GCSE Statistics

Complete Revision and Practice

Contents

Section One — Data Collection

Section Two — Tabulation and Representation

Contents

Here

Section Three — Data Analysis

Section Four — Probability

Published by Coordination Group Publications Ltd.

Editors: Ali Palin, David Ryan, Luke Von Kotze

Contributors: Andrew Ballard, Sally Gill, Sharon Keeley, Val Malcolm, Sam Norman, Andy Park, Richard Parsons, Katherine Reed, Alan Rix, Mark Turner, Julie Wakeling, Sharon Watson, Janet West.

With thanks to Ann Francis and Sarah Hilton for the proofreading.

The tourism earnings data on page 132 is from the National Statistics website: www.statistics.gov.uk.

ISBN: 978 1 84762 149 8
Website: www.cgpbooks.co.uk
Printed by Elanders Hindson Ltd, Newcastle upon Tyne.
Clipart source: CorelDRAW®

Data Sources

Here's the first page — it's on data sources. There are two types of data source you need to know about — primary and secondary. Both types have their pros and cons. Read on...

Primary Data *is Raw Data*

Primary data is any data that hasn't been interpreted by anyone yet (i.e. raw data). That could be:

1) Data you collect especially for your project, e.g. from surveys, questionnaires, experiments, etc.
2) Data from a database that hasn't been processed in any way, e.g. census data.

EXAMPLES:

1. Jane needs to investigate the shopping habits in her local town. She collects data by using a questionnaire in the high street.
2. Peter uses the 2001 census to find out about types of employment in his area.

Collecting primary data gives you control over what data you get, how you get it and how accurate it is. However, the methods can be time consuming and expensive.

Secondary Data *Comes from Other Sources*

Secondary data will definitely have been collected by someone else.

1) It's any processed information that you find in books, databases, internet pages, magazines, newspapers, etc.
2) It often comes in tables or graphs.
3) It could have been collected for a completely different reason from yours.
4) Secondary data is usually a cheaper and easier way of getting data, but you can't be sure how accurate it is and it can often be out of date.

EXAMPLES:

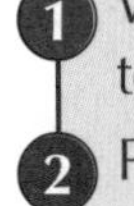

1. When Jane investigates the shopping habits in her local town she could use charts from the evening paper.
2. Peter could use a report written by the careers service to find out about employment in his local area.

*Secondary Data must be **Handled with Care***

Secondary data is often biased, so be careful. For example:

There's more on bias later in the section.

1) The data might not represent what you're interested in...

E.g. It's no good using the Frogatt's Fine Foods customer shopping habits survey to find out the shopping habits of everyone in your town — not everyone shops at Frogatt's Fine Foods.

2) The data collectors might have had different interests from you...

E.g. You want to use Frogatt's Fine Foods' own research into their new opening hours to find out what customers think. You need to bear in mind that Frogatt's will want to show that customers are happy with the new hours — they might have interpreted their results in a way which does this.

Always ask yourself these questions when dealing with secondary data:
1) Is the data relevant to what you want to find out?
2) Is your source of secondary data reliable and accurate — is the data biased?

Primary and secondary data — make sure you know the basics...

You need to know a few different sources of primary and secondary data, and the pros and cons of each type of data. Once you're clear on the facts, you'll be able to comment on data sources in the exam.

Types of Data

Data is collected by measuring or observing things. It can be numerical or descriptive.

Data can be Quantitative or Qualitative

Quantitative Data measures Quantities

1) Quantitative data is anything that you can measure with a number.
2) For example, heights of people, the time taken to complete a task, weights of things, etc.
3) Quantitative data tends to be easier to analyse than qualitative data.

Qualitative Data is Descriptive

1) Qualitative data doesn't use numbers — it's completely descriptive.
2) For example, you observe eye colour, hair colour, etc.
3) Qualitative data is quite often subjective (depending on people's opinions) — e.g. are someone's eyes hazel or brown?
   So this sort of data is usually less reliable than quantitative data.

Discrete or Continuous — Can you Measure it Exactly?

QUANTITATIVE DATA can be broken up into discrete and continuous data.
You need to understand which is which.

1) DISCRETE DATA CAN BE MEASURED EXACTLY

Your data's discrete if it represents something that's countable.
Examples are the number of points scored in a game or the number of people going into a particular shop between 9 am and midday on a Saturday morning.

2) CONTINUOUS DATA CAN ONLY BE MEASURED TO A GIVEN DEGREE OF ACCURACY

Your data's continuous if you can't measure the exact value.

For example — the height of a block

Say you measured the height of a block as 56 cm to the nearest centimetre. That isn't an exact value — you'd get a more accurate height if you measured to the nearest mm or 0.1 mm or 0.01 mm, etc. But you'll never get an exact value for its height, because there'll always be a more accurate way of measuring than the one you use.

You also need to remember that measurements given to the nearest unit can be inaccurate by up to ± ½ unit. E.g. the height of the block is measured as 56 cm to the nearest cm — its actual height could be anything from 55.5 cm up to 56.5 cm.

Other examples are the weight of an object and the time taken to do something.

Quantitative data measures quantities...

Remember that — it should help you remember that quantitative data is numerical.

Classifying Data

Once you've collected your jumbled mass of data, you need to start making sense of it.

You can Split your Data into **Classes**

A good first step when you've got loads of raw data is to split it into different classes. When you do this, it's important that you define the classes well — so you know exactly which class to put each bit of data in.

Here's how NOT to do it:

> A student divides the colour of mice into the following classes:
>
> White, Grey, Greyish white, Brown, Black/Brown, Black
>
> The classes are badly defined because they overlap. The decision of which class to put each mouse into depends on who makes it — it's subjective.

You can put your Data onto **Different Types of Scale**

1 **Categorical** Scales

If you've got qualitative data, it's sometimes useful to give your classes a number to make it easier to process the data.

For example, you might split eye colour into 'blue', 'brown' and 'other'. You could number the 'blue' class 1, the 'brown' class 2 and the 'other' class 3. The numbers can't be used for anything other than labelling the classes — they don't have any other meaning.

2 **Rank** Scales

Here numbers are given to classes, but they are only used to order a list.

For example, a survey could ask people to rank celebrities' attractiveness from 0 (very unattractive) to 5 (very attractive). The difference between a 2 and a 3 might not be the same as the difference between a 4 and a 5.

3 **Interval** Scales

Here, equal steps on the scale do mean something.

An important example is temperature, where the difference between 10 °C and 20 °C is the same as the difference between 30 °C and 40 °C. But an interval scale doesn't have a true zero, so you can't say that 20 °C is twice as hot as 10 °C.

4 **Ratio** Scales

These are "proper scales". Equal steps on the scale mean something and the measurements have a true zero.

For example, two kilometres is twice as far as one kilometre.
Other examples of ratio scales are areas, volumes and data that can be counted.

Learn the four different types of data scale...

Different types of data need different scales of measurement. Read through the info on scales a few times, then turn over the page and write down an example of each type.

More Types of Data

Much of the data you'll come across will be grouped in tables. Take a look at the example below.

Grouping Data — when the Spread of Data's too Big

If you measured the ages of 50 people living on a street, you'd probably get data that's really spread out (e.g. anything from 0-110). You might need to group the data to make it more manageable.

Example

Here's the raw data for the 50 people:

2	10	20	60	89	61	22	42	23	101
65	81	4	22	5	40	70	5	47	44
12	84	32	71	51	35	84	59	37	52
39	71	25	45	85	29	45	86	34	44
40	34	90	22	62	48	62	53	81	53

Here's the same data, grouped in a frequency table:

Age in completed years	0 - 19	20 - 39	40 - 59	60 - 79	80 and over
Number of people	6	13	14	8	9

There are three details to learn...

1) The groups in a frequency table are called class intervals.
So in the table above, the class intervals are 0-19, 20-39, etc.

2) The lower class limits (or class boundaries) are 0, 20, 40, ...

3) The upper class limits are 19, 39, 59, ...

See pages 38 and 39 for more on class intervals.

The problem with grouping data is that you don't know what the exact data values are any more, which means you have to estimate statistics like the mean and median (see Section 3).

Grouping data makes it easier to analyse...

Grouping data is very useful — it makes analysing large sets of data much quicker and easier. On the down side, the exact data values are lost so your analysis is less accurate.

More Types of Data

Here's the last page on types of data...

Bivariate Data — Measuring Two Things

EXAMPLE: This table shows the heights and weights of 10 students:

Student	A	B	C	D	E	F	G	H	I	J
Height (m)	1.34	2.01	1.70	1.51	1.49	1.76	1.85	1.69	1.68	1.49
Weight (kg)	56	77	60	56	54	68	67	65	66	58

In this set of data, each student has had two data items (or variables) measured — height and weight. This type of data is called bivariate — bi for two, variate for variables.

Bivariate data can be: 1) Discrete, 2) Continuous, 3) Grouped, 4) Ungrouped

EXAMPLE 1: Discrete bivariate data — marks out of 20 in a French test and a Maths test for a class of 30 students.

EXAMPLE 2: Continuous bivariate data — the weight and tail length of 25 cats.

EXAMPLE 3: Grouped bivariate data — when you're collecting a lot of bivariate data, you could group it. The two-way table below shows grouped data on the weights of students and the number of hours they spend watching TV every week.

Weight (nearest kg) of students	Number of hours spent watching TV each week (nearest hour)				
	14 or fewer	15 - 19	20 - 24	25 or more	Total
Less than 50	1	0	0	0	1
50 - 59	8	7	1	1	17
60 - 69	3	12	4	0	19
70 - 79	1	4	7	4	16
80 or more	0	0	2	5	7
Total	13	23	14	10	60

You need to be able to interpret two-way tables like this. For example:

- There are 12 students who weigh 60 – 69 kg and who watch 15 – 19 hours of TV every week.
- The total number of students who watch 20 – 24 hours of TV every week is 14.

Bivariate data sounds complicated... but it's not...

Bivariate just means that the data involves two variables rather than one. Look at the two-way table above. There are two pieces of information about each student — weight and hours of TV watched. Make sure you can interpret two-way tables — you're likely to get a question on it in the exam.

Warm-Up and Worked Exam Questions

This stuff is all pretty straightforward, but that doesn't mean you should try and get away with not learning it all. And we all know the best way to learn anything is to do lots of practice questions...

Warm-Up Questions

1) What is the main difference between primary and secondary data?
2) Give two disadvantages of using secondary data rather than primary data.
3) What is qualitative data?
4) Is a person's shoe size discrete or continuous data?
5) To check the efficiency of 'Freddie's Freezers', 200 of them were cooled to -8°C. The power was then cut for 24 hours and the internal temperature of each one was taken again. What type of scale would be best to represent the temperatures after 24 hours?
6) What is the name for data that involves two characteristics of each member of the sample?

Worked Exam Questions

Here's an exam question with the answer already written in. Make sure you understand it.

1 The table below shows data on the number of people and pets per household in a small village. For example, there are 12 households consisting of 1 person with no pets.

Number of pets per household	Number of people per household				
	1	2	3	4	5 or more
0	12	10	6	3	3
1	5	12	7	4	2
2	2	3	5	6	2
3	1	3	4	1	3
4 or more	0	2	3	1	0

(a) How many households consisting of 2 people have 3 pets?

3

(1 mark)

(b) How many households are there in total with 1 pet?

5 + 12 + 7 + 4 + 2 = 30 *This is the total of the '1 pet' row.*

(1 mark)

(c) What is the most common number of pets in households consisting of 4 people?

2

(1 mark)

2

Exam Questions

2 A school in Essex conducted a survey about how students got to school and what their favourite subject was. Each student was asked two questions and the results are shown in the following table.

	Favourite Subject				Transport to School			
	English	Maths	Science	Other	Car	Bus	Walk	Other
Boys		54	38	64	42	38	103	17
Girls	50	68	30	52	63	45	87	5

(a) Fill in the missing box.

(2 marks)

(b) How many students walked to school?

103 + 87 ....

(1 mark)

(c) What was the most popular subject among the girls?

Maths ....

(1 mark)

(d) How many students were surveyed altogether?

Add boys & girls ....

(1 mark)

(e) A school in Dorset decided to use this data to estimate how many school buses they should run. Was this a good or bad idea? Give one reason for your answer.

....

....

(1 mark)

3 Martin wanted to know how popular football on the television was. He asked 50 of his friends to rate it on a scale of 1 to 5, where '1' meant they hated it and '5' meant they thought it was fantastic. Here are his results:

	Hate it				Fantastic
	1	2	3	4	5
Frequency	3	2	10	13	22

(a) What type of scale has Martin used to classify this data?

Rank scales ....

(1 mark)

(b) Is the data discrete, continuous or neither?

Discrete data ....

(1 mark)

(c) Is the data primary or secondary?

Primary ....

(1 mark)

Census Data

Carrying out a census is a way of finding out about every member of a population.

Population *— the Group you Want to Find Out About*

For any statistical project, you need to find out information about a group of people or things. This group is called the population.

Examples of populations are:

1) All the pupils in a school
2) All people who have access to the internet
3) All the boxes of cereal produced by a factory
4) All the newts living in a pond

*A **Census** Surveys **Every Member** of the Population*

When you collect data about every member of a population, it's called a census. This can be easy, but it usually isn't.

Here are two examples of populations where it's easy to carry out a census:

1. Finding out how long it takes every student in a class to get to school in the morning. The population is all the students in the class, so you just ask them.

2. Finding out the Maths exam results for all the students in one year group of a school. The population is all the students in the year group — the school keeps a record of all exam results, so that's easy as well.

These are examples of SMALL, WELL-DEFINED POPULATIONS (meaning it's easy to tell exactly who or what is in them).

*A **Census** Isn't Always **Practical** or even **Possible***

Doing a census is often difficult and sometimes impossible. For example:

1) Suppose you're trying to collect data on the lengths of newts living in a large pond. How will you know that you've surveyed all the newts in the pond?
2) The population census in Britain is only taken every ten years. That's because the population's so large that it takes years to count everyone and make sense of all the data. The really difficult bit is making sure everyone's been counted once and only once (and they probably don't manage it).
3) If a battery manufacturer wanted to find out how long their batteries lasted, it wouldn't be sensible to carry out a census. The population's far too big (and they wouldn't have any batteries left to sell!)

So for LARGE POPULATIONS, CENSUSES AREN'T USUALLY PRACTICAL.

A Census is only practical for some populations...

More often than not it's too difficult or time consuming to carry out a census. You need to be able to decide whether it would be sensible to carry out a census for any given population.

Sampling

When it's not sensible to collect information using a census, you have to use sampling.

Sampling — *a Cheap and Easy Alternative to a Census*

In practice, it's not usually possible to survey whole populations — so a sample is surveyed instead.

EXAMPLES:

1) A battery manufacturer is challenged to check its claims that its batteries last longer than any other brand. They can't test every single battery, so they test a sample of 1000 batteries instead.
2) To find out about the amount of time spent watching TV by the people who live in a large city, a market research company surveys a sample of 2500 people.
3) Pete needs to find out about the heights of trees in a forest for his biology project. He surveys a sample of 500 trees.

Sample Data and Census Data are Different

Some ADVANTAGES of using sample data over census data are:

1) It's often more PRACTICAL to collect
2) It's CHEAPER
3) It's QUICKER

The DISADVANTAGE of using sample data is that you don't have information about every member of a population. It's really important to make sure the sample is representative of the population.

There are different ways of doing this — more about those on the next few pages — but for now, here are some samples that AREN'T representative of their population:

1) In a survey to find out the average age of cars in a town, a sample was taken of 1000 cars crossing a certain roundabout between 8 am and 9 am on a Monday morning. This sample is likely to be mostly people on their way to work, whose cars might be newer than those of, say, pensioners.
2) A survey on the incomes of people in a town uses a sample of 10 households in a certain street. There are two things wrong with this sample:
   - It's likely that the people on the street will have similar incomes.
   - It's far too small. When choosing samples, size matters — basically, the bigger your sample, the better. Any statistics (e.g. mean, variance, etc.) that you work out from a bigger sample are likely to be closer to those of the whole population.

Obviously even if two samples are representative of a population, the data (and hence any statistics you calculate) won't be exactly the same. This is called the variability between samples.

Learn the differences between a census and a sample...

Sampling is a way of finding out about a population without having to survey everyone or everything in it. But the key thing is to make sure that the sample represents your population. You'll need to be able to spot problems with sampling methods in the exam.

Sampling

There are a few different sampling methods you need to know about. The first is simple random sampling.

First Make Sure your ***Population*** *is* ***Well Defined***

Before you do anything else on a statistical project, you need to be clear about what you're trying to find out.

Once you know this, your next step is to decide exactly what your population is.
You need to put together a sample frame — that's a list or map of all the members of the population.

Here are some examples of well-defined populations and their sample frames:

EXAMPLE 1:
You're trying to find out the average Key Stage 3 SATs score for Maths in England in 2003.
Your population would be all students in England who took the Key Stage 3 Maths SAT in 2003.
Your sample frame would be a list of all students who took the Key Stage 3 Maths SAT in 2003.

EXAMPLE 2:
Ahliah needs to find out the average height of the chestnut trees in her local country park for a science project. The population she uses is all the chestnut trees in the country park. Instead of listing the trees, Ahliah makes a map of the country park with all the chestnut trees marked and uses that as her sample frame.

Simple Random Sampling *— Sampling Without Bias*

Once you've decided on your population and made a sample frame, you need to choose a sample that represents the population fairly (without bias).

With relatively small, well-defined populations, you can use a simple random sample.
In a simple random sample, every member of the population has an equal chance of being chosen.

EXAMPLE: If your population was the 2000 students who go to Eastfield Secondary School, your sample frame would be a list of all the students who go to the school.

To get a random sample of 100 students:

1) **Give every student on the list a number.**
2) **Use random number tables, a calculator or a computer to get a list of 100 different random numbers between 1 and 2000.**
3) **The 100 students with those numbers would form your sample.**

See p33 for more on generating random numbers.

Simple random sampling avoids bias...

Simple random sampling should give you an unbiased sample because each member of the population is equally likely to be chosen. Make sure you know what's meant by a well defined population.

Stratified and Systematic Sampling

Two more types of sampling for you here — stratified and systematic.

Stratified Sampling — Representation for all Groups

Using stratified sampling can help you get a true picture (or representative sample) of a population. It's useful when your population's made up of groups (or categories) each containing members that are similar to each other in some way, e.g. age groups.

The number chosen from each group needs to be proportional to the size of the group in the population. Choose the right number from each group at random to make your sample.

Example

The table shows the distribution of students in Years 9, 10 and 11 at Eastfield Secondary School. You want to choose a sample of 50 from the 1000 students.

	Boys	Girls	Total in Year
Year 9	179	221	400
Year 10	196	204	400
Year 11	119	81	200

WITH ONE SET OF CATEGORIES — YEAR GROUPS...

$(400 \div 1000) \times 50 = 20$ should be chosen at random from Year 9
$(400 \div 1000) \times 50 = 20$ should be chosen at random from Year 10
$(200 \div 1000) \times 50 = 10$ should be chosen at random from Year 11

This should give a fairly representative sample — it's got the right proportion of students from each year group.

... OR TWO SETS OF CATEGORIES — YEAR GROUPS AND GENDER

Of the 20 Year 9 students, $(179 \div 400) \times 20 = 8.95$ should be boys.
Round this to 9 boys and 11 girls.
Of the 20 Year 10 students, $(196 \div 400) \times 20 = 9.8$ should be boys.
Round this to 10 boys and 10 girls.
Of the 10 Year 11 students, $(119 \div 200) \times 10 = 5.95$ should be boys.
Round this to 6 boys and 4 girls.

Now, you want the right proportions of boys and girls in each year group as well.

Systematic Sampling — Choosing Every n^{th} Item

EXAMPLE: How would you get a systematic sample of 50 from a list of 2000 students at Eastfield Secondary School?

1) **DIVIDE your population size by your sample size — $2000 \div 50 = 40$.**
2) **Choose a RANDOM start number between 1 and 40 — let's say 3.**
3) **Your sample would be the third person on the list, then every 40th person after that until you have 50 people.**

So the sample would be the 3rd, 43rd, 83rd, 123rd, ... etc. students on the list.

Systematically learn these sampling methods...

Sometimes, the thing you're trying to find out about will vary a lot between different groups within the population. Then it's sensible to use stratified sampling. Make sure you can do the calculations above.

Cluster, Quota and Convenience Sampling

You need to know about three types of non-random sampling that are widely used...

Cluster Sampling — Cheaper than Random Sampling

Sometimes, a large population can be split into smaller groups called clusters. Sampling is then done on a random sample of these clusters, rather than on the whole population.
For the sample to be representative, there should be as little variability between the clusters as possible.

For example, in a county the clusters could be towns or villages.

For CLUSTER SAMPLING:

1) **First a random sample of clusters is chosen**
2) **Then a random sample is taken from each selected cluster**

EXAMPLE: If the government wanted to find out about spending habits in England, they would probably use cluster sampling. The clusters could be all the counties in England. A random sample of counties would be chosen and then a random sample of people within these counties would be surveyed.

It's easy to see that it would be cheaper for interviewers to just cover certain counties rather than the whole country.

Quota Sampling — Often used for Market Research

1) The population is divided up into groups based on age, gender and so on.
2) The interviewer will be told to interview a certain number of people from each group, e.g. 20 men and 20 women over the age of 40, 15 men and 15 women under 40.
3) This method of sampling is often used in interviews carried out on high streets, and the final choice of the sample members is down to the interviewer — it's not random.

Convenience Sampling — Just What it Sounds Like

The sample is chosen for convenience.
It's taken from a section of the population present at one particular place and time.

For example, a researcher interviews the first 50 people entering a supermarket on a particular morning.

These three types of sampling have the disadvantage of being non-random, but they're cheap and easy to use (see the next page for advantages / disadvantages of sampling techniques).

Three more types of sampling for you to learn...

The type of sampling to use depends on what your population is like (see p13). The problem with these three types is that they can produce biased samples. Read the page, then scribble down what you know.

Strengths and Weaknesses of Sampling Methods

Each sampling method has its own advantages and disadvantages. Here they are in detail.
Make sure you're clear on each of the methods on pages 10-12 before you read this page.

1 SIMPLE RANDOM SAMPLING

Every member of the population has an equal chance of being selected, so a simple random sample is completely unbiased. But if the population is spread over a large area, whoever carries out the survey could have a lot of travelling to do.

2 SYSTEMATIC SAMPLING

This should produce an unbiased sample. Problems arise when the sample frame you use has some sort of pattern. For example if every tenth gizmo produced by a machine is faulty and you are sampling every tenth gizmo for quality control, your sample will either be completely faulty or completely without faults. Either way, your sample is biased.

3 STRATIFIED SAMPLING

If you have easy to define categories in the population (e.g. males and females) this is likely to give you a good sample. The number selected from each group or category is proportional to the size of that group. Stratified sampling isn't useful when there aren't any obvious categories or when the categories are hard to define. It can be expensive because of the extra detail involved.

4 CLUSTER SAMPLING

The main advantage of cluster sampling is that it saves on travel when the population is spread over a large area. It's easy to get a biased sample though — e.g. people living in the same postal district could have similar incomes or employment.

5 QUOTA SAMPLING

This is quick to use and any member of the sample can be replaced by one with the same properties. If you have no sample frame (list of the population) — then the only way of getting a sample may be quota sampling or convenience sampling. Quota sampling can easily be biased, though — it's often used in street surveys by market research companies, so the sample chosen depends on the interviewer. The people who refuse to take part may all have similar points of view on the topic being surveyed. For example if the survey was on working hours, those with the longest working hours might not have time to answer the questions.

6 CONVENIENCE SAMPLING

The convenience comes at a price — there's no attempt to make the sample representative of the population being surveyed.

Learn the pros and cons of the six sampling methods...

You should be able to recognise when you'd use the different sampling methods.
Cover the page and write down one advantage and one disadvantage of each method.

Biased Samples

Here are two different ways that bias can creep in when you're sampling...

You need to Sample from the **Right Population**

It sounds obvious, but you need to be absolutely clear about what your population is when you're doing a statistical project. You'd be surprised how easy it is to get this wrong, and if you sample from the wrong population, you'll introduce bias.

EXAMPLES OF SAMPLING FROM THE WRONG POPULATION:

1) A classic example is telephone polling. Say you want to find out about the eating habits of all the people in your town. You choose a sample selected at random from the phone book. The sample is biased — think about it. The population you're interested in is everyone who lives in the town, but your sample excludes anyone who isn't in the phone book (e.g. because they're ex-directory or don't have a phone).

2) A food company wants to find out about the snack preferences of young people in a city. They choose a random sample from all the students who go to a particular secondary school. The sample is biased because the population should be all the young people in the city, not just those that happen to go to that school.

You can get Bias if you choose a **Non-Random Sample**

How to be non-random:

1) Use cluster sampling
2) Use quota sampling
3) Use convenience sampling

See pages 12 and 13 for the details of these sampling methods.

EXAMPLES OF NON-RANDOM SAMPLING TECHNIQUES:

1) You want to find out if the students at your school think the tuck shop provides good value for money. You choose, for your sample, the first twenty people in the queue for the tuck shop at break time. You've got the population right — any student who goes to your school could (in theory) be in the queue. But the sample is non-random — people who think strongly that the tuck shop is bad value for money probably don't shop there. This is an example of convenience sampling.

2) A car manufacturer sends out customer satisfaction questionnaires to all the people who've bought new cars from them in the past year. The sample of questionnaires they get back will be biased. People are more likely to return the questionnaire if they're really happy or really unhappy with the car — or have a lot of time on their hands.

A biased sample doesn't represent your population...

Selecting a completely unbiased sample can be tricky. Sometimes, it's impossible to avoid some bias, no matter how hard you try. The important thing is that you understand the limitations of your results.

Warm-Up and Worked Exam Questions

These warm-up questions should let you know if you understand the basics of sampling. If you struggle with any of them, go back and learn the bits you don't know before attempting the exam questions.

Warm-Up Questions

1) Paul wants to take a census of people in his class to find what their favourite flavour of crisps is. What percentage of the people in his class should he ask?
2) What is the main disadvantage of using sample data?
3) Alison wants to find the average height of the penguins in a zoo. What are the population and sample frame for this investigation?
4) In a school of 300 boys and 50 girls, what type of sampling should be used to select a school committee that represents the proportion of boys and girls in the school? How many boys would be in a committee of 14?
5) E-Z-P-Z want to find out how many people in the UK enjoy their new range of tinned peas. They decide to interview certain numbers of men and women from different age groups. What is this sampling method called?
6) Give two ways in which a sample might be biased.

Worked Exam Questions

Here are a few exam-style questions with the answers written in for you.
They should get you in the mood for the rest of the exam questions that follow.

1 Describe how you would use systematic sampling to select 20 items from a group of 100.

$100 \div 20 = 5$. **(1 mark)** *Pick any starting point between 1 and 5 and take every fifth item of the group after that. E.g. select the 4th, 9th, 14th, ..., 99th items.* **(1 mark)**

This will give a total of 20 selected items.

(2 marks)

2 A sports club consists of 548 golfers, 83 swimmers and 57 tennis players.
A committee of 16 is to be selected to represent the members.

(a) What kind of sampling should be used to give fair representation to each sport?

Stratified

(1 mark)

(b) How many from each group should be on the committee?

Total number of members = $548 + 83 + 57 = 688$ **(1 mark)**

Golfers = $(548 \div 688) \times 16 = 12.7$

Swimmers = $(83 \div 688) \times 16 = 1.9$

Tennis players = $(57 \div 688) \times 16 = 1.3$ **(2 marks for all three correct, 1 mark for two.)**

Rounding to nearest whole number, the committee should consist of:

13 golfers, 2 swimmers and 1 tennis player. **(1 mark)**

(4 marks)

Worked Exam Questions

Worked Exam Questions

3 Why are the following sampling methods biased?

(a) Asking people in a newsagents whether or not they have their newspapers delivered.

People in a newsagents are more likely to go to the shop for their newspaper than have one delivered.

(1 mark)

(b) Asking people going into a shop on a Tuesday afternoon if they are in full time employment or not.

If people are going into shops on a weekday afternoon, they are less likely to be in full time employment.

(1 mark)

(c) Trying to find out the average national salary by asking people who live on your street how much they earn.

People living in the same street (in similar houses) might all have similar salaries, whereas salaries in other areas could be very different.

(1 mark)

Hint: for this type of question, you've got to try and think of reasons why the sample might not be representative of the whole population.

4 Sam wants to find out how many teenage girls in England wear make-up.

(a) What would Sam's sample frame be?

A list of all the teenage girls in England.

(1 mark)

(b) Give one reason why Sam should use sample data rather than a census.

A census would require asking every teenage girl in England, which is a huge task and almost impossible to do successfully.

You could also say that sampling would be quicker or cheaper. *(1 mark)*

(c) Sam decides to ask all the teenage girls in her school whether or not they wear make-up.

(i) What type of sampling is this?

Convenience sampling

(1 mark)

(ii) Give two disadvantages of using this method.

The teenage girls in other schools might be very different from those in Sam's school. ***(1 mark)*** *Also, asking in a school would not cover all ages as few 17 and 18 year olds and almost no 19 year olds would be asked.* ***(1 mark)***

(2 marks)

Exam Questions

5 Natalie and Jack wanted to find out whether people in England preferred to shop in Tasko or Sonsberry's. They each conducted a survey. Natalie stood in her local town centre and asked 100 females over the age of 16. Jack asked 50 people waiting to get on a train at his local station.

(a) Who chose to do convenience sampling?

(1 mark)

(b) Give one reason why Natalie's results could be biased.

(1 mark)

6 Three students, Charlene, Adam and Tom were given data taken from one school in Wales to assist them in their coursework. They each decided to investigate the relationship between the weight and height of all 16 year old girls in Wales. The given data was as follows:

Height (m)	1.83	1.67	1.60	1.62	1.72	1.68	1.73	1.73	1.56	1.69
Weight (kg)	60	52	54	56	51	54	64	50	50	51
Height (m)	1.63	1.62	1.72	1.65	1.65	1.68	1.61	1.61	1.70	1.75
Weight (kg)	48	54	51	66	54	48	54	54	50	56
Height (m)	1.75	1.72	1.68	1.62	1.58	1.65	1.60	1.63	1.57	1.55
Weight (kg)	60	60	48	51	54	54	48	52	48	50
Height (m)	1.62	1.68	1.69	1.60	1.60	1.55	1.70	1.63	1.56	1.61
Weight (kg)	48	50	54	48	45	60	63	48	55	50

Charlene decided to take a systematic sample of 10 girls, Adam used all the data and Tom thought a simple random sample of 20 would be best.

(a) If the height of the first girl chosen by Charlene was 1.67 m, what was the weight of her second girl?

(3 marks)

(b) How could Tom have collected his sample?

(1 mark)

(c) Whose investigation is likely to give the most reliable results and why?

(2 marks)

(d) Is Adam's investigation a census? Explain your answer.

(1 mark)

Planning an Investigation

When you're planning an investigation, you've usually got some kind of research question or statement you're trying to find evidence to support. The fancy word for this is hypothesis.

*Use a **Hypothesis** to Make Things Clear*

When you're planning an investigation you need to be clear about what it is you're trying to find out. So you need to have a research question or hypothesis.

A hypothesis is a statement that you believe is true but that you haven't got evidence to support yet. Once you've got a hypothesis you'll be able to work out what data to collect.

EXAMPLES OF HYPOTHESES:

1) Rick and Alex are playing a dice game. Rick is losing and thinks that since they're using Alex's dice, the dice must be loaded.

   Rick's hypothesis is that the dice are biased.

2) Yvette thinks that students who watch a lot of television are less likely to do well in exams because they don't have as much spare time to study.

   Yvette's hypothesis is that the more time a student spends watching television per week, the less well they do in examinations.

*You can Break Up your Research into **Subquestions***

In the examples above, each problem has just one question. If things are more complicated you'll have to break your investigation down into smaller chunks, called subquestions.

Example

The Comfee furniture company is trying to work out a scale of charges for delivering sofas. They think the journey takes more time (and so will be more expensive) if the delivery address is further away from their storage depot.

The company's hypothesis is that the further a journey is, the longer it takes.

This is a really simple hypothesis, but it doesn't take into account the different types of road a delivery van has to travel on. A 200-mile journey down the motorway might be quicker than a 100-mile journey along country lanes. So the company could break down their delivery areas into three categories:

1) Places that can be reached mainly by motorway
2) Places that can be reached mainly by 'A' roads
3) Other places

They could then investigate each area separately.

My hypothesis is — you'll need to know this in the exam...

Having a clear hypothesis is vital if you're to avoid getting in a muddle later on. Exam questions like to ask you to suggest a suitable hypothesis for an investigation or to find evidence supporting a hypothesis.

More on Investigations

Once you've got a research question or hypothesis, you need to decide what data to collect. It has to be something that will provide evidence either for or against your hypothesis (it's no good having data that doesn't do either). Next, choose how you're going to get the data. Here are four methods:

***Questionnaires**, **Experiments**, **Raw** or **Secondary** Data*

1. QUESTIONNAIRES — the data's collected by questioning members of the sample. The questions can take many different forms and you need to be really careful when you're designing a questionnaire. More on this later.

2. EXPERIMENTS — instead of asking people questions, you could do an experiment, e.g. by measuring their height or how fast they can run. You have to use experiments to collect data on the natural world, such as heights of trees.

3. RAW DATA — this is data that has not been processed in any way, for example, census data.

4. SECONDARY DATA — this is data that has been collected and processed for some other reason than the one you need to use it for. You need to take care when you use it, but it can still be handy. You can find secondary data in newspapers and magazines, on the internet, in databases and historical records, etc.

*Choose the **Best Method** for Your **Hypothesis***

Some examples will make this clearer.

Example 1 — Wartshire County Council's hypothesis:

The people of Wartford travel less far to work than the people living in outlying villages.

The County Council would need to collect data on how far the people of Wartford and the outlying villages travel to work. A questionnaire would be a sensible way to do it.

Example 2 — Mr Phitt the P.E. teacher's hypothesis:

Students who can run faster spend less money at the school tuck shop.

Mr Phitt could do an experiment to see how fast each student can run 100 metres, then get them to complete a questionnaire on how much they've spent at the tuck shop in the last month.

In these two examples, these aren't the only ways of collecting data. In example 2 for instance, Mr Phitt could just ask the students if they can run fast — this mightn't be so accurate though. You need to be able to justify the method you choose and compare it with alternative methods.

Learn these four methods of collecting data...

Deciding how to collect data is a matter of common sense really. You need to think about factors like how practical and efficient each of the possible methods would be, and which should give the most accurate results. As long as you can give reasons for your choice, you should get the marks.

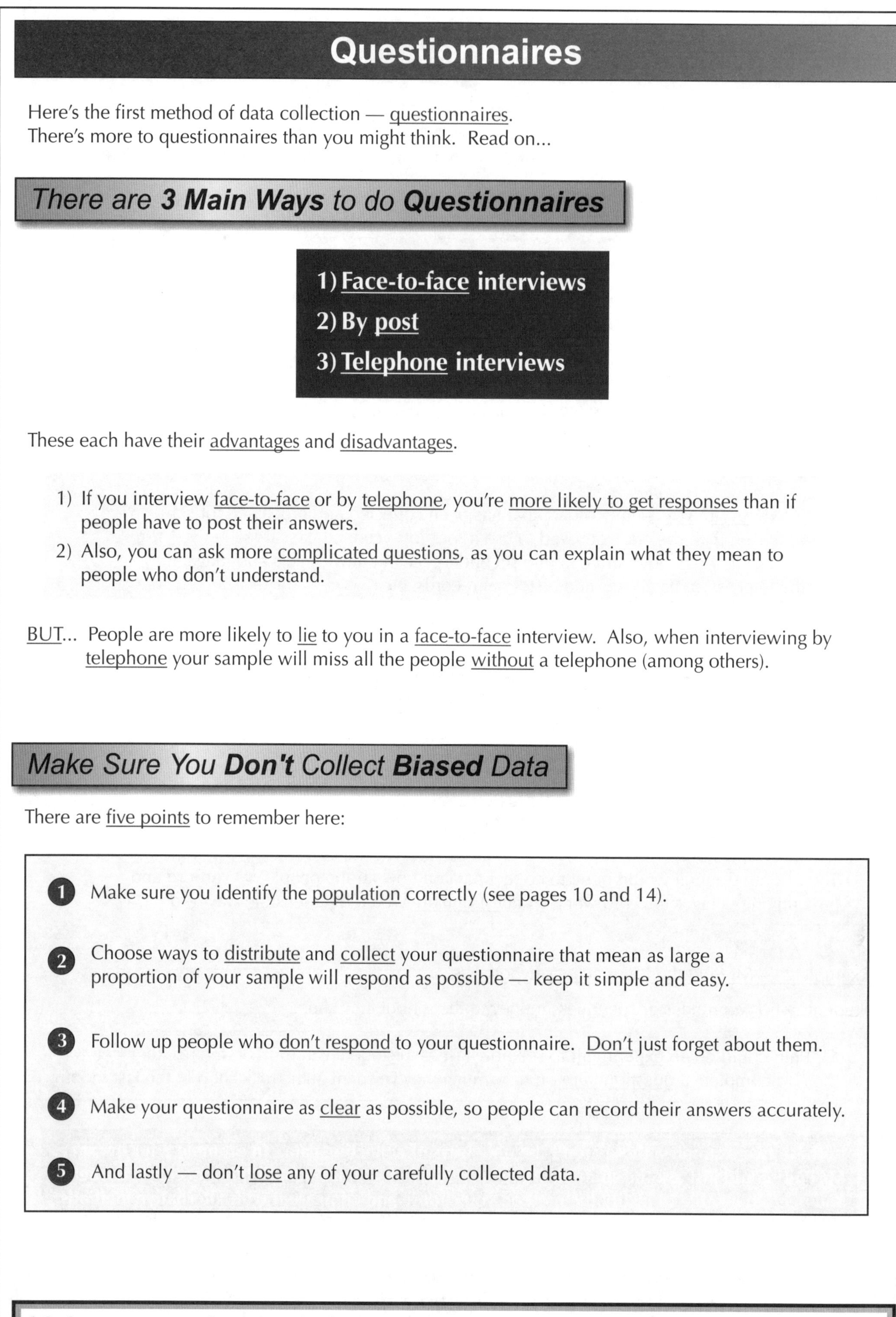

Questionnaires

Here's the first method of data collection — questionnaires.
There's more to questionnaires than you might think. Read on...

*There are **3 Main Ways** to do **Questionnaires***

1) Face-to-face interviews
2) By post
3) Telephone interviews

These each have their advantages and disadvantages.

1) If you interview face-to-face or by telephone, you're more likely to get responses than if people have to post their answers.
2) Also, you can ask more complicated questions, as you can explain what they mean to people who don't understand.

BUT... People are more likely to lie to you in a face-to-face interview. Also, when interviewing by telephone your sample will miss all the people without a telephone (among others).

*Make Sure You **Don't** Collect **Biased** Data*

There are five points to remember here:

1. Make sure you identify the population correctly (see pages 10 and 14).
2. Choose ways to distribute and collect your questionnaire that mean as large a proportion of your sample will respond as possible — keep it simple and easy.
3. Follow up people who don't respond to your questionnaire. Don't just forget about them.
4. Make your questionnaire as clear as possible, so people can record their answers accurately.
5. And lastly — don't lose any of your carefully collected data.

Make sure you're ready for questions on questionnaires...

Getting to know the ins and outs of questionnaires is what the next few pages are about — so make sure you know the pros and cons of different questionnaire types and you've learnt the five key points above.

Questionnaires

Questions come in two main varieties — open or closed.
You'll need to choose the type best suited to your investigation.

Closed *Questions Have a* ***Fixed Number*** *of Possible Answers*

Closed questions list possible answers.
These can be yes/no or tick box questions.

Examples

Are you under 18 years of age?

Yes ☐ No ☐

Tick the mode of transport you use to get to school.

Walking ☐ Bicycle ☐ Bus ☐ Car ☐ Other ☐

The good thing about closed questions is that you can easily process the data collected.
Also, if the question is well designed, the responses won't be ambiguous at all.

Open *Questions Allow* ***Any*** *Answers*

Open questions usually just leave a space for the answer.
This means there's no limit to the possible responses.

Example

What is your favourite TV program? _

What do you like to do on Saturdays? _

Open questions are particularly good in face-to-face interviews because you can follow up the answers. The problem is that you might end up with such a wide range of answers that the data is really hard to process.

Open and closed — there are only two kinds of question...

There isn't too much to learn on this page. If there are a fixed number of answers, it's a closed question. If there are an unlimited number of answers, it's open. Closed questions are simpler and easier to use — open questions get you more detail. Pick the one that suits your investigation best.

Problems with Questions

Bad questions can make the best statistical investigation turn pear-shaped, and there are quite a few pitfalls to watch out for — you've got to be ready for them.

Design your Questionnaire ***Carefully***

Bear these six points in mind when you design a questionnaire:

1) Make sure your questions are relevant.

The data from the questionnaire should provide evidence either for or against your hypothesis. It's no good asking really fascinating questions if the answers aren't going to be useful.

2) Questions should be clear and easy to understand.

You need to check that there's no possible way your questions can be misunderstood.

3) Allow for all possible answers to your question.

E.g. "What is your favourite subject — Maths, English or Science?"

This is difficult to answer truthfully if you like Art best.

4) Questions shouldn't be leading.

Leading questions are ones that are more likely to get a certain answer.

For example: "Do you agree that thrash metal is really good music?"

The problem with this question is that it could make the interviewee feel pressurised into saying 'yes'. A better question would be "What type of music do you prefer to listen to?"

5) Questions should be unambiguous.

Here's an example: "Do you play computer games a lot?"

This question could be interpreted differently by different people. One person who plays 20 hours a week could answer yes, while another who plays the same amount could answer no. A better question would be "How many hours do you play computer games per week?"

6) People may not answer questions truthfully.

This is often because they're embarrassed about the answer.

For example: "Do you wear fashionable clothes?" (see next page for a way round this).

Test *your Questionnaire with a* ***Pilot Study***

You should always use a pilot study to check for problems with your questionnaire.
This is where you try the questionnaire out on a small group of people. The pilot study should help you spot any questions that are unclear or ambiguous, as well as any other unexpected problems.

After doing your pilot study, make sure you keep a record of any problems that came up and the changes that you made to put them right.

Where questionnaires go wrong — six key points to remember...

A poorly designed questionnaire could lead to biased data — or data irrelevant to your investigation. Learn these six points so you know how to get the data you want — and double check it with a pilot study.

Opinion Scales and Random Response

Now you know how to put a questionnaire together — here's a page of tools to make them great.

Opinion Scales** — Good for Getting **More Detail

1) Opinion scales give you more information than yes/no questions.
2) People are given a statement and asked to use a scale of, say, 1 to 5, to say how strongly they agree or disagree with the statement.
3) The most commonly used scales are 1 to 5 or 1 to 10. But whatever scale you use, it's really important that people understand what the scale means.

Example

A sweet manufacturer wants to find out whether it would be worth introducing a chocolate bar with an orange centre. As part of their market research they want to find out if people like the combination of chocolate and orange.
They could use this question:

Do you like the flavours of chocolate and orange together? Yes/No

The problem is, this wouldn't show any difference between people who think the combination is just OK and the people who really love it and would buy loads of the chocolate.

It would be more useful to ask people to —

> Circle the response that best describes how you feel about this statement, where 1 means strongly agree, 2 means agree, 3 means neutral, 4 means disagree and 5 means strongly disagree.
>
> I like the flavours of chocolate and orange together. 1 2 3 4 5

Random Response** — Useful for **Sensitive Questions

You might need to ask a question that people may be embarrassed to, or not want to answer truthfully, such as, "Have you committed a crime in the last 12 months?"

The random response technique is handy for reducing this problem.
Here's how you could use it to get more accurate data from the question above:

> Toss a coin. If it lands on heads, tick the yes box; if it lands on tails, answer the question.
> Have you committed a crime in the past 12 months? Yes ☐ No ☐

If 100 people are surveyed you'd expect roughly 50 of them to toss heads and roughly 50 to toss tails. But if there are 60 ticks in the yes boxes, then it suggests that about 10 of the roughly 50 people who have tossed tails have committed a crime in the past 12 months. So it's likely that about 20 people in the sample of 100 have committed a crime in the past 12 months. The bigger your sample, the more accurate the results will be.

The person analysing the data doesn't know if someone ticked yes because they got 'heads' or because they had committed a crime. This means that people are more likely to answer the sensitive question truthfully (if you explain how the system works to them beforehand).

"I know the stuff on this page inside out" — 1 2 3 4 5...

Opinion scales give you more detailed data than a simple yes/no question — but still deliver data that's easy to process. As long as you make the questions clear you shouldn't have any problems.

Interviews

Instead of asking people to complete a written questionnaire, you can get data for your statistics project by doing interviews.

In **Interviews** You Question Each Person **Individually**

1) In interviews, you speak one-to-one with each person in your sample.
2) An interview could be a questionnaire which you complete for the interviewee, or it could just be a list of topics that you want to find out their opinions on.
3) Interviews have pros and cons when compared to questionnaires.
   Make sure you know what they are...

Interviews Have **Advantages**...

1) You can ask more complex questions in an interview.
   If someone doesn't understand the question, you're there to explain what it means.
2) Face-to-face interviews usually have a higher response rate.
   A person asking you questions is a lot harder to ignore than a piece of paper.
3) You know the right person answered the questions.
   If a questionnaire is sent out to the sample it's possible for anyone to fill it in.
   As a prank, children sometimes fill in questionnaires intended for their parents.
4) You can follow up answers to questions if you think more information is needed.

...and **Disadvantages**

1. Interviews take a long time to carry out.
   Each interviewer can only talk to one person at a time.
   If you want to survey 100 people it'll take... well, ages.
2. Interviewing can be expensive too.
   If you're running a market research company, employing interviewers will cost much more than sending out questionnaires.
3. The interviewees are more likely to lie.
   People are much more likely to not tell the truth in a face-to-face interview if they're embarrassed about their answer.
4. It's hard to get information from a geographically spread out sample.
   If a sample included people living across a large area, it'd be very difficult to interview them all face-to-face. An interviewer would have a lot of travelling to do, whereas a questionnaire could just be mailed.
5. The answers could be recorded in a biased way.
   This could be by accident if the interviewer isn't very well trained, or deliberate if the interviewer has strong views on a subject.

Interviews — get to know the pros and cons...

Interviews can be expensive, slow and they risk putting bias in your data — but they also offer more detail, especially if you're the one doing the interviewing. It's all about weighing up the pros and cons.

Warm-Up and Worked Exam Questions

Warm-up questions — free gym membership for the stats brain...

Warm-Up Questions

1) Fineton Library is trying to come up with a system for estimating how long books will be out for when they're borrowed. They think that books with more pages will be out for longer as they take longer to read.

   Suggest a suitable hypothesis for the library.

2) What is the main disadvantage of using email to distribute questionnaires?
3) Say what is wrong with the question — "You don't really like maths, do you?"
4) What can you do to reduce the risk of having problems with your questionnaire?
5) For each of the following questions state whether they are open or closed.

   a) What make of car do you drive?
   b) Do you prefer plain or milk chocolate?

6) Chris wants to know to what extent people are bored by politics.
   What type of scale should he use for his questionnaire?
7) Vicky, an attractive blonde, thinks that most men prefer blondes. She wants to interview a sample of men to find out. Why would it be unwise for her to conduct the interviews?
8) When using an opinion scale is it better to use a scale of 1-3 or 1-5?

Worked Exam Questions

If only all exam questions had the answers written down for you already. Enjoy it while it lasts...

1 For each of the following questions state whether they are leading, ambiguous or neither.

(a) You don't like me, do you?

Leading *People are likely to react by saying "No, I do like you".*

(1 mark)

(b) How many hours do you spend on the internet each week?

Neither *It calls for an exact answer.*

(1 mark)

(c) Do you spend a lot of money on Christmas presents?

Ambiguous *How much is a lot of money? A lot to some people may seem very little to others.*

(1 mark)

(d) Reality programmes are rubbish, aren't they?

Leading *It is making the person feel they should agree.*

(1 mark)

Worked Exam Questions

Worked Exam Questions

2 Tina gave a questionnaire to eighty Yr 11s, asking if they had ever cheated in an exam. She wasn't sure if she would get honest answers so she asked them to toss a coin, answer 'Yes' if it landed on heads and answer the question truthfully if it landed on tails. Fifty said 'Yes'.

(a) What is this technique called?

Random response

(1 mark)

(b) Estimate how many of the students have cheated in an exam. Show your working.

Expected number of people getting heads and saying 'Yes' is

80 ÷ 2 = 40 **(1 mark)**

50 said 'Yes' and 50 - 40 = 10 — so assume 10 out of the expected 40

who answered truthfully have cheated. **(1 mark)**

If 10 of 40 have cheated, an estimate for the whole sample is

10 x 2 = 20 students have cheated **(1 mark)**

(3 marks)

(c) Tina used a closed question in her survey.
Give one general advantage of using closed questions in questionnaires.

It's easy to process the data.

Or you could say that the questions and answers should be unambiguous. *(1 mark)*

3 Julia has designed a questionnaire to try and find out about people's reading habits.
Here is one of her questions:

On average, how many books do you read? Please tick one box.

1-5 ☐ 5-10 ☐ 10-15 ☐ > 15 ☐

What three things are wrong with this question?

There is no time period specified so people may say how many books they

read in a month, say, rather than in a year. **(1 mark)**

The groups overlap – for example an answer of 10 could go in one of two boxes. **(1 mark)**

For someone who doesn't read any books there is no box to tick. **(1 mark)**

(3 marks)

Exam Questions

4 Hayley, the owner of a small factory, thinks that half an hour of exercise in the morning before work would improve her employees' performance. She decides to test this hypothesis by asking her employees to exercise before they get to work and then fill in a questionnaire about their performance at the end of the day.

(a) Why is Hayley's method flawed?

....

(1 mark)

(b) How could she test her hypothesis more effectively?

....

....

....

(2 marks)

5 Miss Prim is investigating people's attitudes to household chores.
Here's one of her questions:

> Do you agree that ironing is more fun than spring cleaning?
> Please tick the box that applies.
> Yes ☐ No ☐

(a) State one thing wrong with this question.

....

(1 mark)

(b) Improve the question by redesigning it with at least two changes.

(2 marks)

6 Jan thinks that most dog walkers don't pick up their dog's mess when they're out walking. She decides to use a random response technique to see if she is right or not. She asks forty people out walking their dogs if they pick up their dog's mess and uses an unbiased dice to prompt their response.

(a) How could she use the dice for this investigation?

....

....

(2 marks)

(b) 32 people say 'No'. Estimate how many of the 40 people don't clear up after their dog.

....

....

(3 marks)

More on Obtaining Data

Statistical experiments are used to measure how one variable changes when you change a second variable.

You need to **Identify** your **Variables** Clearly

It's important that you define your variables carefully. You need to vary one variable and record its effect on another variable, while everything else should be kept constant (controlled):

1) The variable you vary is called the "explanatory" or "independent" variable.
2) The variable you then observe changes in is the "response" or "dependent" variable.
3) On a graph, you always plot the explanatory variable on the horizontal (x) axis and the response variable on the vertical (y) axis.

EXAMPLE: A walker measures his pulse rate for different walking speeds. Here's a graph of his data:

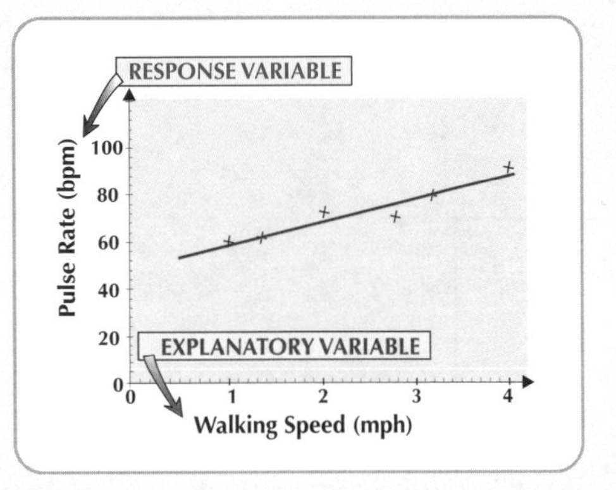

The explanatory variable is his walking speed, because he varies that. The speed he walks at affects his pulse rate (the response variable). The faster he walks, the higher his pulse rate.

If he'd got his variables the wrong way round, this graph would suggest that increasing his heart rate makes him walk faster — which doesn't make a lot of sense.

Design your Experiment **Carefully** — Keep it **Fair**

The walking experiment above would take some careful planning.
Some of the things the experimenter would need to think about are:

1) The walker needs to be walking at each of the different speeds for some time before measuring his pulse, so that his pulse has a chance to 'settle down' to the right value for that speed.
2) Any measuring devices need to be checked for accuracy and reliability.
3) Several measurements should be taken for each speed. Taking an average will increase the reliability of the results.

A good way of taking these measurements would be to use a data collection method called data logging.

1) Data logging is the automatic collection of data at given intervals of time.
2) You program an instrument or machine to take readings of whatever you're measuring at set intervals. E.g. you could program a heart rate monitor to record the walker's pulse rate once every 60 seconds, say.
3) Data logging is an accurate way of collecting lots of data. It's also efficient because you don't need a person to manually take each of the measurements — it's all done automatically.

Know your explanatory variable from your response variable...

There are two important definitions here. The explanatory variable is the one you change yourself — it's independent. The response variable changes as a result of varying the explanatory variable — it depends on it. If you're even slightly confused, read through this page again.

More on Obtaining Data

If you're designing an experiment, you need to think about all the factors that might affect the results.

Keep all your Other Variables Constant

It's really important to keep any extraneous variables (a mathsy term for any variables other than the two you're interested in) constant, so they don't influence the response variable. Then, any change in the response variable has to be due to changes in the explanatory variable.

Going back to the walking experiment...

EXAMPLE:

Other variables which might have affected the walking experiment include:

1) **WALKING SURFACE AND GRADIENT** — all walking needs to be done on the same surface (e.g. tarmac, gravel, grass, etc.), and at the same gradient.
2) **CONDITIONS** — changes in weather and wind direction can affect how difficult it is to walk. Since you can't actually control the weather, you just have to choose times to do the experiment when conditions are similar.
3) **TIREDNESS** — the walker's pulse rate should be back at rest rate before each trial. This means he's always starting from the same "zero" point.

Each of these must be kept as constant as possible, otherwise they might affect the results. They might even have more of an effect on the pulse rate than the walking speed.

It's Important to Identify all Extraneous Variables

It's not always possible to control all the variables in an experiment, but it's important that you realise what they all are — otherwise you could draw some invalid conclusions.

EXAMPLE: 100 individuals take part in an experiment over one year. The average number of hours they each slept, per 24 hours, was plotted against their age.

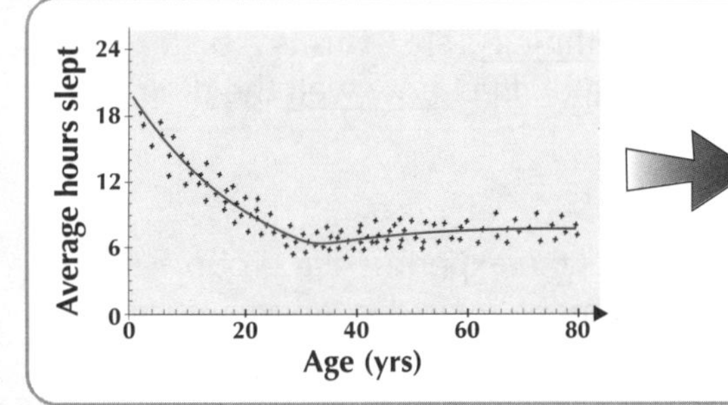

It would be easy, from this data, to conclude that the amount of sleep you need per day decreases until you reach your mid-thirties, then increases very slightly with age. But the situation is a bit more complicated than that...

You need to think about all the other factors that might have an influence on the length of time you sleep for. Stressful jobs or young families to look after can reduce the amount of sleep you get per night. Diet plays a significant role as well — for example, adults are likely to have much higher levels of caffeine in their diet than children, decreasing the number of hours they sleep for.

Extraneous is a strange but important word...

Don't be put off by the mathsy speak here. Basically, the other variables need to remain constant — otherwise you can't tell if your results are down to changes you've made or something else altogether.

More on Obtaining Data

If you want your experiment to test the effectiveness of a particular factor, you need a control group.

Control Groups make your Results Meaningful

A 'control group' is a group that isn't part of the experiment, but is as similar to the experimental group as possible. You compare any changes in the experimental group with the control group.

You can then tell whether the changes are due to your experiment or might have happened anyway.

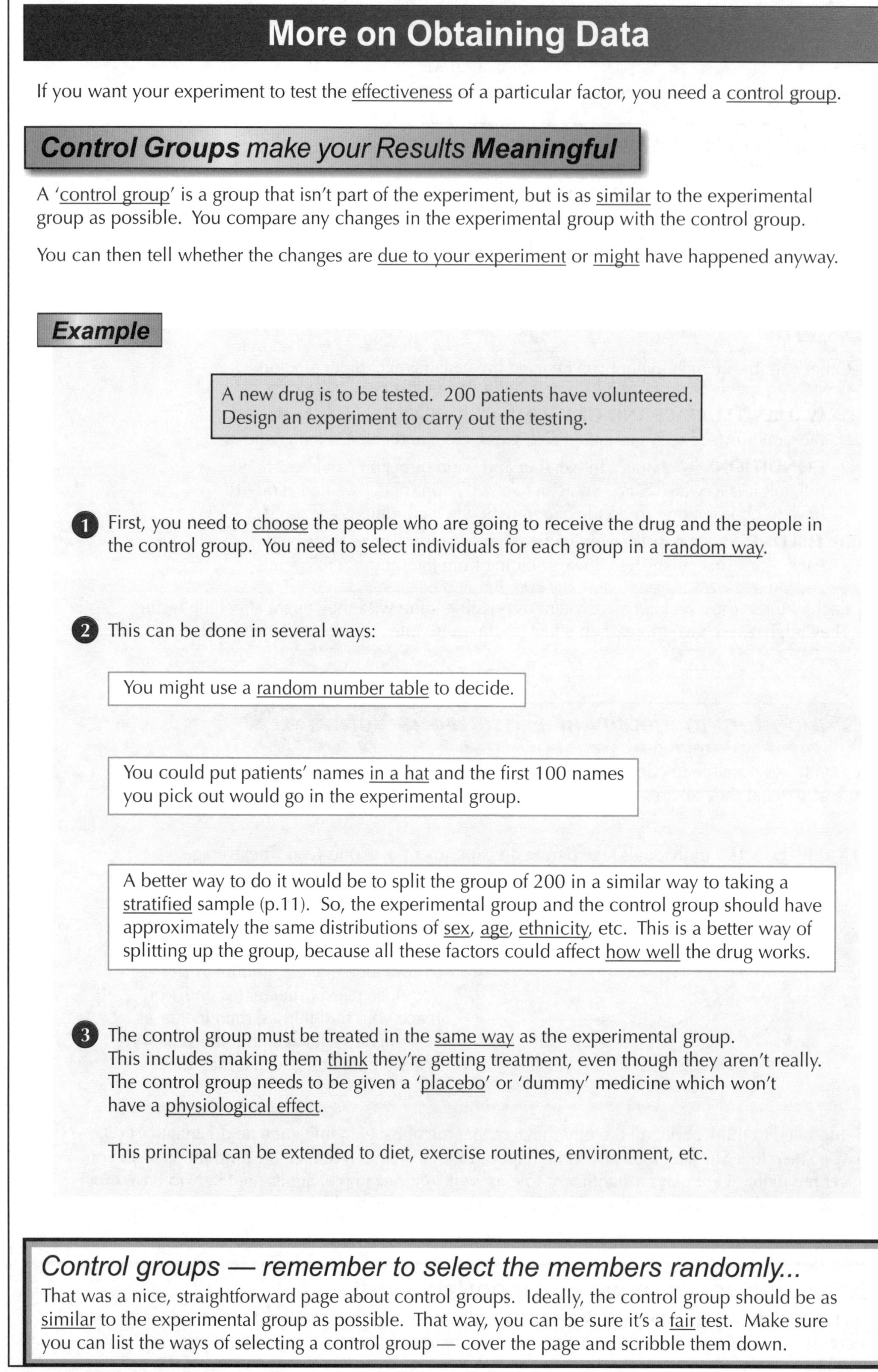

Example

A new drug is to be tested. 200 patients have volunteered. Design an experiment to carry out the testing.

1. First, you need to choose the people who are going to receive the drug and the people in the control group. You need to select individuals for each group in a random way.

2. This can be done in several ways:

   You might use a random number table to decide.

   You could put patients' names in a hat and the first 100 names you pick out would go in the experimental group.

   A better way to do it would be to split the group of 200 in a similar way to taking a stratified sample (p.11). So, the experimental group and the control group should have approximately the same distributions of sex, age, ethnicity, etc. This is a better way of splitting up the group, because all these factors could affect how well the drug works.

3. The control group must be treated in the same way as the experimental group. This includes making them think they're getting treatment, even though they aren't really. The control group needs to be given a 'placebo' or 'dummy' medicine which won't have a physiological effect.

   This principal can be extended to diet, exercise routines, environment, etc.

Control groups — remember to select the members randomly...

That was a nice, straightforward page about control groups. Ideally, the control group should be as similar to the experimental group as possible. That way, you can be sure it's a fair test. Make sure you can list the ways of selecting a control group — cover the page and scribble them down.

Matched Pairs & Before-and-After

Making sure your experiment isn't affected by outside factors is a tricky business.
Here are two ways of keeping that risk down.

Matched Pairs are **Identical** apart from the Test Variable

You can use 'matched pairs' to investigate the effect of one factor alone.

1) You take pairs of members of your population who are alike in every way.
Identical twins are used a lot in matched pair studies by sociologists and psychologists.
2) Put one member from each pair into each of two groups.
3) The groups are then treated differently in some way, and any changes to the response variable noted.
4) Since the two groups are identical in every way, any differences in the response variable must be due to the different treatment.

Example

Tim wants to investigate the effects of two different soils on the fruit of a strawberry plant. He decides to do this using matched pairs.

To make sure the two plants are identical in every way, Tim uses strawberry plants grown from cuttings off the same plant.
He puts the two young plants in pots containing the test soils, side by side in the greenhouse, and waits for the fruit to appear.

1) To make this a completely fair test, all extraneous variables need to be controlled. The two plants need to be kept at the same temperature, get the same amount of light and the same amount of water.
2) Since the only difference between the two plants will be the soil they've grown in, any differences in the size, colour or taste of the fruit will be due to the soil.

Before-and-After Experiments test the **Same Group** Twice

1) Like matched pairs, before-and-after experiments keep all but one factor constant.
2) For these experiments, the same group of people (or things), are given a similar test before and after an event to see how they're affected by it.

Example

A company that gives courses on improving your memory skills wants to test out a new system. Thirty volunteers are shown a list of twenty numbers and asked to write down as many as they can remember. After training in the memory system, the same group of people are given a similar test again.

If the system works, the results of the second test will be better than those of the first.

This sort of experiment has been used to test the effect of the long school summer holiday.

Matched pairs — first find your twins...

These methods are about getting just one factor at work in your experiment. Write down all you know about each method, go back through the page, then test yourself again. "Before-and-after" in action...

Capture / Recapture Method

Capture/recapture is a clever way to estimate the size of a constant population.

Both the *Capture* and *Recapture* need to be *Random*

EXAMPLE:

Work out an estimate of the number of fish in a lake, given the following information:

(i) A fisherman nets 50 fish from the lake. He marks all of them with a small tag and returns them alive to the lake.

(ii) A few days later another fisherman nets 60 fish. 15 of them are found to have been tagged by the first fisherman.

If you can assume that the sample of 60 fish is representative of the whole population, you can work out roughly how many fish there are in total.

Method 1 — Ratios

1) The ratio of tagged to untagged fish in the second net is 15:45 (which cancels to 1:3).
2) You know there are 50 tagged fish in the population.
3) So, multiply the ratio by 50 to get the total numbers of tagged and untagged fish: $(1 \times 50):(3 \times 50)$ or 50:150.
   So there are about 200 fish in the lake.

Method 2 — Fractions

1) The fraction of tagged fish in the second net will be the same as the fraction tagged in the whole lake.
2) Call the total population N.

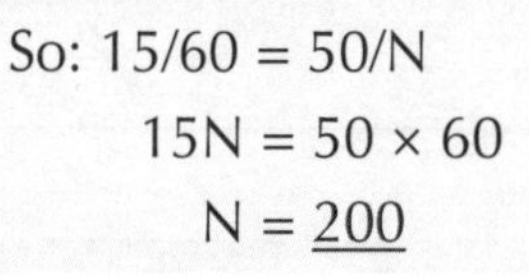

So: $15/60 = 50/N$

$15N = 50 \times 60$

$N = 200$

> BE VERY CAREFUL:
> Capture/recapture only works in constant populations, i.e. the population has to be made up of exactly the same members when the two samples are taken.

It doesn't matter which method you use, so do the one you find easiest to remember. Remember to show all your working though.

You Need to Make a Lot of *Assumptions*

You make a lot of assumptions when you use this method — so it's only an estimate.

1) You assume that the second net is perfectly representative of the whole population. For this to be true, the tagged fish will need to have had time (and opportunity) to fully mix back in with the rest of the population before the second sample is taken.
2) You have to assume that the capture and recapture are completely random. If the person doing the catching can see the tags, you could end up with a biased second sample.
3) You also assume the fish are unaffected by the first capture or the tagging/marking. They're returned alive and well, but some types of tag would make them easier to catch.

Make sure you capture the points on this page...

For the maths bit of capture and recapture, learn one of the two methods on this page — otherwise you'll risk getting them confused. Bear in mind that it's only an estimate — know the assumptions you're making.

Simulation

You can use random numbers to 'simulate' real random events (like rolling a dice).

Use **Random Number Tables** to Simulate Real Data

EXAMPLE: The table below contains random numbers. You can use it if you want to simulate the results of rolling a fair dice.

5712	2839	6210	5335	7691	7748	4452
5586	1784	7362	2731	1790	4283	5166
9000	8012	3502	7523	3450	3718	8926

Random number tables are usually much bigger than this one, and the individual values can have any number of digits.

There are loads of ways to do this using the table:

1) Probably the most obvious way is to read across each row and take the first digit of each number to be the result of a roll of the dice. You ignore any numbers with a first digit of 7 or more. The first 10 results using this method are: 5, 2, 6, 5, 4, 5, 1, 2, 1, 4.
[Don't be tempted to read a 7 as a 1, an 8 as a 2, etc. If you do that, you've got more chance of generating a 1, 2 or 3 than a 4, 5 or 6 (1 = 1 or 7, 2 = 2 or 8, 3 = 3 or 9, 4 = 4, etc.).]
2) You could use the second, third or fourth digit of each random number instead, or read down the columns rather than across the rows. You could even use all the digits — reading left to right, right to left, up and down and back up again...
3) However you choose to read the table, you need to make your method clear and stick to it.

You can use your **Calculator** to Generate **Random Numbers**

Your calculator will probably have a random number button. Look for "RAN" or "RAN#" (if you've got a graphical calculator, you might have a RAN function instead — read the manual).

Chances are you'll have to press the 'Shift' or '2nd Fn' button first (on some calculators it's "shift •"), but it depends on the make of your calculator.

Calculators usually generate random numbers between 0 and 1 to 3 decimal places.
e.g. 0.693, 0.581, 0.002, 0.014, 0.088, 0.639

In the dice example above you might chose the last digit to simulate your roll score (ignoring 0 and anything above 6).

Or you can use a **Computer**

There are loads of different computer programs you can use to generate random numbers, but this example just tells you how to do it in Excel — you can make yourself a random number table.

1) Open a new worksheet in Excel.
2) In cell A1, type =RAND() and press enter — this gives you a random number between 0 and 1 with loads of decimal places.
3) Copy and paste this into as many cells as you need.

Random numbers — table, calculator or computer...

There are three methods for you to learn here. They're pretty simple so long as you remember that point about simulating dice rolls — no 0's or anything above a 6 — it's easy marks.

Warm-Up and Worked Exam Questions

What's this I see — oh, it's some more warm-up questions...

Warm-Up Questions

1) What is the other name for the explanatory variable?
2) An experiment was done to find out how the stopping distance of a car varies with the speed of the car. What are the explanatory and response variables in this experiment?
3) Simon takes readings from his thermometer at hourly intervals. He wants to display his results on a graph. Which variable should be plotted on the y-axis — temperature or time?
4) Laura is doing an experiment using a group of people and needs a control group. Describe the role of a control group in an experiment.
5) In what kind of experiment do you test the same group twice?
6) An experiment was done to test the theory that exercise increases appetite. On one morning, a group of people went jogging outside before breakfast. The next day the same group of people stayed indoors and rested before eating breakfast. The amounts of food eaten for breakfast each day were compared. What is the extraneous variable in this experiment?
7) Use your calculator to randomly generate 10 three-digit numbers.

Worked Exam Questions

As that old saying goes, wherever there's a warm-up question...

1 An environmental health inspector visited 'Tastiest Bite' fast food restaurant and found mice in the kitchen. She caught ten mice and tagged each of them. She returned later and caught eight mice, two of which had tags on.

(a) Estimate how many mice there are in the kitchen.

Let n = total number of mice

So $2 \div 8 = 10 \div n$, $2n = 80$, $n = 40$

(2 marks for correct answer, otherwise 1 mark for correct method.)

(2 marks)

(b) Write down one assumption you have made about the mice population.

The tagged mice are well mixed with the non-tagged mice before the second sample is taken.

There are several other correct answers here — you're assuming a lot in part (a).

(1 mark)

(c) State whether the capture/recapture method would be suitable for estimating each of the following. Give a reason for your choice.

(i) Number of people on a cruise ship.

Yes. They are in a confined area so the population is constant, and they move around.

(1 mark)

(ii) Number of cats in a neighbourhood.

No. They don't stay in a confined space, so a tagged sample might not be representative of the whole population.

(1 mark)

Exam Questions

2 Here is a table of 20 randomly generated three-digit numbers.

371	706	955	499	981	546	374	177	167	928
230	266	123	106	142	962	310	243	022	787

(a) How could these numbers be used to simulate the results of spinning a five-sided spinner numbered 1-5?

....

....

(2 marks)

(b) Using the method you have described in part (a), what would the first nine numbers be?

....

(1 mark)

3 A doctor believes he has found a pill that will dramatically reduce patients' cholesterol levels in one week. He chooses eight matched pairs and puts one member from each pair into each of two groups, A and B. He records their cholesterol levels and starts the experiment. Every day for one week, he gives one of his pills to each member of group A and a dummy pill to each member of group B.

(a) What is the name given to group A?

....

(1 mark)

(b) What is the name given to group B?

....

(1 mark)

(c) Give another name for the dummy pill.

....

(1 mark)

(d) How should the doctor make sure that the patients' lifestyles, e.g. diet and exercise, don't make the experiment unfair?

....

....

(1 mark)

(e) What will the doctor do at the end of the week?
Explain how he will know if his pill works.

....

....

(2 marks)

Revision Summary for Section One

Phew — that was a bit of a monster of a first section, but there's loads of useful stuff in there. It'll come in handy wherever you are... well, particularly if you're in a Statistics Exam. Use these questions to test what you know, and what you don't. Keep practising them till you can get them all right without looking back at the section. Go on — you know you want to.

Keep learning the basic facts until you know them

1) Define "primary data" and give three possible sources of it.
2) Define secondary data. What things do you have to be sure of before you use secondary data for a statistical project?
3) Define qualitative and quantitative data.
4) What is the difference between discrete and continuous data? Give one example of each.
5) Give a definition and an example for each of the following:
   a) categorical scale, b) rank scale, c) interval scale, d) ratio scale.
6) Give one problem with grouping data.
7) What is bivariate data?
8) What does the word "census" mean?
9) Give an example of a population that it wouldn't be practical to take a census of.
10) Describe how to take a simple random sample of 25 from a population of 5000.
11) What is a stratified sample? Describe a method of selecting a stratified sample.
12) Describe how to take a systematic sample of 25 from a population of 5000.
13) List three non-random sampling methods.
    Give one advantage and one disadvantage of each of these methods.
14) Describe two possible causes of bias when you're taking a sample.
15) What is a hypothesis and why do you need one?
16) Give three different ways to carry out questionnaire surveys.
17) What advantages do closed questions have over open questions?
18) What can you do to reduce the chances of collecting biased data from a questionnaire?
19) List three things you need to bear in mind when designing each question in a questionnaire.
    What's the best way to test the quality of a questionnaire once you've written it?
20) What is an opinion scale?
21) What's the advantage of using an opinion scale instead of a simple "yes/no" question?
22) Describe the method of random response questioning.
    What sort of question would random response be suitable for?
23) Give four advantages and four disadvantages of carrying out face-to-face interviews rather than asking your sample to fill out a paper questionnaire.
24) Explain what the "explanatory variable" and "response variable" are in the context of statistical experiments.
25) Why do you need to keep all other variables, apart from the explanatory and response variables, constant during experiments?
26) What is a control group?
27) What are matched pairs?
28) Explain the process of capture/recapture for estimating population sizes.
29) What condition needs to be true of the population for you to be able to use capture/recapture?
30) What assumptions do you make when you use capture/recapture?
31) How might you use random number tables to simulate the results of tossing a fair coin?
32) Explain how you can generate random numbers on your calculator.

Frequency Tables

Frequency tables can be done either in columns or rows, and let you see lots of raw data more easily.

Frequency Tables Contain Raw Data

1) The word frequency just means how many, so a frequency table is just a "how many in each group" table.
2) All frequency tables have 3 columns (or 3 rows).
3) The first column (or row) just gives the group labels — the different categories (e.g. 1 goal, 2 goals, etc.)
4) The second column (or row) gives the actual data — in the form of a tally.
5) The last column (or row) is the frequency, which you get by adding up the tally marks.

Example

A hockey team lists the number of goals they score in each match of a season.
Draw a frequency table for the data.

1, 2, 0, 3, 2, 1, 0, 2, 3, 2, 2, 1, 2, 0, 1, 5

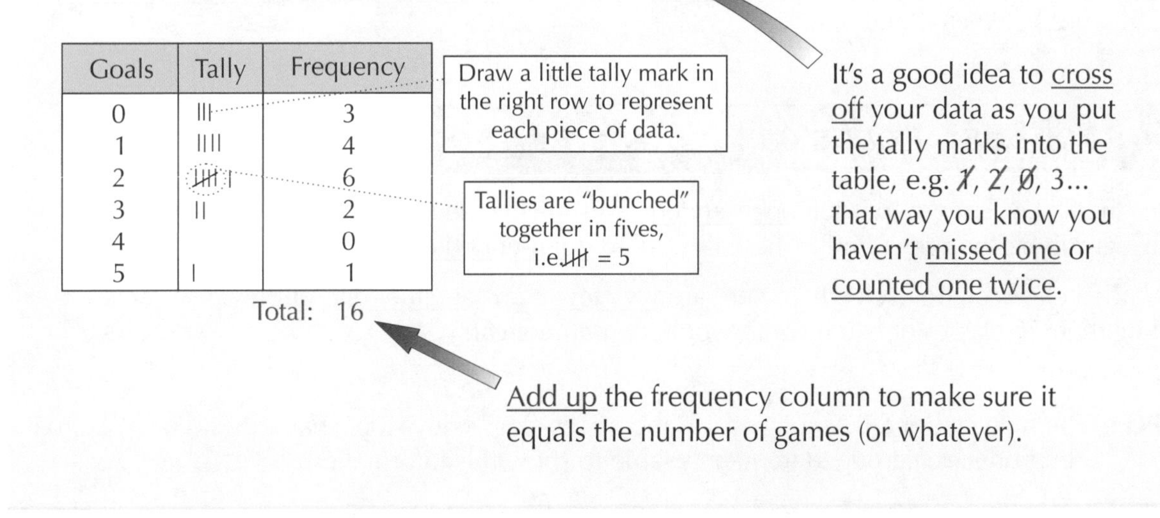

Goals	Tally	Frequency
0	III	3
1	IIII	4
2	~~IIII~~ I	6
3	II	2
4		0
5	I	1

Total: 16

Don't be clever and just fill in the frequency column by sight without doing the tally column. You'll just end up making mistakes that way.

*You can Draw Frequency Tables **Horizontally** or **Vertically***

This table is the same as the top one, just turned around — easy.

Goals	0	1	2	3	4	5
Tally	III	IIII	~~IIII~~ I	II		I
Frequency	3	4	6	2	0	1

A frequency table is just a "how many in each group" table...

As so often in maths, the words they use can be really off-putting. Once you realise that a frequency table really just shows you how many things are in each group, life becomes a lot easier.

Grouped Frequency Tables

Grouped frequency tables split data into groups using class intervals. They're a bit trickier than simple frequency tables because the group labels are now intervals rather than single items.

Use **Grouped Frequency Tables** When you've got **Lots** of Data

You often use grouped frequency tables when you've got too many pieces of data to think about individually, or when they are all different.

EXAMPLE: Amanda recorded the number of runs she scored in 12 school cricket matches:

10, 1, 9, 5, 8, 6, 15, 5, 12, 5, 16, 0

Runs	0 - 4	5 - 9	10 - 14	15 - 20
Tally	||	𝍸 |	||	||
Frequency	2	6	2	2

Here, there are gaps between each upper class limit and the next lower class limit (e.g. the first class ends at 4 and the second class starts at 5). That's because the data's discrete (see p.2), so nothing comes between 4 and 5, etc.

The **First** or **Last** groups can be **Open-ended**

Sometimes the first or last group is left open-ended. This means the first group has no lower limit and the last group has no upper limit. These are called open-ended classes.

An open-ended class can be used when there are very few items at either end of the data — so recording them in classes of equal width would be impractical.

EXAMPLE: The manager of a TV shop records the prices of 15 televisions that are sold one Saturday. He produces a grouped frequency table to show this information.

£449, £250, £479, £499, £549, £525, £534, £1099,
£650, £600, £589, £650, £599, £230, £689

Cost of TV (£)	less than 400	400 - 499	500 - 599	600 - 699	700 and over
Tally	||	|||	𝍸	||||	|
Frequency	2	3	5	4	1

In the above example you'd need nine class intervals to show the data without using open-ended classes and four of those intervals would be empty.

Remember that the details of the raw data are lost whenever information is grouped, especially when open-ended classes are used.

Grouped frequency tables make large sets of data easier to handle...

Make sure you can take raw data and turn it into a grouped frequency table. You should also know when it's appropriate to use open-ended classes in your table. The fun never stops with Statistics.

Grouped Frequency Tables

You can also make grouped frequency tables for continuous data...

Be Careful with Class Intervals for **Continuous Data**

If you've got continuous data, you can use inequalities to define your class intervals.

Remember that:

$>$ means "Greater than"

$<$ means "Less than"

$\geq$ means "Greater than or equal to"

$\leq$ means "Less than or equal to"

Example

Adam measured the heights of 12 plants in a biology experiment to the nearest 0.1 cm. Draw a frequency table for his results:

6.2 1.3 5.0 7.2 3.1 8.8 13.7 7.1 4.9 19.6 10.0 15.0

1) First, choose the class widths (unless you're told what to use). What class widths you choose depends on how detailed you want your table to be (see p.42).

2) Using inequalities, define your class intervals. Every possible value needs a group to go into:

Height (cm)	$0 \leq h < 5$	$5 \leq h < 10$	$10 \leq h < 15$	$15 \leq h < 20$
Tally	|||	𝍸	||	||
Frequency	3	5	2	2

So, 5.0 would go in the 2nd group, and anything less than 5.0 would go in the 1st group. There should be no gaps or overlaps between your class intervals. E.g. if the class interval of the 3rd group was changed to $10 \leq h \leq 15$ and the other groups left the same, there would be an overlap between the 3rd and 4th groups. Recording a height of 15 cm would be impossible because you wouldn't know which group to put it in.

3) Remember when you're using tables like this, that they're only as accurate as the original data. E.g. if you measured the heights of the plants to the nearest 0.01 cm, you might find the plant you thought was 5.0 cm tall was actually only 4.97 cm tall. That would put it in the first group, not the second.

Use inequalities to define class intervals for continuous data...

When you're making grouped frequency tables for continuous data, remember that every possible value needs a single group to go into. There should be no gaps or overlaps between any class intervals.

Simplifying and Analysing Data

Having lots of data is all well and good, but big complicated tables are really hard to analyse. Simplifying tables makes them easier to get your head round, but you do lose detail in the process.

Whenever you simplify tables of data, you're likely to end up with less information in the new table than you started with (not surprising really).

You need to know the different ways of simplifying tables, as well as how and why simplifying affects the usefulness of your data.

EXAMPLE: *Five species of butterfly are found in the Marshy-Lea conservation area. The table below shows the number of each species recorded in Marshy-Lea by year.*

Species	2003	2004	2005	2006	2007
A	112	82	98	72	61
B	52	30	41	28	25
C	63	57	52	45	41
D	14	17	23	25	27
E	22	18	20	19	4

There's a lot of information in this table, which makes it very difficult to spot trends (general patterns in the data).

*The **Easiest** Way of Simplifying is **Totalling***

If you total the data for each year you get:

Total number of butterflies recorded in Marshy-Lea by year.

Year	2003	2004	2005	2006	2007
Total	263	204	234	189	158

This new table is much easier to form useful conclusions from.

1) The trend seems to be that numbers are generally decreasing.
2) It's useful to look at any bits of the data that don't follow the general trend as well. So, between 2004 and 2005, there was actually an increase in recorded butterflies. But look at the year before that — there had been a big drop between 2003 and 2004.
3) You could go on to compare the data with earlier and later years, or other sites, if you had similar data for them.

DISADVANTAGES OF TOTALLING:

1) **You've lost all the detail about individual species.**
2) **Whilst you can see the overall number decreasing, look at the 'species D' row in the original table — the numbers are actually increasing slightly. Facts like this one are lost by totalling.**

Simplifying makes data much easier to analyse...

It can be difficult to spot trends in tables with lots of data in. You should be able to simplify data by totalling and spot patterns in the data. But remember that totalling is only one way of simplifying...

Simplifying and Analysing Data

Totalling is not the only way of simplifying data.
Turning numbers into percentages can make things clearer sometimes.

*You Can Work Out **Percentages***

You can look at changes in the proportion of butterflies of each species by calculating percentages. Just looking at 2006 and 2007:

Percentage breakdown, by species, of butterflies recorded at Marshly-Lea — 2006/2007.

Species	2006	2007
A	38.1%	38.6%
B	14.8%	15.8%
C	23.8%	25.9%
D	13.2%	17.1%
E	10.1%	2.5%

So in 2007, 15.8% of the butterflies recorded at Marshy-Lea were of species B.

1) This table lets you look at the proportion of each year's butterfly numbers by species.
2) Clearly the proportion of butterflies of species D is greater in 2007 than 2006, and the percentage of butterflies of species E is down dramatically.
3) The proportion of species A has stayed steady, and is by far the highest.

DISADVANTAGES OF PERCENTAGE BREAKDOWN TABLES:

1) We don't know from this table whether total butterfly numbers have increased or decreased from one year to the next.

2) Nor do we know how many butterflies of each species were found.

A COMBINATION of the table showing the total data for each year and the percentage breakdown table gives you a good overview of the data.

Remember that details are lost whenever data is simplified...

You should be aware of the advantages and disadvantages of the different methods of simplifying tables. Sometimes you may need a couple of different simplified tables to be able to draw useful conclusions from the data. There's yet more about different ways of simplifying data over the page.

Simplifying and Analysing Data

Here's another page on simplifying data. Only one more to go after this... promise.

Simplify Data by **Grouping** it

If you have lots of data that's all different, it can help to put it in a grouped frequency table.
You have to be very careful not to distort your data when you're simplifying though.

Example

A 100 m sprinter runs the following practice times (in seconds):

11.56... 10.47... 10.03... 10.94... 11.89... 11.62... 10.81... 11.77... 10.20... 11.91... 10.55...

He records them, accurate to 0.1 seconds...

11.6 10.5 10.0 10.9 11.9 11.6 10.8 11.8 10.2 11.9 10.6

...and shows them in a grouped frequency table.

Time (s)	Frequency
$9.0 < t \leq 9.5$	0
$9.5 < t \leq 10.0$	1
$10.0 < t \leq 10.5$	2
$10.5 < t \leq 11.0$	3
$11.0 < t \leq 11.5$	0
$11.5 < t \leq 12.0$	5

The data's much easier to handle in this format, but the way he's put the table together is a bit misleading. By reducing the number of significant figures of his measurement, the sprinter has distorted his data.

His fastest time was actually 10.03... seconds.
He rounded this to 10.0 and counted it in the $9.5 < t \leq 10.0$ group.
This suggests he broke the 10 second barrier, which he didn't.

Be careful when grouping data together...

When you're making a grouped frequency table, make sure the accuracy and class intervals you choose don't give misleading results. There's more about frequency tables and class intervals on pages 37-39.

Simplifying and Analysing Data

Here it is – the final page on simplifying data. It might seem dull, but these pages are really important. It's very difficult to analyse data without putting it in the right form, and that usually means simplifying.

Combining Class Intervals gives you a Simpler Table

You can simplify a grouped frequency table by combining classes.

Example

The sprinter from the previous example (see page 42) decides to simplify his table by halving the number of classes:

Time (s)	Frequency
$9.0 < t \leq 10.0$	1
$10.0 < t \leq 11.0$	5
$11.0 < t \leq 12.0$	5

ADVANTAGE:

1) The new table is much smaller and simpler to look at.

DISADVANTAGES:

1) Important details have been lost.

   For example, the second and third groups (10-11 and 11-12) now have the same frequencies. This masks the fact that most of his times were either really slow or quite fast. There was a big gap in the original data between 11 and 11.5 seconds.

2) The 9-10 second group is completely unnecessary. Using the original data, none of the sprinter's times would actually go in it. It just distorts the data even further than the first table did. (It might also be worth noticing that most of this group is well below the Olympic 100 m record — hmmm...)

Learn to look for trends in data, but be careful not to oversimplify the situation.

Simplifying GOOD... Oversimplifying BAD...

It's important to realise how oversimplifying data can distort your results. Make sure you know the advantages and disadvantages of the different ways of simplifying data inside out. It's just easy marks.

Warm-Up and Worked Exam Questions

These warm-ups shouldn't be too stretching — if you find them really tricky go back through the section.

Warm-Up Questions

1) Ben has six lessons at school each day. Ben records the number of lessons he enjoys each day over a two week period.

   4, 3, 0, 6, 2, 3, 4, 3, 1, 2

   Complete the frequency table below for Ben's data. One frequency has already been done.

Lessons enjoyed	0	1	2	3	4	5	6
Tally			||				
Frequency			2				

2) The data below shows the number of goals scored in each of 20 football matches.

   0 2 4 1 2 6 1 4 2 5 4 2 0 3 1 7 2 3 6 5

   Record this data in a grouped frequency table with four class intervals.

3) In your answer to Q2, what does the total of the numbers in the frequency row represent?

Worked Exam Questions

Once every little bit of this makes sense, move on to the exam questions opposite.

1 The times taken for various cars to reach 60 mph from a stationary start are recorded. The times are rounded to the nearest 0.1 seconds and are summarised in a grouped frequency table:

Time, t (sec)	$5.0 < t \leq 6.0$	$6.0 < t \leq 7.0$	$7.0 < t \leq 8.0$	$8.0 < t \leq 10.0$
Number of cars	12	8	5	5

(a) Give one reason why the processing of the data means that the table may be misleading.

By rounding to the nearest 0.1 seconds some data may have been placed in an inappropriate group. For example, a time of 6.04 would be rounded down to 6.0 and recorded in the $5.0 < t \leq 6.0$ group. But it should really be in the $6.0 < t \leq 7.0$ group.

Hint: always be a little bit wary if rounding has taken place. *(1 mark)*

(b) A second grouped frequency table has been made to show the data.

Time, t (sec)	$5.0 < t \leq 5.5$	$5.5 < t \leq 6.0$	$6.0 < t \leq 6.5$	$6.5 < t \leq 7.0$	$7.0 < t \leq 7.5$	$7.5 < t \leq 8.0$	$8.0 < t \leq 8.5$	$8.5 < t \leq 9.0$	$9.0 < t \leq 9.5$	$9.5 < t \leq 10.0$
Number of cars	5	7	4	4	4	1	1	0	2	2

Give two ways in which this second table is a better form of grouping than the first one.

Unlike in the first grouped table the class widths are the same. **(1 mark)**

More information is included in the second table. **(1 mark)**

Another reason would be that the shape of the distribution is clearer. *(2 marks)*

Exam Questions

2 A charity fundraiser walked the length of the country in 58 days. The following table shows a summary of the number of miles, m, she walked each day.

Miles, m	$m \leq 5$	$5 < m \leq 10$	$10 < m \leq 15$	$15 < m \leq 20$	$20 < m \leq 25$	$25 < m \leq 30$	$30 < m$
Frequency	0	1	17	22	15	x	0

(a) Find x — the number of days she walked over 25 miles but not more than 30 miles.

....

(2 marks)

(b) On how many days did she walk 20 miles or less?

....

(1 mark)

(c) The charity decides to summarise the data in a second table. Complete the table.

Miles, m	$5 < m \leq 15$	$15 < m \leq 25$	$25 < m \leq 35$
Frequency			

(1 mark)

(d) Give one way in which the method of grouping in the first table is better than that in the second table.

....

(1 mark)

3 The table below shows the number of hours flown by oil rig support helicopters from 1985 to 2006 by helicopter type. The data is in 1000s of hours.

Helicopter Type	Year			
	85-89	90-94	95-99	00-06
A	80	70	90	90
B	160	150	160	130
C	200	260	300	300
D	70	110	120	150
E	80	50	40	60
F	90	70	70	80
All Helicopters	680	710		

(a) Complete the table.

(1 mark)

(b) Describe the trend in total flying hours between 1985 and 2006 for all helicopters.

....

(1 mark)

(c) 10.3% of the 1985-1989 flying hours were flown by Type D helicopters. Compare this to the proportion of hours flown by Type D helicopters in the period 2000-2006.

....

....

(2 marks)

Bar Charts

There are several different ways of drawing bar charts. You know how to do simple bar charts already — from "normal" maths, but bar charts can also be used to compare data.

Pictograms use *Pictures* to Represent Data

EXAMPLE:
A council employee did a survey of customer satisfaction on the buses by questioning passengers on a Saturday afternoon. 70 people were happy with the service, but 50 people thought it wasn't good enough. A similar survey was also done the following afternoon. On this occasion there were 160 people who were happy and 80 who were unhappy.

The pictograms on the right show this data.

People questioned on Saturday

Happy
Unhappy
= 20 people

People questioned on Sunday

Happy
Unhappy
= 20 people

Multiple Bar Charts Can be Used to Compare Data

Multiple bar charts have more than one bar for each category. This makes it easy to compare data.

EXAMPLE:

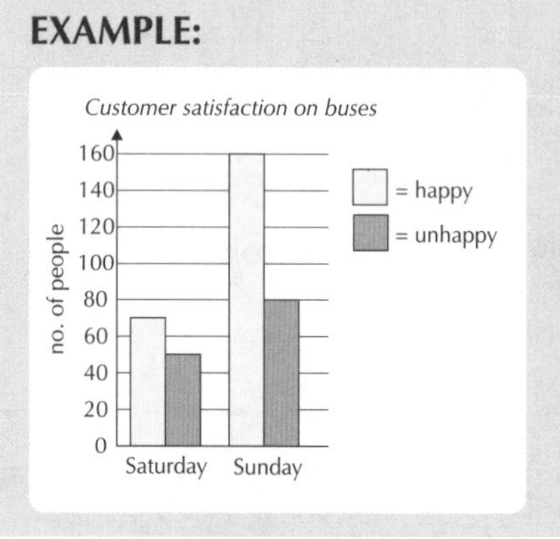

Going back to the previous example — here's a multiple bar chart for the same data.

It is easy to compare customer satisfaction on the two days. However, it is difficult to draw useful conclusions, as different numbers of people were questioned on the different days.

Composite Bar Charts show Proportions in the Data

A composite bar chart has a single bar for each category. Each bar is split into sections. They can be thought of in terms of percentages, with the length of the whole bar representing 100%.

EXAMPLE:
Returning to the above example again — this is a composite bar chart for the same data.

This chart shows that a higher proportion of those passengers questioned on Sunday were happy with the service than those questioned on Saturday.

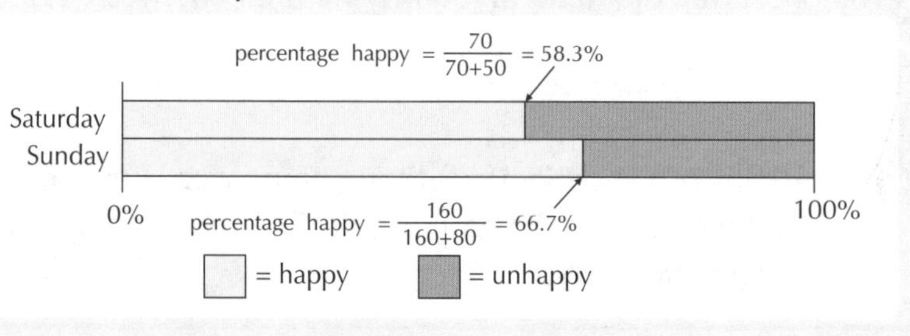

Make sure you know the different types of bar charts...

Just like that old saying about cats, there's more than one type of bar chart. You should be happy with all the details about the bar charts on this page and be able to draw any of them from a table of data.

The basic stuff on pie charts is covered in "normal" maths, so here's a page on the more interesting bits you need to know.

Comparative Pie Charts use Areas

Comparative pie charts use the same area for each unit of data.

The council employee from the example on page 46 decides to draw comparative pie charts for her data.

1. She decides that Saturday's pie chart will have a radius of 1.4 cm. Working out the angles is fairly easy:

Total number of people interviewed = 120
Happy = 70, so angle = (70/120) × 360 = 210°
Unhappy = 50, so angle = (50/120) × 360 = 150°

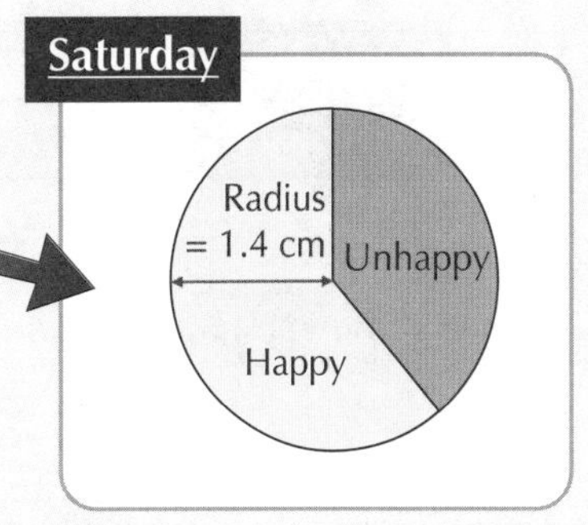

2. Now she wants a comparative pie chart for Sunday's data.

Saturday's chart has a radius of 1.4 cm and represents 120 people.

So: area for 120 people = $\pi r^2 = 1.4^2\pi$ cm^2
area for 1 person = $1.4^2\pi \div 120$ cm^2

Use this to work out the radius of the other pie chart:

Sunday's survey had 240 people.
1 person = $1.4^2\pi \div 120$ cm^2

So: area for 240 people = $240 \times 1.4^2\pi \div 120 = 1.4^2\pi \times 2$ cm^2.

Work out its radius:
area = πr^2

So: radius = $\sqrt{(\text{area} / \pi)} = \sqrt{1.4^2\pi \times 2 / \pi} = 1.98 \text{ cm} \approx 2 \text{ cm}$

Finally, work out the angles...

Happy = (160/240) × 360 = 240°
Unhappy = (80/240) × 360 = 120°

Sunday
radius
= 2 cm
Unhappy
Happy

It's important you understand how this example works...

It's quite tempting to skip through this page and think "I've seen one pie chart, I've seen them all". Unfortunately you won't get any marks in the exam for skipping. Make sure you know how comparative pie charts are different from the regular ones you've seen before. Save the skipping for P.E.

Discrete Data and Step Polygons

Graphs of discrete data look different from graphs of continuous data — and you need to be an expert at both types. The discrete graphs on this page use vertical lines and steps.

A *Line Graph* is a bit like a *Bar Chart* — but with *Lines*

These are used to show frequency distributions for discrete data.

EXAMPLE: It is claimed that boxes of matches have an average content of 48 matches. George counts the exact number of matches in each of 10 boxes. The frequency table and line graph below show his results.

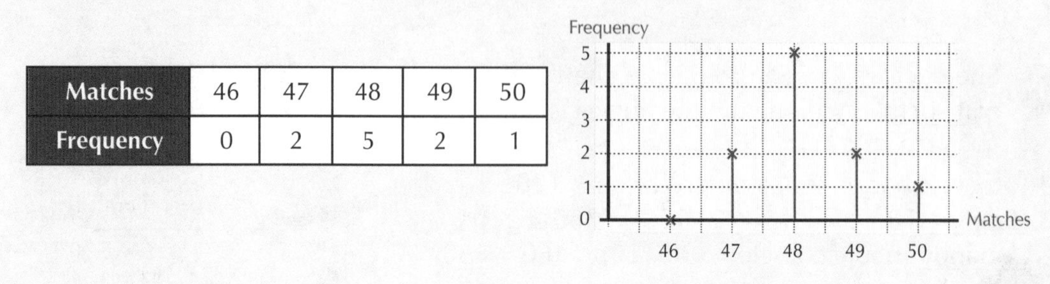

Matches	46	47	48	49	50
Frequency	0	2	5	2	1

Cumulative Frequency Step Polygons

Cumulative frequency is just a 'running total' of the frequencies.

EXAMPLE: Using the matches example from above:

1) Make a new table for cumulative frequency — this is the running total of the frequencies.

Matches	≤ 46	≤ 47	≤ 48	≤ 49	≤ 50
Cumulative Frequency	0	0 + 2 = 2	2 + 5 = 7	7 + 2 = 9	9 + 1 = 10

2) For discrete data, the cumulative frequency polygon is plotted as a step graph like this:

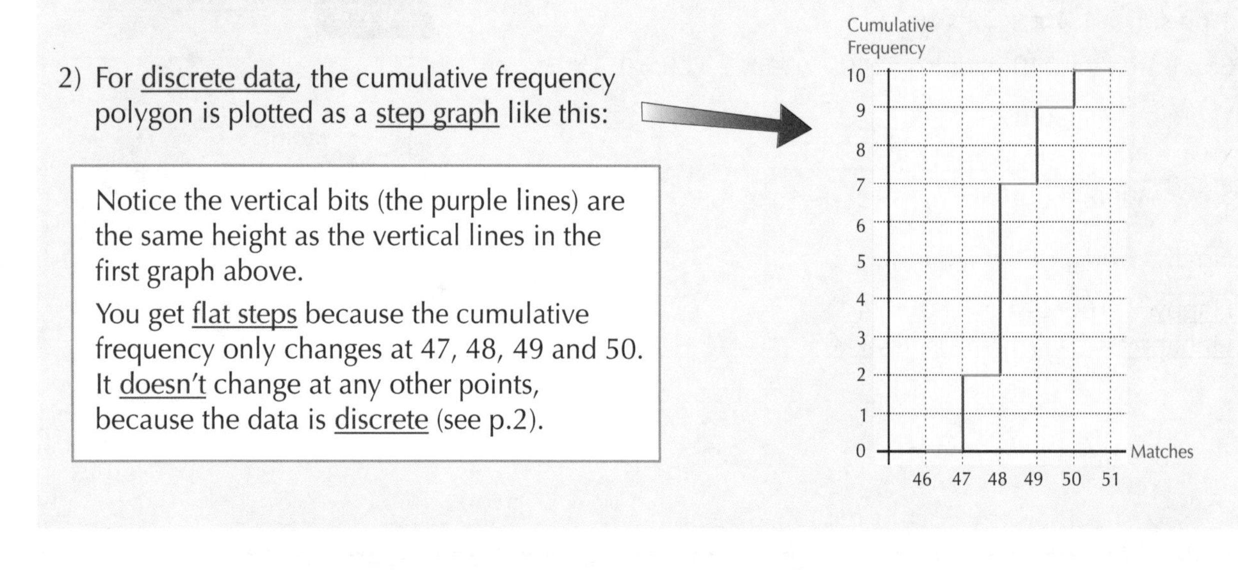

Notice the vertical bits (the purple lines) are the same height as the vertical lines in the first graph above.

You get flat steps because the cumulative frequency only changes at 47, 48, 49 and 50. It doesn't change at any other points, because the data is discrete (see p.2).

Learn how to draw these two graphs of discrete data...

When you're drawing graphs of discrete data, remember that there are gaps between the data values. So you'll use vertical lines and steps — the data points shouldn't be joined with a line or curve.

Warm-Up and Worked Exam Questions

Statistics is very much like international athletics — it's best if you warm up first.

Warm-Up Questions

1) This frequency table shows how many of three types of fruit Jonathan eats in a week.

Fruit	Apples	Bananas	Oranges
Frequency	12	10	8

Construct a pie chart to show the information using a radius of 3 cm.

2) Below is a line graph showing the number of trees in the gardens on one street.

a) How many gardens have two trees?

b) How many gardens does the street have altogether?

3) A hockey team records the total number of goals scored in each match they play. The information is summarised in the table below.

Goals Scored	0	1	2	3	4
Frequency	1	3	5	2	1

a) Draw a cumulative frequency table for the data.

b) How many matches have the team played?

Worked Exam Questions

These are quite tricky — so make sure you can follow them step by step...

1 The phone company T4 sold a total of 150 000 mobile phones in 2006. They show this on a pie chart with a radius of 10 cm. The phone company wants to construct a comparative pie chart to represent their 2007 sales of 120 000 mobile phones.

(a) Calculate the radius of the 2007 chart. Give your answer to 2 significant figures.

2006: Area $= \pi r^2 = \pi \times 10^2 = 100\pi$ cm^2

150 000 phones $= 100\pi$ **(Hint: π has been left in to avoid rounding errors later on.)**

So, 10 000 phones $= 100\pi/15$ cm^2 **(1 mark)**

(Hint: you could work out the area for 1 phone but the answer is small and you could easily introduce rounding errors.)

2007: 10 000 phones $= 100\pi/15$ (from 2006)

So area for 120 000 phones $= 12 \times 100\pi/15 = 80\pi$ cm^2 **(1 mark)**

$A = \pi r^2 = 80\pi$ (now divide by π both sides) **(3 marks for the correct answer, otherwise marks for working as shown.)**

$r^2 = 80$, so $r = \sqrt{80} = 8.94 = 8.9$ cm (2 s.f.)

(3 marks)

(b) Sales of the T4 Omega phone were 30 000 in 2006 and 20 000 in 2007. What angle should represent the Omega phone in each pie chart? Show your working.

Omega Sector 2006: $30\,000 \div 150\,000 \times 360° = 72°$ **(1 mark)**

Omega Sector 2007: $20\,000 \div 120\,000 \times 360° = 60°$ **(1 mark)**

(2 marks)

Exam Questions

2 Members of a cycling club meet up once a week. Each member picks one of three routes to ride. There's a Long Route, a Medium Route and a Short Route.

The table shows the number of cyclists doing each route for two weeks.
The composite bar chart below displays the data for Week 1.

Route	Long	Medium	Short
Number of Cyclists — wk.1	15	3	2
Number of Cyclists — wk.2	12	15	3

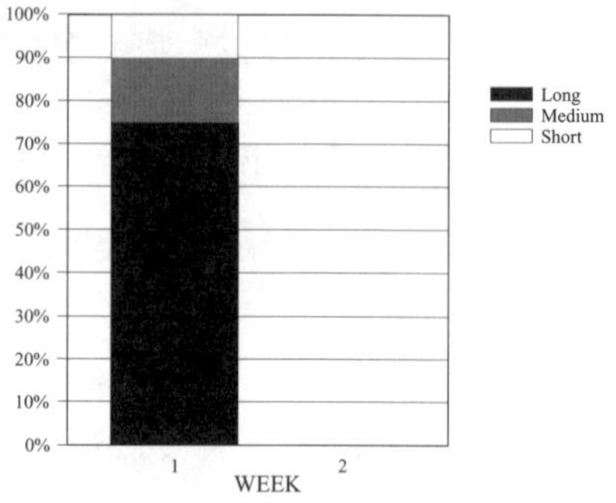

100%
90%
80%
70%
60%
50%
40%
30%
20%
10%
0%
1
2
WEEK
Long
Medium
Short

(a) Show how the height of the 'Medium Route' bar was calculated.

....

(1 mark)

(b) Complete the composite bar chart above by drawing the bar for Week 2.
Show your working below.

....

....

(2 marks)

(c) State one similarity between the data for both weeks.

....

(1 mark)

(d) Riders who complete thirty-five 'long' rides in a year are given a club badge.
Eddy kept a record of the number of long rides he managed in each month of last year.

Long rides per month	1	2	3	4	5
Frequency	0	3	2	5	2

(i) Complete this cumulative frequency table for the data.

Long rides per month	≤ 1	≤ 2	≤ 3	≤ 4	≤ 5
Cumulative Frequency					

(1 mark)

(ii) Draw a cumulative frequency step polygon for the data on the axes below.

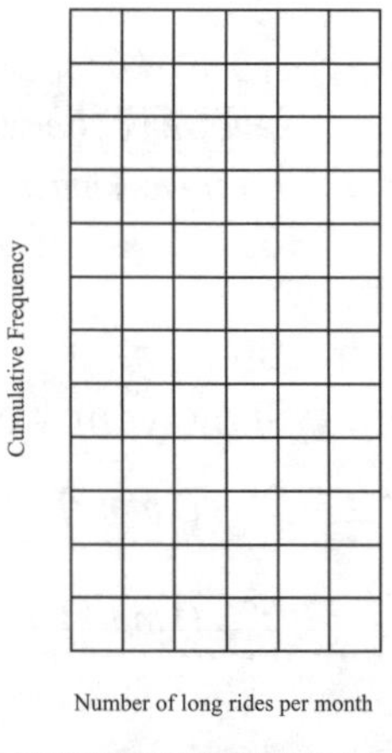

Cumulative Frequency

Number of long rides per month

(2 marks)

Frequency and Cumulative Frequency Polygons

When your data's continuous, you draw polygons and curves instead of steps.

I'm going to use the example on plant heights from page 39 to demonstrate — Adam came up with this table:

Height (cm)	$0 \le h < 5$	$5 \le h < 10$	$10 \le h < 15$	$15 \le h < 20$
Frequency	3	5	2	2

A Frequency Polygon Uses the Midpoint of Each Class

1) You need to work out the midpoints of each class of heights first:

Height (cm)	$0 \le h < 5$	$5 \le h < 10$	$10 \le h < 15$	$15 \le h < 20$
Midpoint	2.5	7.5	12.5	17.5
Frequency	3	5	2	2

2) Then plot the frequency polygon:

   Plot the midpoint of each class against its corresponding frequency.

   Because it's a polygon (rather than a curve), you join the points with straight lines.

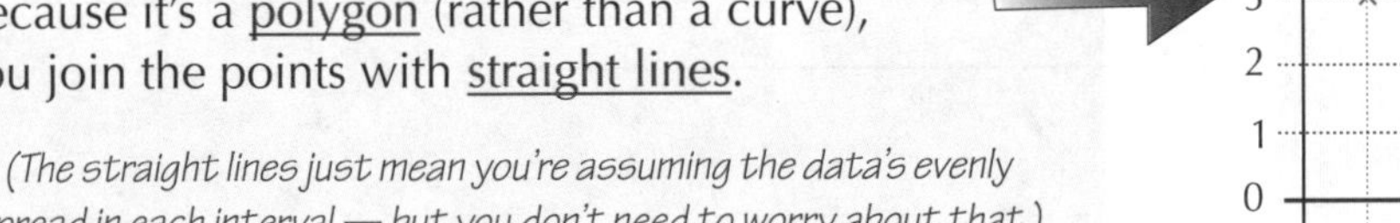

(The straight lines just mean you're assuming the data's evenly spread in each interval — but you don't need to worry about that.)

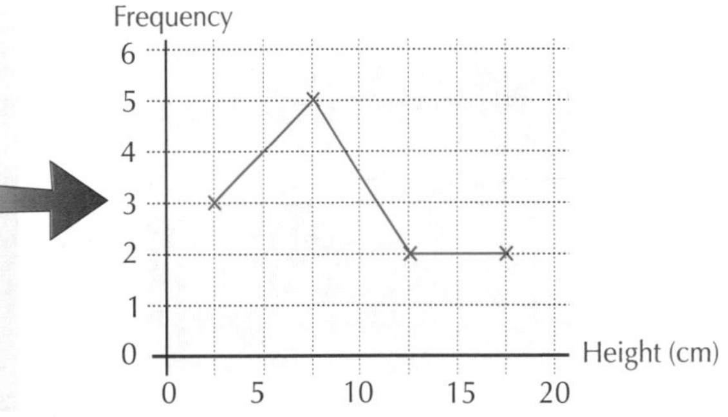

You can Plot Cumulative Frequency Polygons

The cumulative frequency is the 'running total' of heights (or whatever) — see page 48. You plot the cumulative frequency against the highest value in each class. That's because this data can only tell you for sure how many plants are less than these heights.

Height (cm)	$h < 5$	$h < 10$	$h < 15$	$h < 20$
Cumulative frequency	3	8	10	12

1) The points in a cumulative frequency polygon are joined with straight lines.
2) You might be asked to draw a 'cumulative frequency curve' instead. Then you need to draw a smooth curve through the points.
3) If you're just asked for a 'cumulative frequency diagram', you can draw either.

(If you're interested — you can draw either because they both work for continuous data. Which one you draw depends on what assumptions you're making about the distribution of the data.)

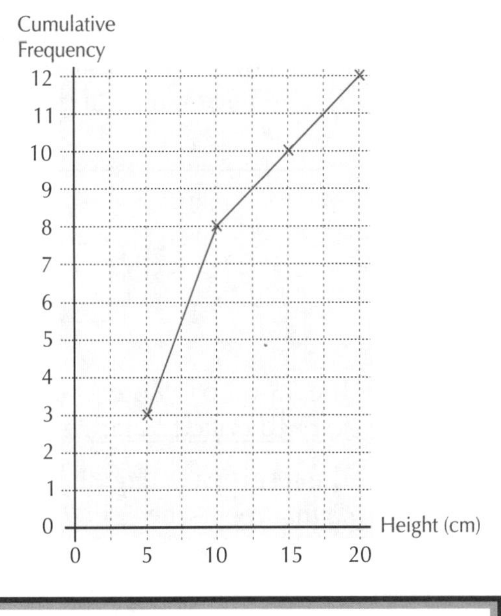

Some more lovely diagrams for you to learn...

Make sure you understand how these two diagrams are constructed and how they're different from each other. You should be able to convert a frequency polygon into a cumulative frequency polygon.

Histograms and Frequency Density

On the next couple of pages you're going to have the pleasure of seeing some more types of diagram...

Histograms *are a bit like* ***Bar Charts*** *— but Not*

Histograms show frequency, but it's the area of the bars that represents the frequency, not their height. So, instead of easy-to-understand bar charts you get seemingly incomprehensible monsters, and yes, that makes them a firm favourite with the examiners.

The vertical axis of a histogram shows frequency density — and there's a handy formula for calculating it. You use this formula to work out how high each bar should be when you're drawing a histogram.

FREQUENCY DENSITY = FREQUENCY ÷ CLASS WIDTH

EXAMPLE:

Say you've got a grouped frequency distribution with a frequency of 40 in the $5 < x \leq 10$ class — your frequency is 40, your class width is 5, so your bar needs to be $40 \div 5 =$ 8 units high.

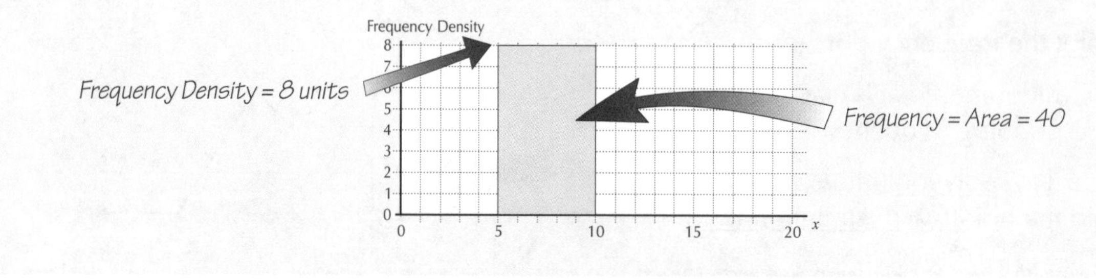

Histograms *Can be Used to Find* ***Frequencies***

You might also be asked to find frequencies from a histogram.
This is no trouble if you follow these two easy steps:

1) Work out what frequency is represented by each unit of area (e.g. each cm^2).
2) Find the area (e.g. in cm^2) of each bar, and so work out the frequency.

Example

The histogram below represents the age distribution of people arrested for slurping boiled sweets in public places in 1995. Given that there were 36 people in the 55 to 65 age range, find the number of people arrested in all the other age ranges.

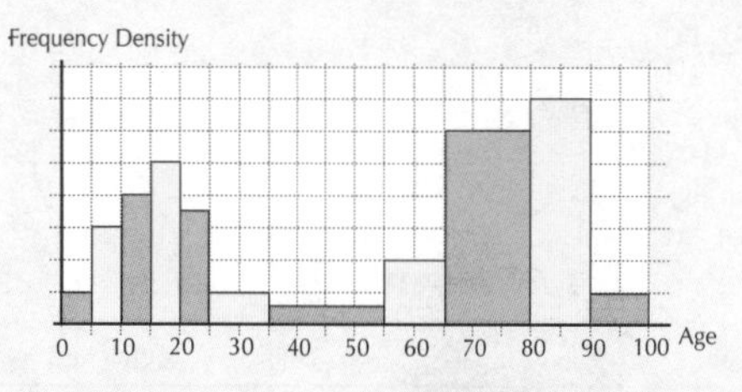

The 55-65 bar represents 36 people and contains 4 dotted squares, so each dotted square must represent 9 people.

The rest is easy. E.g. the 80-90 group has 14 dotted squares, so that represents $14 \times 9 =$ 126 people.

With histograms it's area not height that matters...

The histogram is an odd beast — like a bar chart with funny columns. If you're asked to draw one, just use the formula to work out the frequency density — that tells you how high your bars need to be.

Population Pyramids and Shading Maps

Here are two more diagram types, and one of them doesn't even have any bars...

Population Pyramids are made of Bar Charts

Population pyramids consist of two bar charts side by side to contrast two lots of information.

EXAMPLE: The students at St Thomas' College who gained a gold certificate in this year's Maths Challenge competition have been split up by gender and age in the table below.

Draw a population pyramid to show this data.

Age in complete years	Boys (%)	Girls (%)
16-17	25	10
14-15	15	30
12-13	10	10

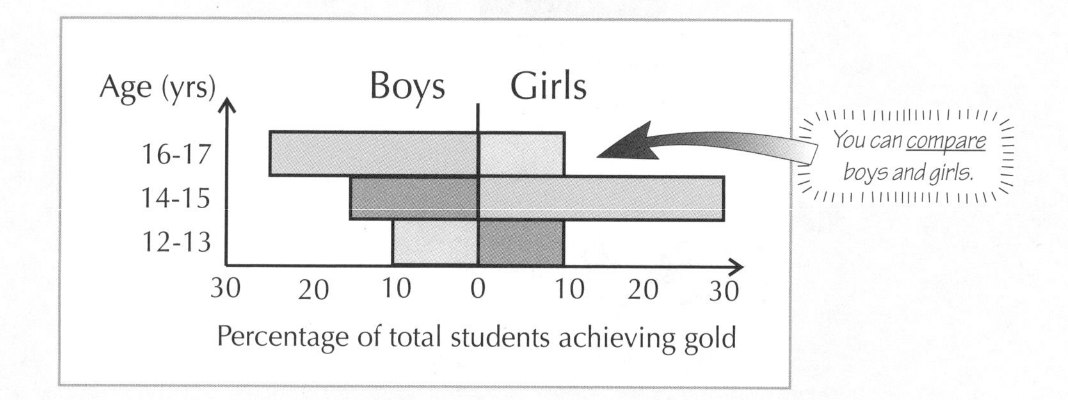

Choropleth Maps use Shading, Hatched Lines or Dots

1) Different regions of the map are shaded differently — the darker the shading (or closer together the hatching or dots), the higher the value of the data for that region.
2) You get a key with a choropleth map that tells you what each type of shading means.

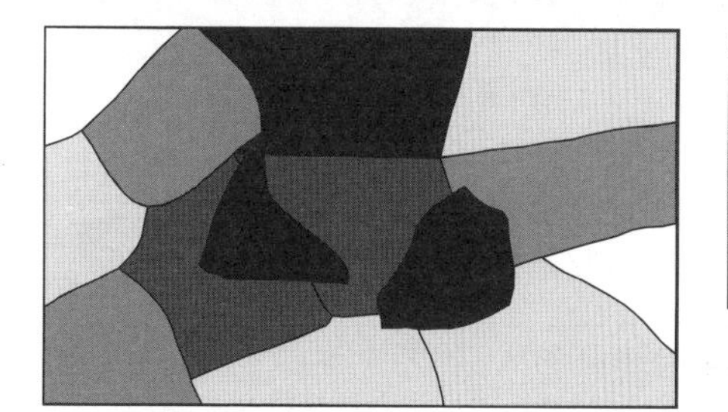

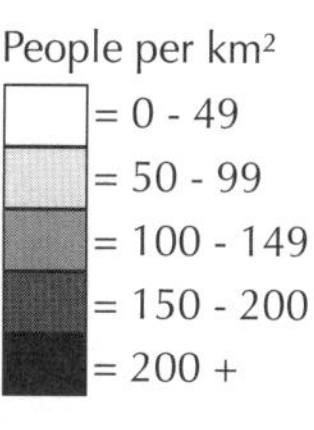

3) You'll be expected to be able to 'read' a map using the key, shade simple maps using data from a table and make connections between two different maps (e.g. a choropleth map of population density and a road map).

Another two diagram types for you to learn...

Nothing too tricky here. Make sure you know these two diagram types like the back of your hand. You should be able to draw a population pyramid from a table of data. Never a dull moment eh?

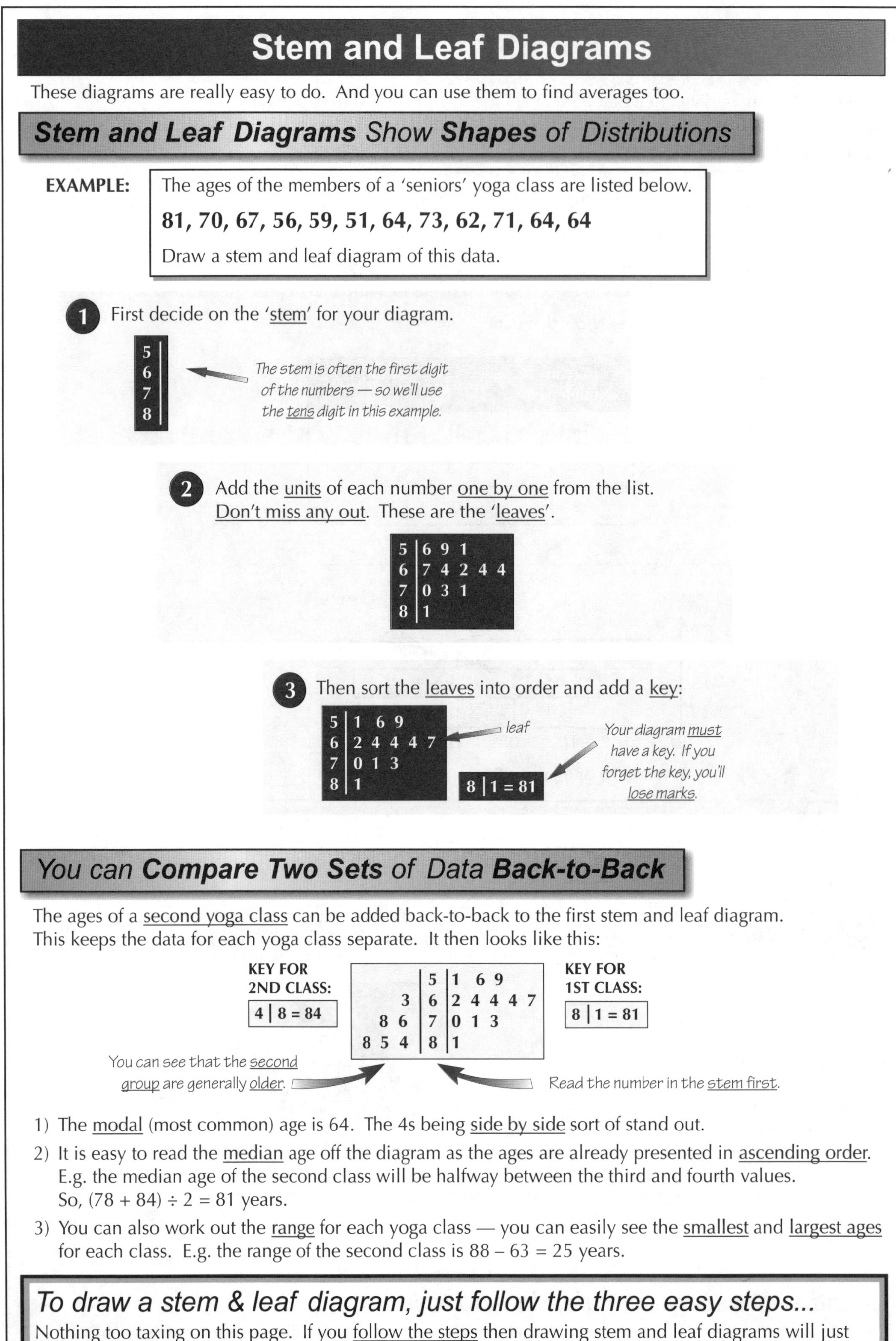

Stem and Leaf Diagrams

These diagrams are really easy to do. And you can use them to find averages too.

Stem and Leaf Diagrams Show Shapes of Distributions

EXAMPLE: The ages of the members of a 'seniors' yoga class are listed below.

81, 70, 67, 56, 59, 51, 64, 73, 62, 71, 64, 64

Draw a stem and leaf diagram of this data.

1 First decide on the 'stem' for your diagram.

Stem
5
6
7
8

2 Add the units of each number one by one from the list. Don't miss any out. These are the 'leaves'.

Stem	Leaves
5	6 9 1
6	7 4 2 4 4
7	0 3 1
8	1

3 Then sort the leaves into order and add a key:

Stem	Leaves
5	1 6 9
6	2 4 4 4 7
7	0 1 3
8	1

8 | 1 = 81

You can Compare Two Sets of Data Back-to-Back

The ages of a second yoga class can be added back-to-back to the first stem and leaf diagram. This keeps the data for each yoga class separate. It then looks like this:

KEY FOR 2ND CLASS: 4 | 8 = 84

2nd class	Stem	1st class
	5	1 6 9
3	6	2 4 4 4 7
8 6	7	0 1 3
8 5 4	8	1

KEY FOR 1ST CLASS: 8 | 1 = 81

1) The modal (most common) age is 64. The 4s being side by side sort of stand out.
2) It is easy to read the median age off the diagram as the ages are already presented in ascending order. E.g. the median age of the second class will be halfway between the third and fourth values. So, (78 + 84) ÷ 2 = 81 years.
3) You can also work out the range for each yoga class — you can easily see the smallest and largest ages for each class. E.g. the range of the second class is 88 – 63 = 25 years.

To draw a stem & leaf diagram, just follow the three easy steps...

Nothing too taxing on this page. If you follow the steps then drawing stem and leaf diagrams will just be easy marks in the exam. Make sure you're happy with finding the median, mode and range too.

Frequency Distributions

A frequency distribution can be as simple as a bar chart. You might get distributions like these from doing a survey or a probability experiment. See Section 3 for Mean, Median and Mode.

Frequency Distributions have Different Shapes

Here are five examples showing possible shapes of frequency distributions. You need to be able to describe the shape of a distribution. Notice that the frequency density always goes up the y-axis.

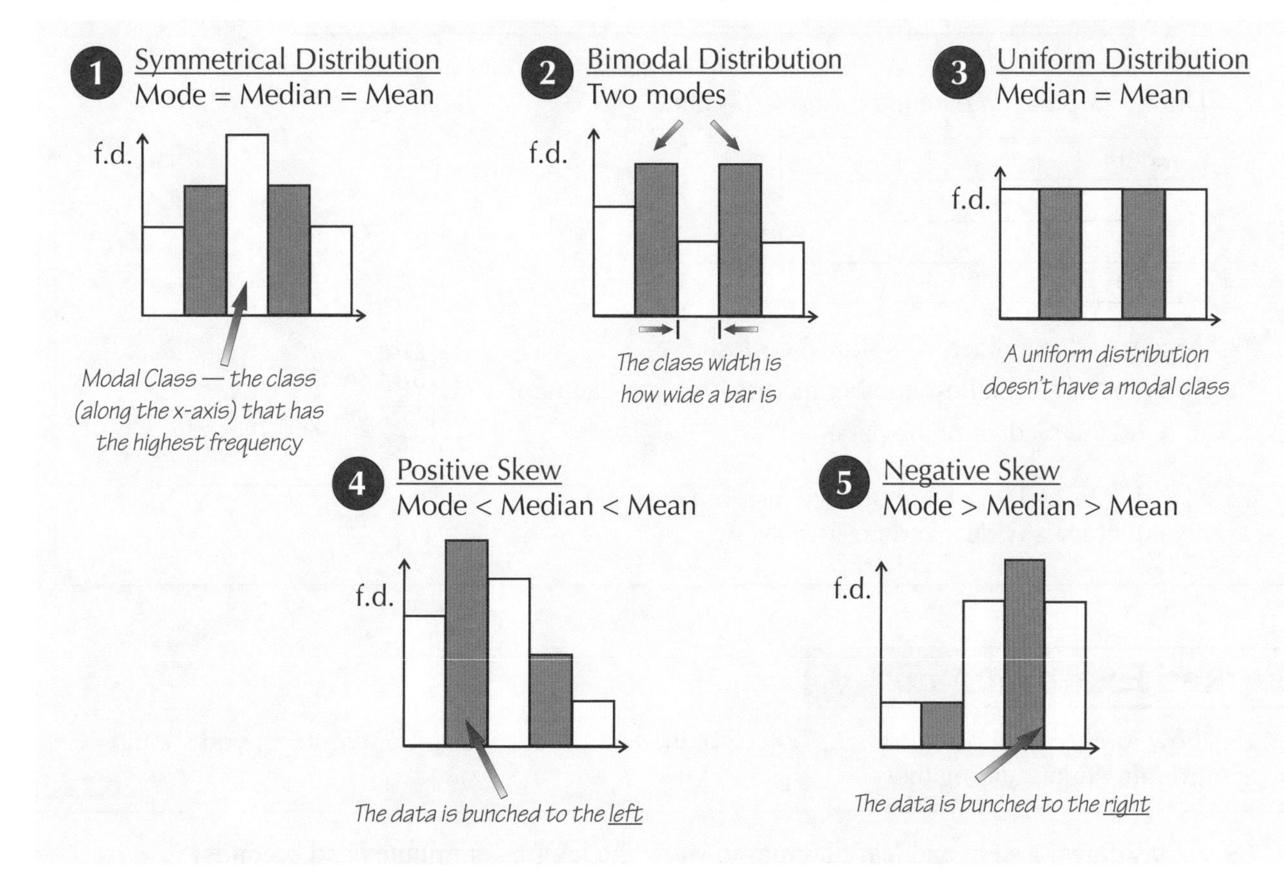

A Normal Distribution is Drawn as a Smooth Curve

Take the symmetrical example above. If you make the class widths smaller and smaller, so you've got more and more bars, you eventually get a smooth curve. This is called a Normal Distribution.

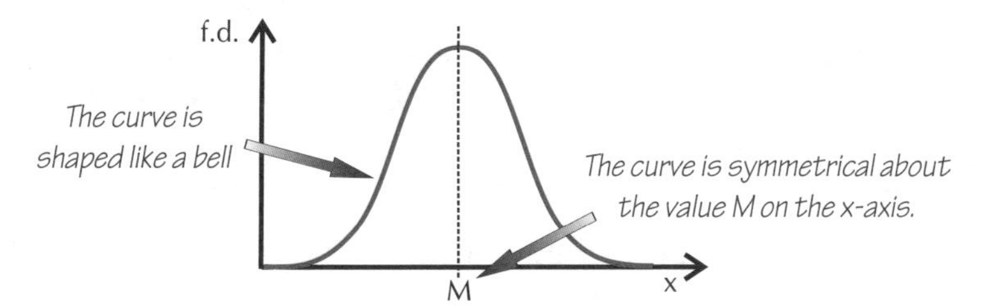

1) The mean, median and mode are all the same and equal to M.
2) The distribution is symmetrical around M.
3) About 95% of values are within two standard deviations (see p.80) either side of M.
   Almost all of the values are within three standard deviations either side of M.

Make sure you learn all about data distributions...

You should be able to name and recognise all the different distributions on this page. The stuff about normal distribution is a bit tricky — make sure you learn the three points and can sketch the graph.

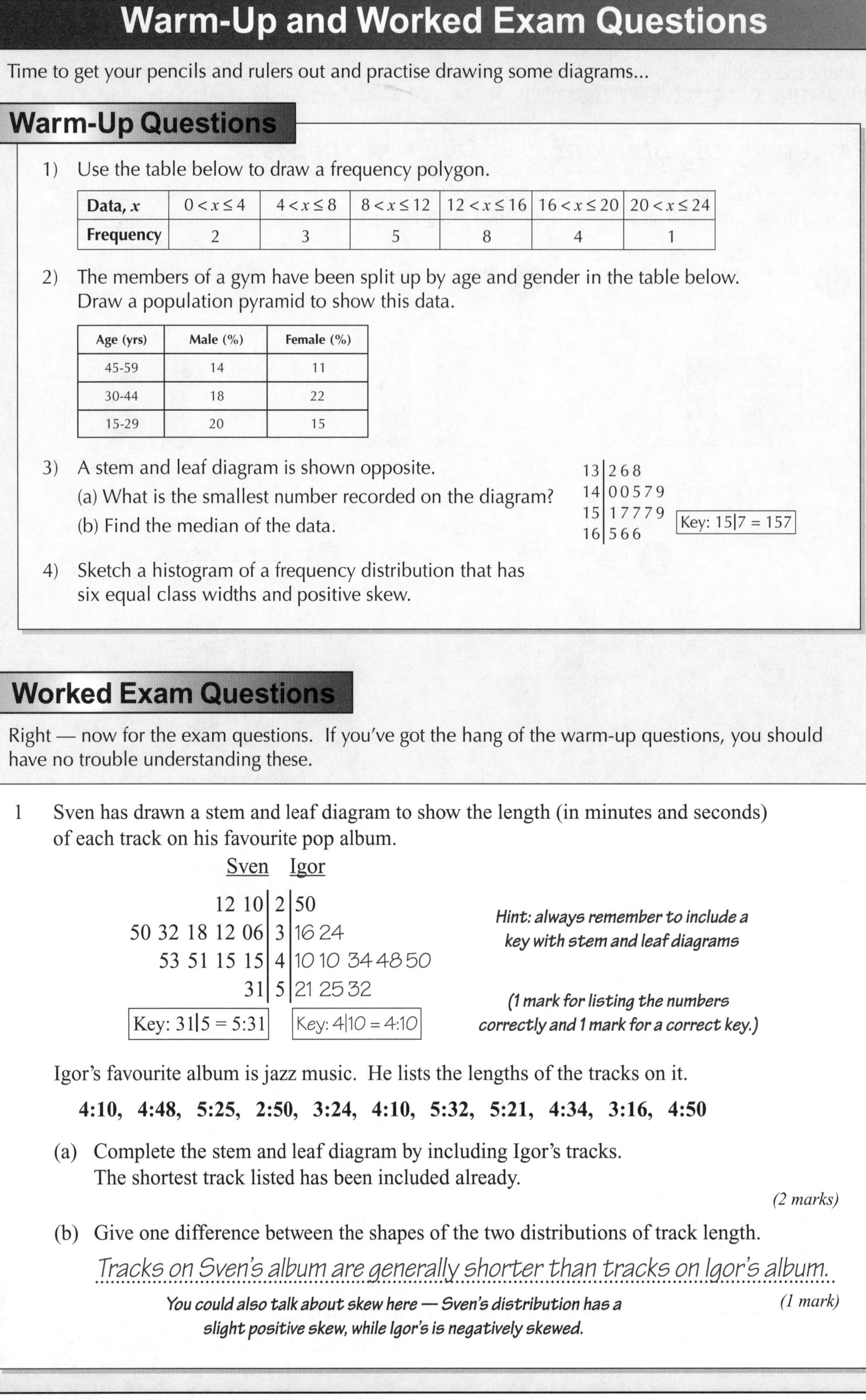

Warm-Up and Worked Exam Questions

Time to get your pencils and rulers out and practise drawing some diagrams...

Warm-Up Questions

1) Use the table below to draw a frequency polygon.

Data, x	$0 < x \leq 4$	$4 < x \leq 8$	$8 < x \leq 12$	$12 < x \leq 16$	$16 < x \leq 20$	$20 < x \leq 24$
Frequency	2	3	5	8	4	1

2) The members of a gym have been split up by age and gender in the table below. Draw a population pyramid to show this data.

Age (yrs)	Male (%)	Female (%)
45-59	14	11
30-44	18	22
15-29	20	15

3) A stem and leaf diagram is shown opposite.
   (a) What is the smallest number recorded on the diagram?
   (b) Find the median of the data.

```
13 | 2 6 8
14 | 0 0 5 7 9
15 | 1 7 7 7 9
16 | 5 6 6
```

Key: 15|7 = 157

4) Sketch a histogram of a frequency distribution that has six equal class widths and positive skew.

Worked Exam Questions

Right — now for the exam questions. If you've got the hang of the warm-up questions, you should have no trouble understanding these.

1 Sven has drawn a stem and leaf diagram to show the length (in minutes and seconds) of each track on his favourite pop album.

Sven		Igor
12 10	2	50
50 32 18 12 06	3	16 24
53 51 15 15	4	10 10 34 48 50
31	5	21 25 32

Key: 31|5 = 5:31   Key: 4|10 = 4:10

Hint: always remember to include a key with stem and leaf diagrams

(1 mark for listing the numbers correctly and 1 mark for a correct key.)

Igor's favourite album is jazz music. He lists the lengths of the tracks on it.

4:10, 4:48, 5:25, 2:50, 3:24, 4:10, 5:32, 5:21, 4:34, 3:16, 4:50

(a) Complete the stem and leaf diagram by including Igor's tracks. The shortest track listed has been included already.

(2 marks)

(b) Give one difference between the shapes of the two distributions of track length.

Tracks on Sven's album are generally shorter than tracks on Igor's album.

You could also talk about skew here — Sven's distribution has a slight positive skew, while Igor's is negatively skewed.

(1 mark)

Worked Exam Questions

Worked Exam Questions

2 Anna measures the heights of players on two different school football teams.
Her results are shown in this table:

Height, x (cm)	$150 \le x < 160$	$160 \le x < 170$	$170 \le x < 180$	$180 \le x < 190$	$190 \le x < 200$
Team A	0	1	2	7	1
Team B	1	4	5	1	0

Anna shows her results for Team A on a frequency polygon:

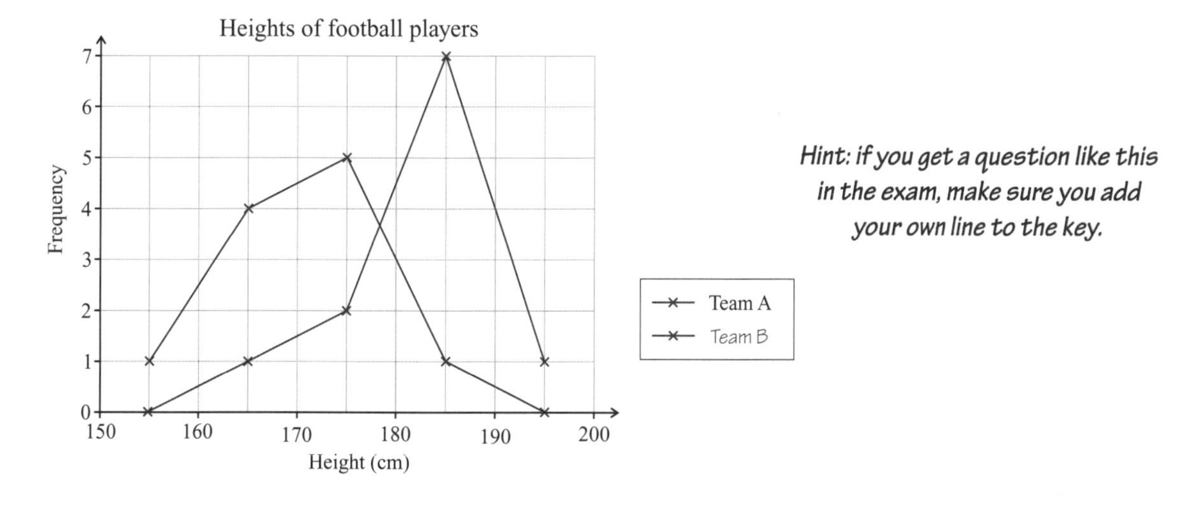

(a) Show Team B's results on the same graph.

(1 mark)

(b) Anna says that the players on Team A are generally taller than those on Team B.
Explain how Anna's frequency polygon supports this view.

Team A's polygon is skewed to the right more than Team B's.

(1 mark)

(c) Draw a cumulative frequency polygon for Team B's results on the grid below.

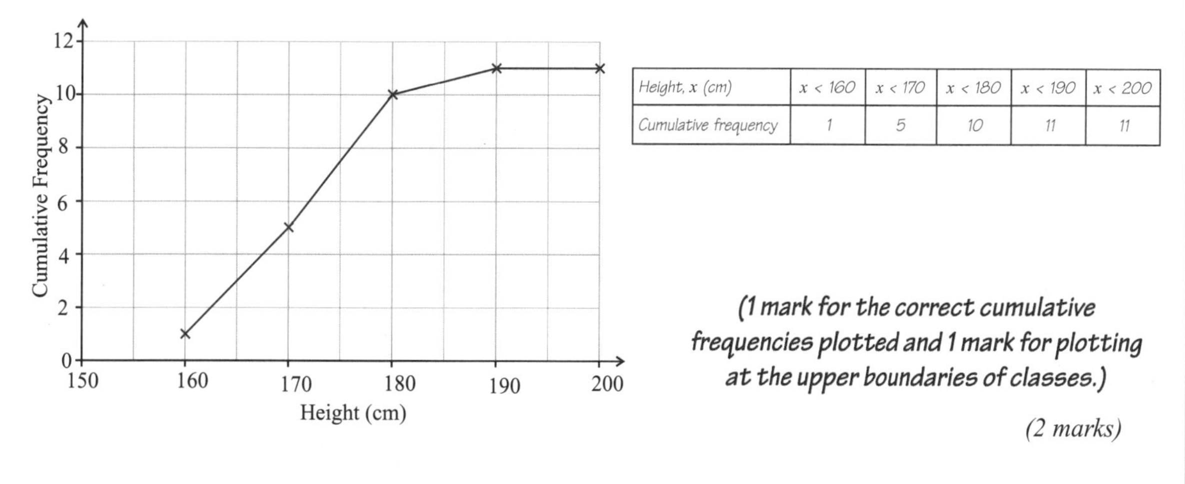

Height, x (cm)	$x < 160$	$x < 170$	$x < 180$	$x < 190$	$x < 200$
Cumulative frequency	1	5	10	11	11

(1 mark for the correct cumulative frequencies plotted and 1 mark for plotting at the upper boundaries of classes.)

(2 marks)

Hint: remember that you plot the cumulative frequency against the upper boundary of each class, not the midpoint of the class.

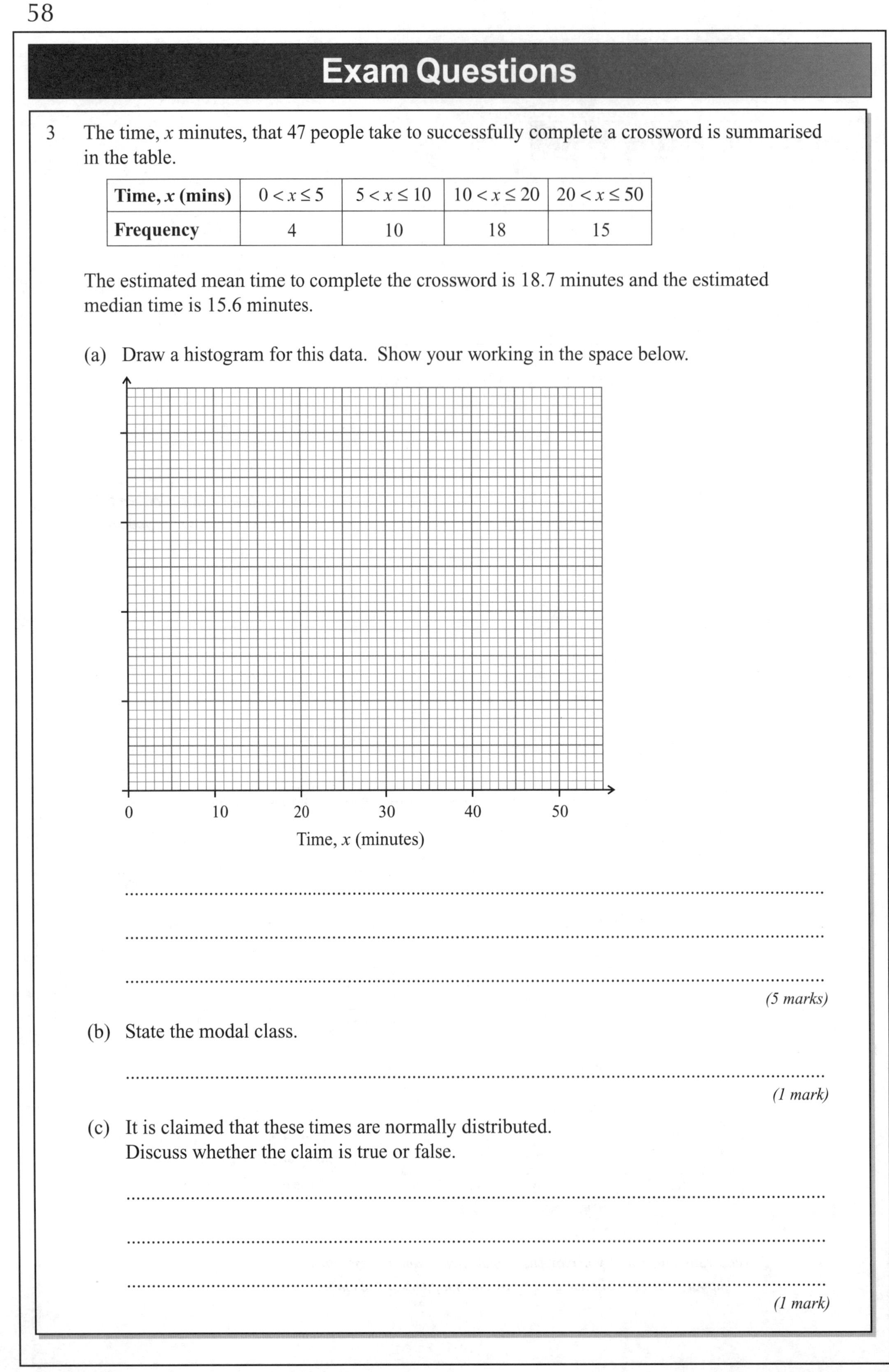

Exam Questions

3 The time, x minutes, that 47 people take to successfully complete a crossword is summarised in the table.

Time, x (mins)	$0 < x \leq 5$	$5 < x \leq 10$	$10 < x \leq 20$	$20 < x \leq 50$
Frequency	4	10	18	15

The estimated mean time to complete the crossword is 18.7 minutes and the estimated median time is 15.6 minutes.

(a) Draw a histogram for this data. Show your working in the space below.

....

....

....

(5 marks)

(b) State the modal class.

....

(1 mark)

(c) It is claimed that these times are normally distributed.
Discuss whether the claim is true or false.

....

....

....

(1 mark)

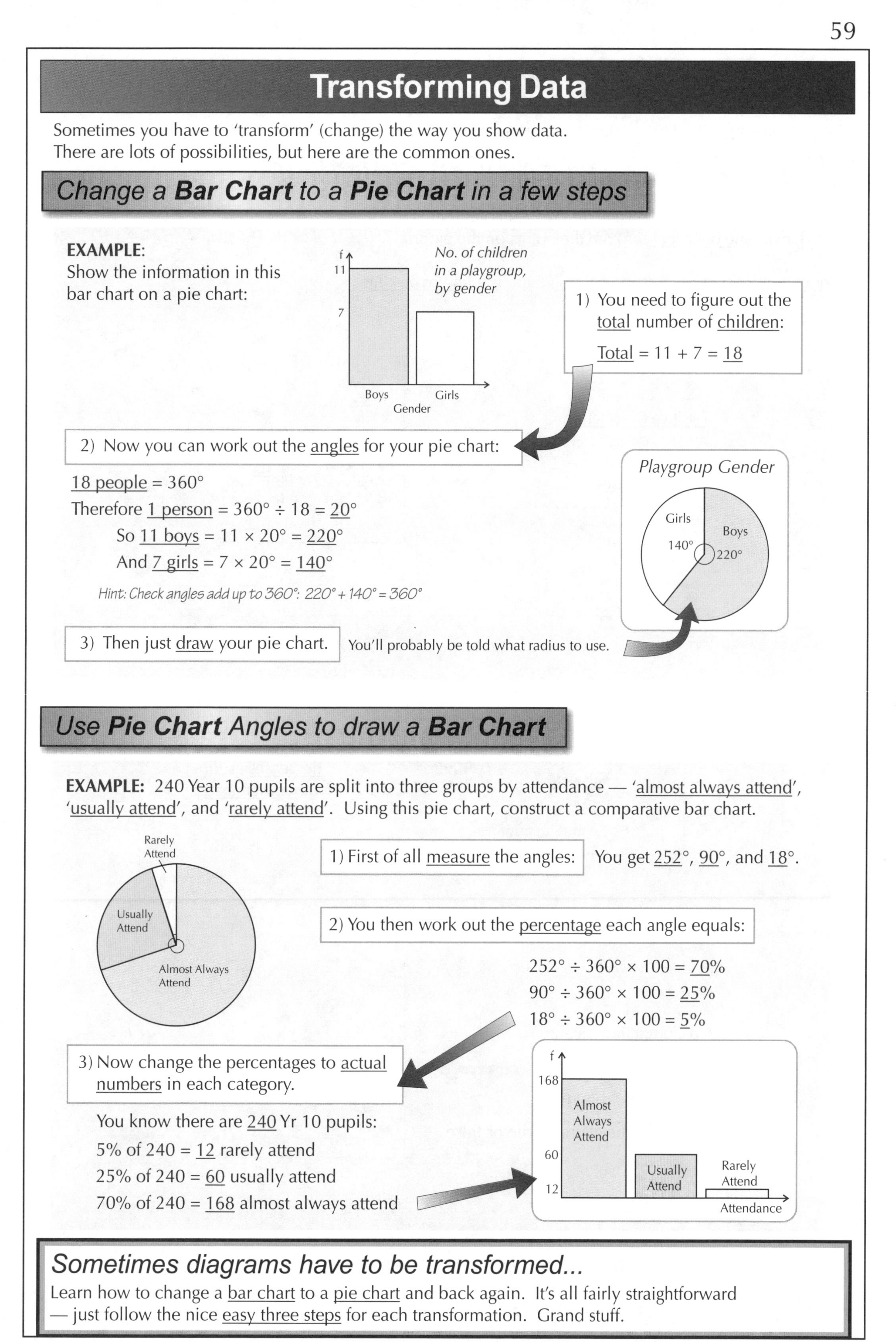

Transforming Data

Sometimes you have to 'transform' (change) the way you show data.
There are lots of possibilities, but here are the common ones.

*Change a **Bar Chart** to a **Pie Chart** in a few steps*

EXAMPLE:
Show the information in this bar chart on a pie chart:

1) You need to figure out the total number of children:

Total = 11 + 7 = 18

2) Now you can work out the angles for your pie chart:

18 people = 360°
Therefore 1 person = 360° ÷ 18 = 20°
So 11 boys = 11 × 20° = 220°
And 7 girls = 7 × 20° = 140°

Hint: Check angles add up to 360°: 220° + 140° = 360°

3) Then just draw your pie chart. You'll probably be told what radius to use.

*Use **Pie Chart** Angles to draw a **Bar Chart***

EXAMPLE: 240 Year 10 pupils are split into three groups by attendance — 'almost always attend', 'usually attend', and 'rarely attend'. Using this pie chart, construct a comparative bar chart.

1) First of all measure the angles: You get 252°, 90°, and 18°.

2) You then work out the percentage each angle equals:

252° ÷ 360° × 100 = 70%
90° ÷ 360° × 100 = 25%
18° ÷ 360° × 100 = 5%

3) Now change the percentages to actual numbers in each category.

You know there are 240 Yr 10 pupils:
5% of 240 = 12 rarely attend
25% of 240 = 60 usually attend
70% of 240 = 168 almost always attend

Sometimes diagrams have to be transformed...

Learn how to change a bar chart to a pie chart and back again. It's all fairly straightforward — just follow the nice easy three steps for each transformation. Grand stuff.

Scatter Diagrams

Scatter diagrams show two variables on the same graph, and whether there's a relationship between them.

Draw a Line of Best Fit if there is a Relationship

If there is a relationship between the two variables then you can draw a line of best fit through the points on the graph.

Correlation describes the connection if there is a line of best fit:

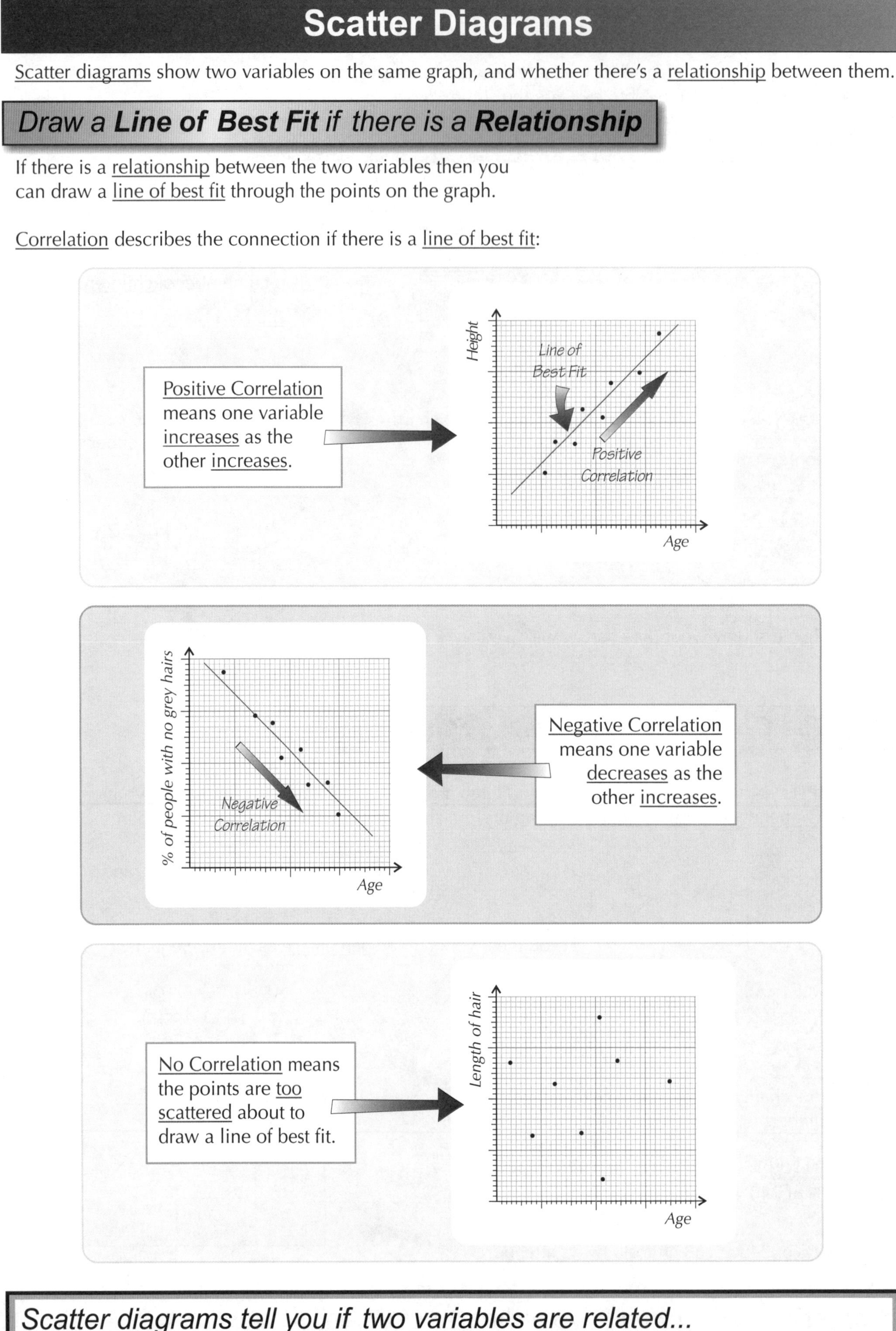

Scatter diagrams tell you if two variables are related...

Learn the definition of correlation. You need to be able to draw lines of best fit and recognise positive and negative correlation in scatter graphs. There's more about correlation on pages 98 to 101.

Time Series

Often, we want to see how a chosen variable varies with time...

Time Series are plotted with Time on the x-Axis

A time series is a set of data values obtained at successive times.
They are plotted with time on the x-axis — and you join the points together.

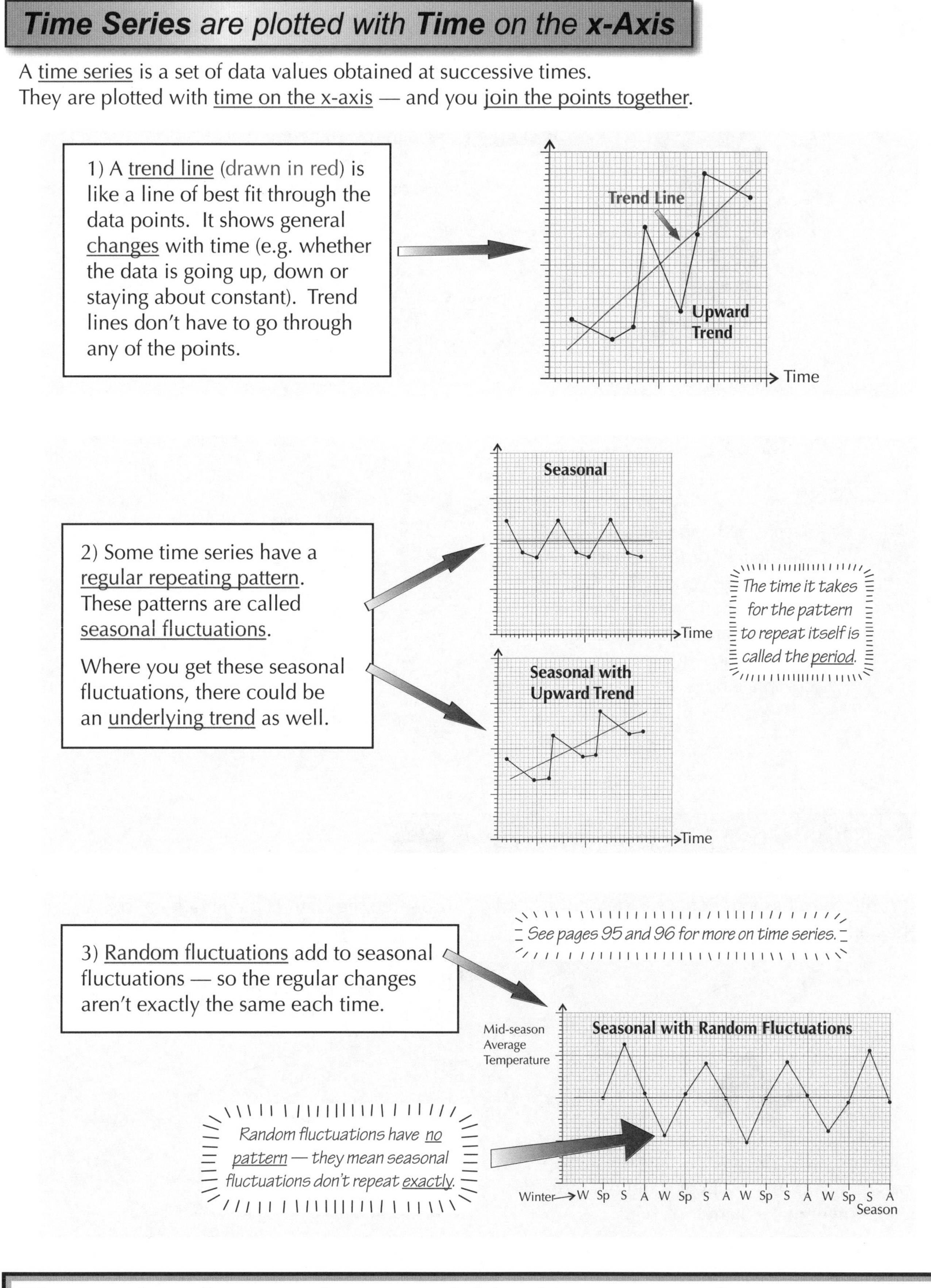

1) A trend line (drawn in red) is like a line of best fit through the data points. It shows general changes with time (e.g. whether the data is going up, down or staying about constant). Trend lines don't have to go through any of the points.

2) Some time series have a regular repeating pattern. These patterns are called seasonal fluctuations.

Where you get these seasonal fluctuations, there could be an underlying trend as well.

See pages 95 and 96 for more on time series.

3) Random fluctuations add to seasonal fluctuations — so the regular changes aren't exactly the same each time.

Time series show you how a variable changes over time...

Make sure you learn the definitions of time series, trend lines, seasonal fluctuations and period.
You should be able to recognise and name the different time series shown on this page.

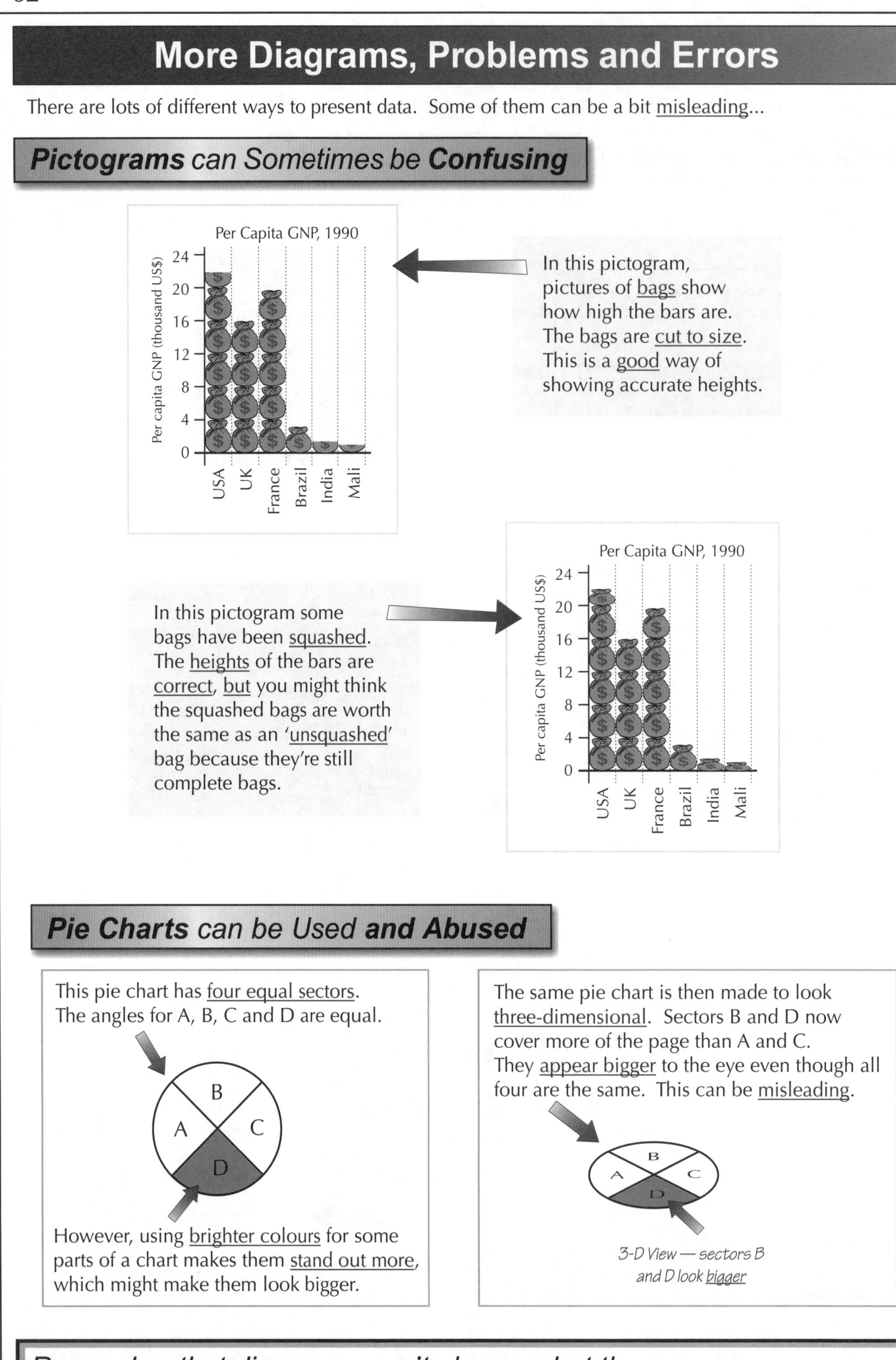

More Diagrams, Problems and Errors

There are lots of different ways to present data. Some of them can be a bit misleading...

Pictograms can Sometimes be Confusing

In this pictogram, pictures of bags show how high the bars are. The bags are cut to size. This is a good way of showing accurate heights.

In this pictogram some bags have been squashed. The heights of the bars are correct, but you might think the squashed bags are worth the same as an 'unsquashed' bag because they're still complete bags.

Pie Charts can be Used and Abused

This pie chart has four equal sectors. The angles for A, B, C and D are equal.

However, using brighter colours for some parts of a chart makes them stand out more, which might make them look bigger.

The same pie chart is then made to look three-dimensional. Sectors B and D now cover more of the page than A and C. They appear bigger to the eye even though all four are the same. This can be misleading.

3-D View — sectors B and D look bigger

Remember that diagrams aren't always what they seem...

It's easy to manipulate diagrams to be misleading and it's also easy to be confused by them. Always check your diagrams to make sure that they're clear to read and not confusing... and then check again.

More Diagrams, Problems and Errors

Diagrams can also be shown as having volume. But there are a few things to watch out for...

Volume should be treated with Care

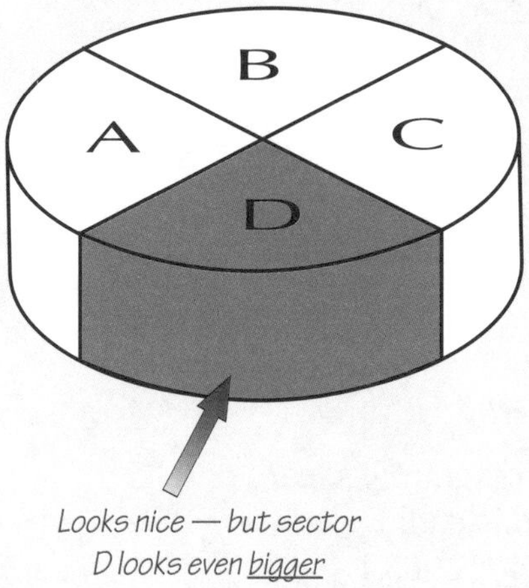

B
A
C
D

The same pie chart from page 62 now has volume. Sector D covers more of the page than any of the other three. The pie chart is still accurate, but sector D looks more important than the others. You often see this sort of thing in reports and the press.

Looks nice — but sector D looks even bigger

In the diagrams below, bars A and C are equal in height:

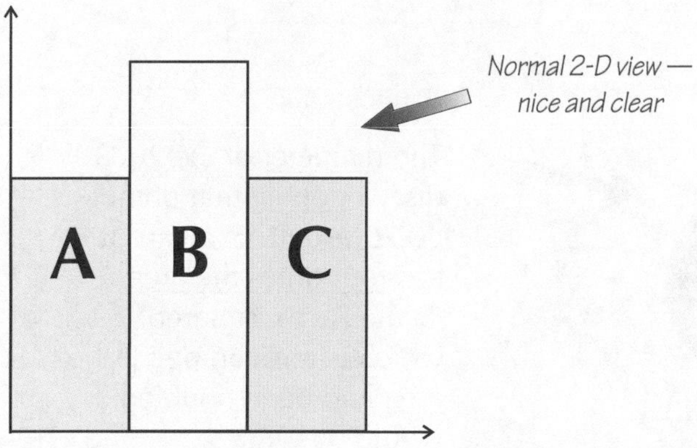

A B C

Normal 2-D view — nice and clear

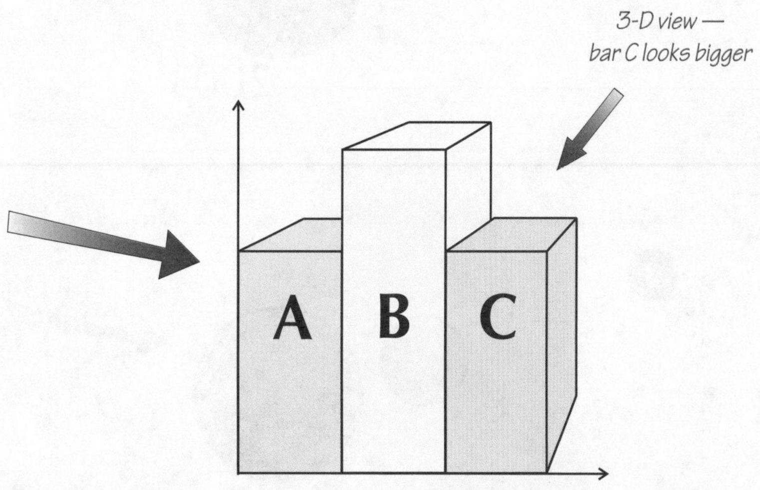

3-D view — bar C looks bigger

The same diagram now has volume. Bar C now appears to be bigger. It covers about the same area of the page as bar B. Bar A might seem less important as it is partly hidden behind bar B.

A B C

You need to think when using three dimensions. There's nothing actually wrong with these diagrams, but you need to read them more carefully because they can be a bit misleading.

Be careful when showing volume...

Make sure you know how three-dimensional diagrams can be misleading. If you're shown a diagram with volume and asked to interpret it, just take a minute to look at it carefully.

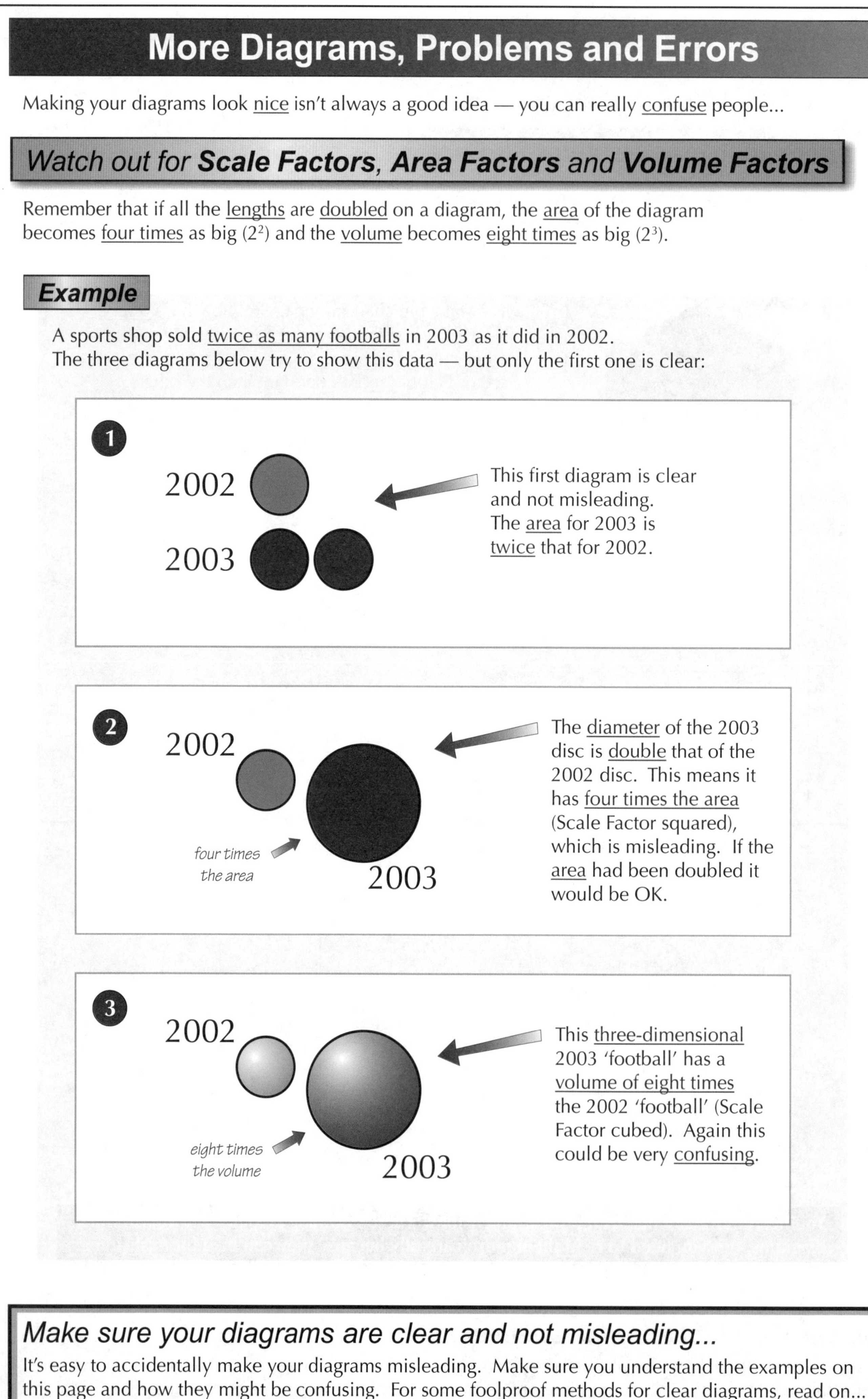

More Diagrams, Problems and Errors

Making your diagrams look <u>nice</u> isn't always a good idea — you can really <u>confuse</u> people...

Watch out for **Scale Factors**, **Area Factors** and **Volume Factors**

Remember that if all the <u>lengths</u> are <u>doubled</u> on a diagram, the <u>area</u> of the diagram becomes <u>four times</u> as big (2^2) and the <u>volume</u> becomes <u>eight times</u> as big (2^3).

Example

A sports shop sold <u>twice as many footballs</u> in 2003 as it did in 2002.
The three diagrams below try to show this data — but only the first one is clear:

Make sure your diagrams are clear and not misleading...

It's easy to accidentally make your diagrams misleading. Make sure you understand the examples on this page and how they might be confusing. For some foolproof methods for clear diagrams, read on...

More Diagrams, Problems and Errors

Sometimes you may want to show areas or volumes in your diagrams. Here's how to do it.

*If you want to use **Area** and **Volume** — Do it **Properly***

If you decide you do want to use area or volume — here's how to do it right.

Example

The salary bonus for a company employee trebles from one year to the next. The company manager wants to show this in a diagram. She decides to do it in three ways — as a linear increase, an area increase and a volume increase.

Method 1:

Linear Increase — starting with a 10 mm long bar

This is like a bar in a chart. Its length becomes three times what it was. Nice and easy...

10 mm

30 mm

The thickness of the bar / line does not increase. It's a one-dimensional change.

Method 2:

Area Increase — starting with a 10 mm square

The area must be three times what it was — i.e. 3×100 mm^2 = 300 mm^2

10 mm

The new square has sides of x mm.

$x \times x = 300$ $x = \sqrt{300}$ $x =$ 17 mm (2 S.F.)

17 mm

Simply multiplying the sides of the square by three would be wrong, and would make the bonus look nine times the original value.

Method 3:

Volume Increase — starting with a 10 mm cube

Here the new volume must be three times what it was — i.e. 3×1000 mm^3 = 3000 mm^3

10 mm

The new cube has sides of: $\sqrt[3]{3000}$ = 14 mm (2 S.F.)

14 mm

Make sure you learn these techniques...

There's nothing tricky here, it's just a case of remembering what to increase. If you learn these three methods inside out you shouldn't have a problem using area or volume in your diagrams.

More Diagrams, Problems and Errors

More things can go wrong with graphs than you would think...

Graphs can lead you up the Garden Path...

Graph A below shows some information clearly — the others are more confusing or misleading.

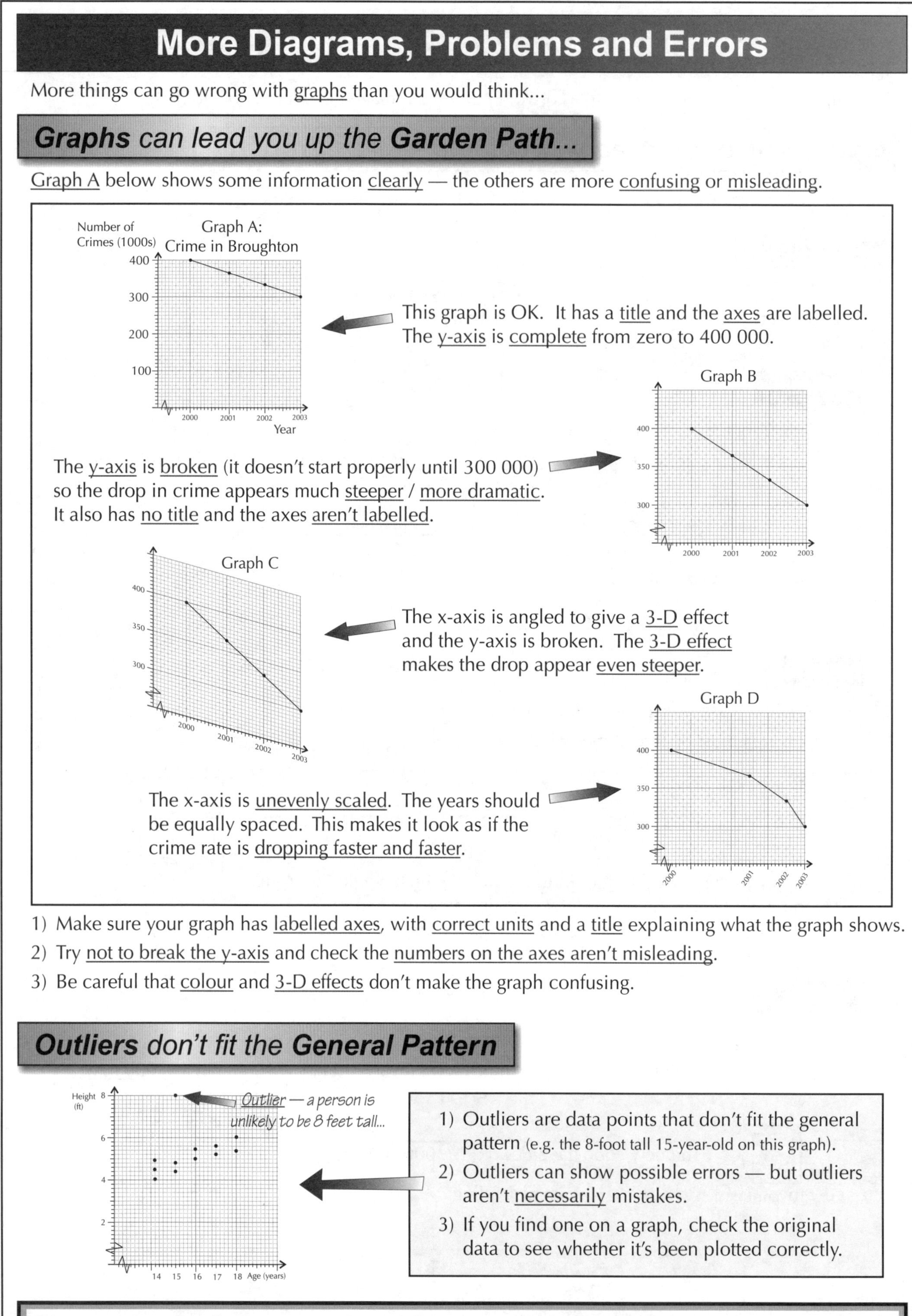

This graph is OK. It has a title and the axes are labelled. The y-axis is complete from zero to 400 000.

The y-axis is broken (it doesn't start properly until 300 000) so the drop in crime appears much steeper / more dramatic. It also has no title and the axes aren't labelled.

The x-axis is angled to give a 3-D effect and the y-axis is broken. The 3-D effect makes the drop appear even steeper.

The x-axis is unevenly scaled. The years should be equally spaced. This makes it look as if the crime rate is dropping faster and faster.

1) Make sure your graph has labelled axes, with correct units and a title explaining what the graph shows.
2) Try not to break the y-axis and check the numbers on the axes aren't misleading.
3) Be careful that colour and 3-D effects don't make the graph confusing.

Outliers don't fit the General Pattern

1) Outliers are data points that don't fit the general pattern (e.g. the 8-foot tall 15-year-old on this graph).
2) Outliers can show possible errors — but outliers aren't necessarily mistakes.
3) If you find one on a graph, check the original data to see whether it's been plotted correctly.

Be aware of all the ways in which graphs can mislead people...

I bet you never thought graphs could be so tricky. Make sure you understand what's wrong with graphs B, C and D above. Make sure you know what an outlier is and what to do if you find one.

Warm-Up and Worked Exam Questions

You should know the script by now — go through these warm-up questions to make sure you know the basics. If you struggle with anything, go back over the last few pages and learn it again.

Warm-Up Questions

1) Post is delivered to a particular area on six days each week. The time series below shows the time taken for deliveries to be completed each day over a four-week period.
   Describe the fluctuations in the series.

2) The three pie charts below show the same data.
   Which pie chart could be misleading? Explain why.

   Chart 1 Chart 2 Chart 3

3) Describe the correlation in this scatter diagram:

Worked Exam Questions

Here are some questions just like the ones you'll get in your exam — and the first two even have the answers written in. You'd be daft not to go through them all carefully till you know them inside out.

1 A graph in a report shows the increase in the number of flights per day, n, from a particular airport over time.

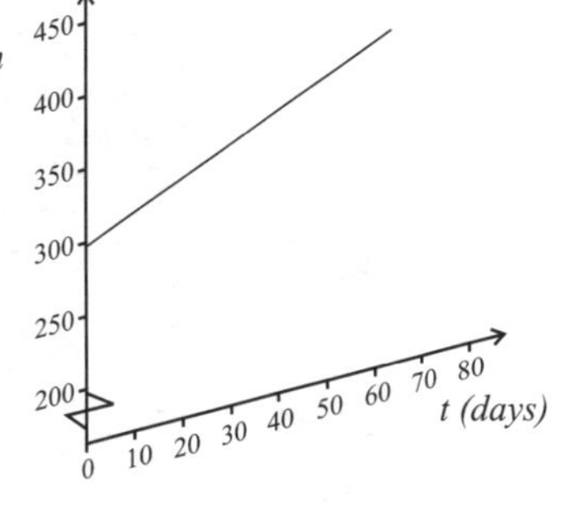

Give two reasons why this graph is misleading.

The time axis is angled upwards, which exaggerates the slope of the line showing the number of flights increasing. **(1 mark)** *Also, the vertical axis is broken which makes the rise in the line seem even steeper.* **(1 mark)**

(2 marks)

Worked Exam Questions

Worked Exam Questions

2 A container ship carrying bananas has had a refrigeration fault. A sample of 960 bananas is taken and the state of the fruit assessed. The results are shown in this pie chart:

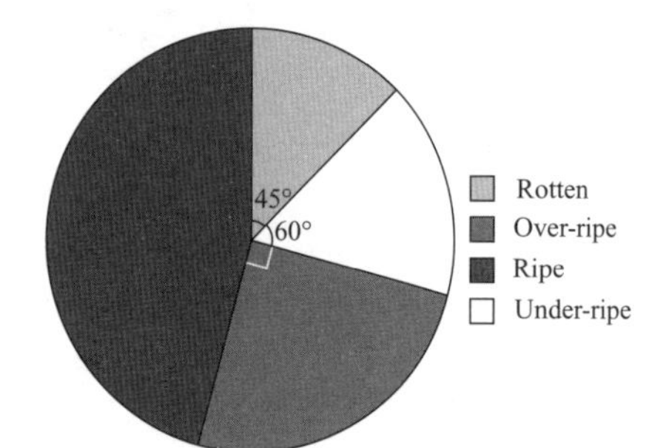

Condition	Number
Rotten	120
Over-ripe	240
Ripe	440
Under-ripe	160

(a) Use the pie chart to complete the table showing the number of bananas in each condition.

Angle of ripe on pie chart = 360 – (90 + 60 + 45) = 165°

Number of rotten = (45 ÷ 360) × 960 = 120

Number of over-ripe = (90 ÷ 360) × 960 = 240

Number of ripe = (165 ÷ 360) × 960 = 440

Number of under-ripe = (60 ÷ 360) × 960 = 160

(3 marks for correct table, otherwise 1 mark for finding angle of 'ripe' section and 1 mark for at least 2 numbers filled in correctly.)

(3 marks)

(b) Use your table to complete a bar chart showing the number of bananas in each condition.

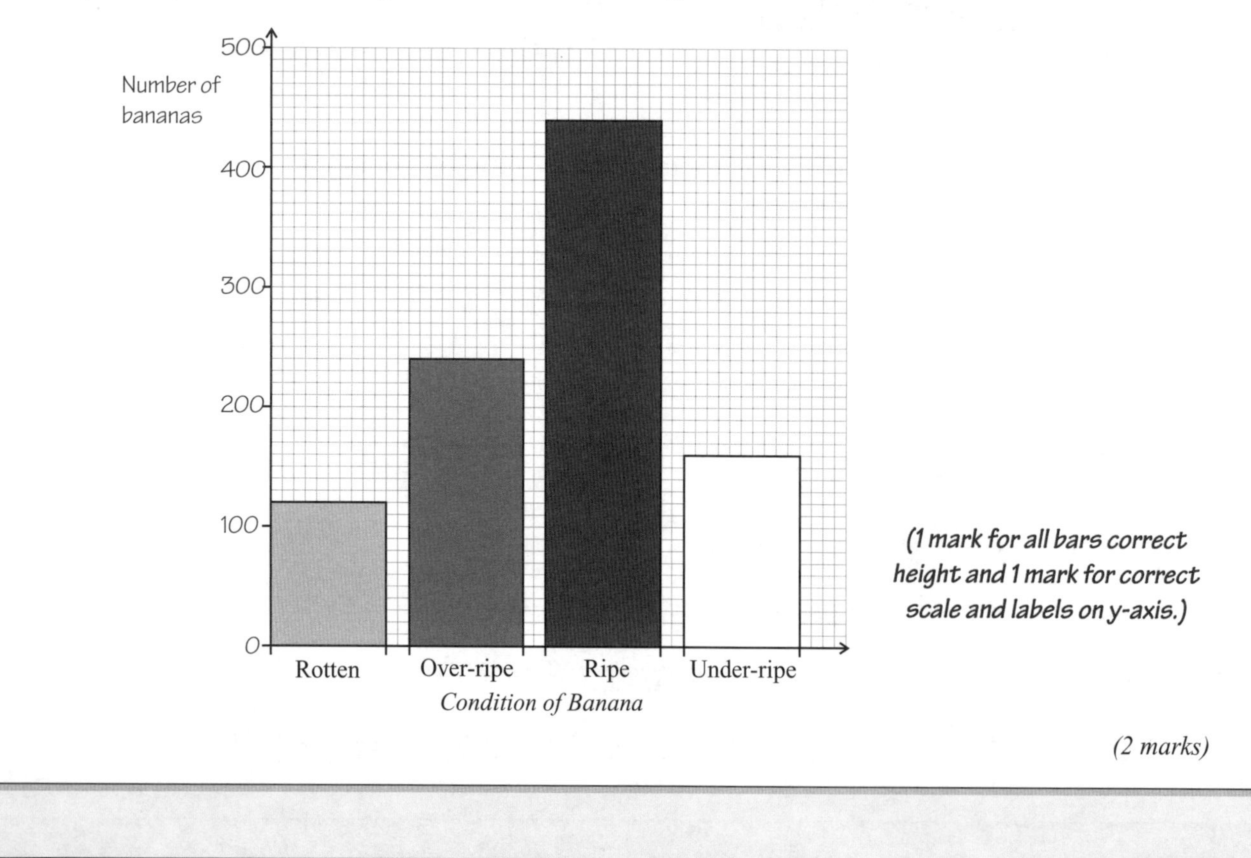

(1 mark for all bars correct height and 1 mark for correct scale and labels on y-axis.)

(2 marks)

Exam Questions

3 Adult humans have a maximum of 32 teeth.
A dentist takes a sample of 20 patients. She records each patient's age in years, x, and the number of teeth they have with no fillings, t.

Age, x (yrs)	30	40	25	31	20	35	10	46	54	60	25	40	50	60	50	45	50	15	55	42
Number of teeth without fillings, t	28	22	27	26	28	24	28	25	22	22	25	24	25	20	20	22	23	31	20	18

(a) Draw a scatter diagram for this data on the axes below.

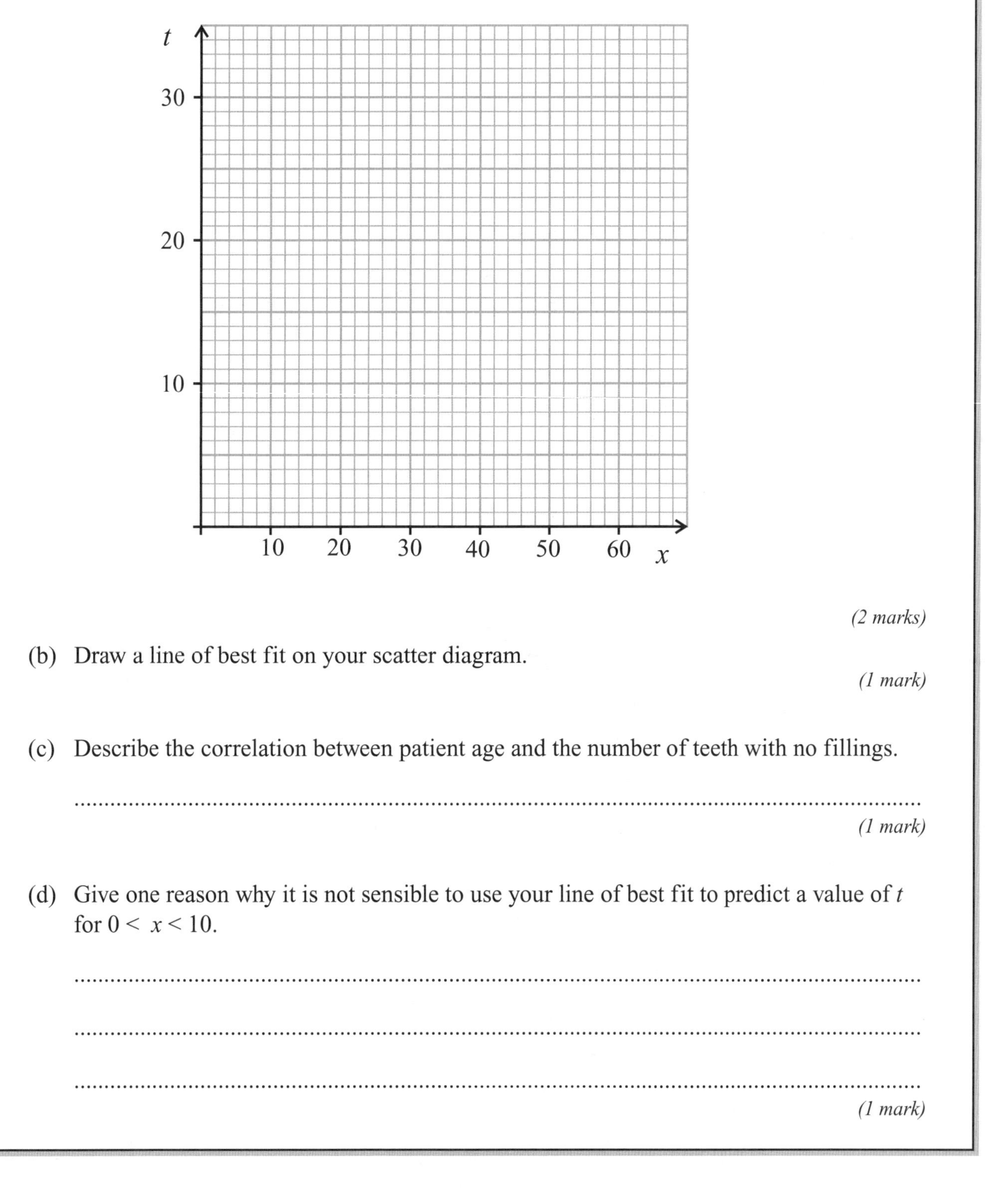

(2 marks)

(b) Draw a line of best fit on your scatter diagram.

(1 mark)

(c) Describe the correlation between patient age and the number of teeth with no fillings.

....

(1 mark)

(d) Give one reason why it is not sensible to use your line of best fit to predict a value of t for $0 < x < 10$.

....

....

....

(1 mark)

Revision Summary for Section Two

Here's what you've really been waiting for — a nice page of quick-fire questions to get your teeth into. Doing these questions will give you the clearest idea of where you need to do more revision. If you struggle with any, go back and go over that part of the section again...

Keep learning the basic facts until you know them

1) Why is it important to keep a tally when doing a frequency table?
2) When and why do you use grouped frequency tables?
3) When might you use an open-ended class interval?
4) Describe the advantages and disadvantages of simplifying a table by totalling.
5) Why might you convert the data in a table into percentages?
6) How can reducing the number of classes in a grouped frequency table make the table misleading?
7) How is data represented in pictograms?
8) Describe the difference between multiple and composite bar charts.
9) What can you say about the areas of comparative pie charts?
10) Describe two types of graph for representing discrete data.
11) How do graphs of discrete data differ from graphs of continuous data?
12) Describe how to plot a frequency polygon.
13) Describe how to change a frequency polygon into a cumulative frequency polygon.
14) Is a histogram the same as a bar chart? If not, describe how they are different.
15) What is frequency density in a histogram? How do you calculate frequency density?
16) How do you find the frequency represented by a bar in a histogram?
17) How is a population pyramid useful for making comparisons?
18) How is information represented on a choropleth map?
19) What is the 'stem' and what is the 'leaf' in a stem and leaf diagram?
20) Describe one advantage of using a stem and leaf diagram.
21) Sketch a frequency distribution with positive skew.
22) Sketch a normal distribution.
23) Describe the process for changing a bar chart into a pie chart.
24) What's the method for changing a pie chart into a bar chart?
25) What is the purpose of a scatter diagram?
26) Describe what it means for two variables to be negatively correlated.
27) On a time series graph:
    a) What does a trend line show? b) What are seasonal fluctuations?
28) Why should you be careful when using area, volume and colour in diagrams? Give examples.
29) What is an outlier? Does an outlier always mean there has been an error in plotting a graph?

Mean, Median and Mode

Once you've collected your data, you need to make sense of what you've got — you need the 3 M's.

The *Arithmetic Mean* is the *"Average"*

The "arithmetic mean" is usually just called the "mean".

Add together all the data values and divide by the total number of values in the sample.

Example: Number of people living in each of nine three-bedroomed houses:
3 5 1 3 7 5 5 5 2

Mean = (3 + 5 + 1 + 3 + 7 + 5 + 5 + 5 + 2) ÷ 9 = 4

The mean changes if you add or remove a data value from the sample (unless it's equal to the mean itself).
If you add a value greater than the mean or take away a value less than the mean — the mean increases.
If you add a value less than the mean or take away a value greater — it decreases.

Finding the *Mean* for *Large Numbers*

A neat little trick — take a number away from all the values (so you only have to deal with small numbers) and find the mean of those. Then add the number you took away back onto the result.

For example, to find the mean of the following numbers, take away 190 first.
191 192 199 198 196 194 195
Mean = 190 + (1 + 2 + 9 + 8 + 6 + 4 + 5) ÷ 7 = 190 + 5 = 195

Calculating the *Weighted Mean*

This is used to combine different sets of data when one is more important than another.

Example: If 25% of your GCSE is coursework then this carries a weight of 0.25, and the exam marks will carry a weight of 0.75.
So, if you score 70% for coursework and 55% for your exam then your percentage result will be (70 × 0.25) + (55 × 0.75) = 58.75%

The *Median* is the *Middle Value*

First put the data in ascending order, then find the middle value.
It's easy to find if you've got an odd number of values.
If there's an even number of values, the median is halfway between the two middle values.

For example, with data values: 5 8 ↑ 10 12,
the median comes halfway between the 8 and the 10, so Median = 9

If there are n data values, the position of the median is $(n + 1)/2$.

The *Mode* is the One that Appears *Most Often*

You can find the mode either by inspection (just looking at the data) or using a tally chart.
So in the data set: 3, 5, 1, 3, 7, 5, 5, 5, 2, the Mode is 5 (it appears 4 times).

Make sure you know the three M's — and how to find them...

It's important you understand everything on this page — it's the basis of lots of stuff still to come.

Mean, Median and Mode

It can make sense to record your data in a table — you get what's called a frequency distribution.

Discrete *Frequency Distributions are for* ***Countable Data***

Countable things like shoe sizes or the number of fish in a pond are discrete data (see p.2).

Example: Number of sweets in each of one hundred packets sampled:

Number of sweets per packet	38	39	40	41	42	43
Number of packets	5	18	29	33	13	2

A table like this is just a set of raw data put into a different format.
The table shows that there are 5 packets of 38 sweets, 18 packets of 39 sweets, etc.

Finding the ***Mean*** *— Add a* ***Third Row***

You can find the mean in exactly the same way as you did before — add all the values together and divide by the total number of values. To make things easier, add a third row to your table.

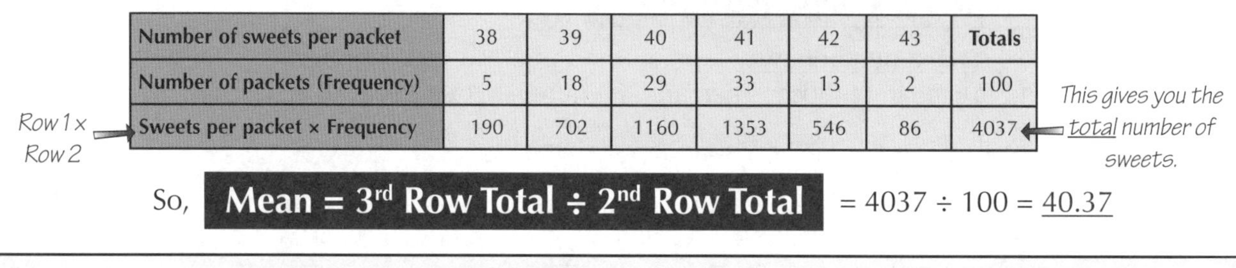

Number of sweets per packet	38	39	40	41	42	43	Totals
Number of packets (Frequency)	5	18	29	33	13	2	100
Sweets per packet × Frequency	190	702	1160	1353	546	86	4037

So, **Mean = 3rd Row Total ÷ 2nd Row Total** = 4037 ÷ 100 = 40.37

A more formal way of writing this method down is to use the following formula:

$$\bar{x} = \frac{\sum fx}{\sum f}$$

$\bar{x}$ is the symbol for the mean
$\sum$ is the Greek letter sigma — it means "the sum of"
x stands for the data values
f stands for the frequencies

This is the formula you'll get on your formula sheet in the exam.
It looks tricky but you'll see it's just a different way of labelling the rows in your table.

Back to the example, x is the number of sweets per packet and f is the frequency (number of packets).

$$\text{So } \bar{x} = \frac{\sum fx}{\sum f} = \frac{\text{Sum of (Frequency} \times \text{sweets per packet)}}{\text{Sum of (Frequency)}} = \frac{3^{rd}\text{ Row Total}}{2^{nd}\text{ Row Total}} = \frac{4037}{100} = 40.37$$

Finding the ***Median*** *is* ***Easy...***

The median is still the middle value but you have to count down through the table to find it.
One advantage of the table is that the data's already in ascending order.
Median position = $(n + 1) \div 2 = (100 + 1) \div 2 = 50.5$ (see p.71)
This means that the median value lies between the 50th and the 51st packets.
Looking at the table, there are 5 + 18 = 23 values in the first two columns.
And 23 + 29 = 52 in the first three.
So, the 50th and 51st values must be in the third column, and the median must be 40.

...So is Finding the ***Mode***

The mode is easy to find from a frequency table as the frequencies have already been worked out.
The mode is 41 as more packets hold 41 sweets than any other number.

Finding the mean from a frequency table — add a third row...

Make your third row by multiplying the other two — learn the method and it'll be easy marks.

Mean, Median and Mode

Continuous data is often recorded in a grouped frequency table, using inequalities (see p.39).
This page shows you how to estimate the mean and median values from the table.

Continuous Data tends to be Recorded in Groups

Since you don't know the individual data values, you can only estimate the mean.
You do this by using the midpoint values from each group. E.g. for the table below the midpoint of the first group is (85 + 90) ÷ 2 = 87.5. It's best to add two more rows to the basic frequency table.

Example:

Length (mm)	$85 < x \leq 90$	$90 < x \leq 95$	$95 < x \leq 100$	$100 < x \leq 105$	$105 < x \leq 110$	Totals
Frequency	3	7	15	10	5	40
Midpoint (mm) (New 3rd row)	87.5	92.5	97.5	102.5	107.5	—
Frequency × Midpoint (New 4th row)	262.5	647.5	1462.5	1025	537.5	3935

Mean = Overall Total (4th Row) ÷ Frequency Total (2nd Row)

So Mean = 3935 ÷ 40 = 98.375 mm.

The Modal group is the group with the most entries, which is $95 < x \leq 100$.

The Median is the value in position number (40 + 1) ÷ 2, which is also in the group $95 < x \leq 100$.

Estimating the Median More Accurately...

In the example above you've already worked out that the median is the value in position number (40 + 1) ÷ 2 which is value number 20.5. So to estimate the median, you need to estimate the 20.5th value.

METHOD:

1) **FIND THE MEDIAN'S POSITION IN ITS GROUP**
Overall position – number of positions below median group

The median's overall position is 20.5 and there are 10 values in the groups below the median group (3 + 7). So position in group = 20.5 – 10 = 10.5 — i.e. you want to estimate the 10.5th value in the group $95 < x \leq 100$.

2) **FIND THIS POSITION AS A PROPORTION**
Position in the group ÷ number of values in the group

The median is the 10.5th value in the group out of a total of 15 values.
So it's 10.5 ÷ 15 = 0.7 of the way through the group $95 < x \leq 100$.

3) **MULTIPLY YOUR ANSWER BY THE SIZE OF THE MEDIAN GROUP**

The group starts at 95 mm and goes to 100 mm so the size of the group is 5 mm. As the median is 0.7 of the way through the group you can estimate it'll be at 0.7 of the way through that 5 mm. So, 0.7 × 5 = 3.5 mm into the group.

4) **ADD THIS NUMBER TO THE MEDIAN GROUP'S LOWER CLASS BOUNDARY**

The group's lower class boundary is 95 mm — estimate for the median is 95 + 3.5 = 98.5 mm.

Grouped data — now there are two rows to add...

When you haven't got the actual data values, things get a bit tricky — you need to know how to work out estimates. Use midpoints to estimate the mean, and the four-step method for your median estimates.

Mean, Median and Mode

Averages are only useful if they suit your data.

There are **Advantages** and **Disadvantages** to each **Average**

	Advantages	Disadvantages
Mean	Uses all the data Usually most representative	Is not always a data value May be distorted by outliers
Median	Easy to find in ordered data Not distorted by outliers	Is not always a data value Not always a good representation of the data
Mode	Easy to find in tallied data Always a data value	Doesn't always exist Sometimes more than one

Different Averages are **Appropriate** in **Different Situations**

The MEAN:

1) It tends to be the most useful, since it uses all the data in its calculation.
2) Outliers affect its accuracy, but you can reduce the effects by choosing a larger sample.
3) The mean's often used to compare performances of people or items, e.g. cricketers' batting averages, golfers' handicaps or the lifetimes of batteries.

The MEDIAN:

1) It only gives you the middle value, but becomes more useful when used together with the range and interquartile range (see p.77-79).

The MODE:

1) It's an easy way of telling you which data value is most likely to appear.
2) It's mainly used with discrete data, as continuous data might not have two values the same.
3) It can give a misleading value. Look at this data giving you the mass in grams of each of ten eggs:
   59 65 66 64 63 69 68 69 61 62
   The mode is 69 g — which is a long way from the mean mass, 64.6 g.
4) One advantage the mode has over the mean and median is that it can be used in qualitative data. E.g. Which school subject is the most popular? What flavour ice cream sells the most?

There's a **Geometric Mean** as well as the Arithmetic Mean

You can use the geometric mean to combine two or more interest rates into one.
The geometric mean of n numbers is:

$$\text{Geometric Mean} = \sqrt[n]{x_1 \times x_2 \times \ldots \times x_n}$$

Example: An investment receives 3% interest in the 1st year, 4% in the 2nd and 8% in the 3rd. What annual rate of interest would give the same return over the three years?

To find the value of the investment after three years, multiply it by 1.03 × 1.04 × 1.08

Geometric Mean $= \sqrt[3]{1.03 \times 1.04 \times 1.08} = 1.04978$

So, Annual Interest = 4.978%

Mean, median, or mode — first check your data...

If it's a large sample of quantitative data, the mean is usually the most useful. If it's qualitative — try the mode. As for the median, well you'll be getting to know it a lot better a little further on...

Warm-Up and Worked Exam Questions

You know the score by now — first some warm-up questions to make sure you know the basics...

Warm-Up Questions

1) What is the median of the consecutive numbers 1-10?
2) Which digit is the mode in the consecutive numbers 1-10?
3) Find the mean of the numbers 981, 985, 986 and 992 using the "large numbers" method.
4) Which average should be used for qualitative data?
5) What advantage does the median have over the mean?
6) Calculate the geometric mean of the numbers 1, 4 and 16.

Worked Exam Questions

...And then some questions like you'll get in your exam. Make sure you get your head round these.

1 Jo couldn't decide which dress to buy: the red one or the blue one, so she decided to give each dress a percentage score for looks, price and practicality.

	Looks	Price	Practicality
Red	40%	30%	60%
Blue	45%	35%	20%

She then weighted these scores using weights of 30%, 50% and 20% respectively.

Using the scores and weights above, which dress should Jo buy? Show your working clearly.

Red dress: $(0.3 \times 40) + (0.5 \times 30) + (0.2 \times 60) = 39$

Blue dress: $(0.3 \times 45) + (0.5 \times 35) + (0.2 \times 20) = 35$

Jo should buy the red dress as it scored higher.

(4 marks for correct answer with working, otherwise 1 mark for correct method and 1 mark for finding each weighted mean.)

(4 marks)

2 A quality control department did a check on the number of nails in bags claiming to contain 100 nails. The results are shown below:

Number of nails per bag	96	97	98	99	100	101	102	103	104	*Total*
Number of bags	2	4	23	53	108	72	27	6	5	*300*
Nails per bag × frequency	*192*	*388*	*2254*	*5247*	*10 800*	*7272*	*2754*	*618*	*520*	*30 045*

(a) Calculate, to 1 decimal place, the mean number of nails in a bag.

Total number of nails ÷ total number of bags = $30\,045 \div 300 = 100.2$ (1 d.p.)

(3 marks for correct answer, otherwise 1 mark for correct method and 1 mark for correct answer but incorrectly rounded.) *(3 marks)*

(b) What is the modal number of nails per bag?

100

(1 mark)

(c) What is the median number of nails per bag?

$(300 + 1) \div 2 = 150.5$. The 150.5^{th} value is 100.

(2 marks for correct answer, otherwise 1 mark for finding 150.5.) *(2 marks)*

Exam Questions

3 The time taken to get to work by employees of 'Booksrus' is recorded as follows:

Time, t (mins)	$0 \le t < 10$	$10 \le t < 20$	$20 \le t < 30$	$30 \le t < 40$	$40 \le t < 50$
Frequency	22	32	45	18	3

(a) Calculate the estimated mean journey time.

....

....

(3 marks)

(b) Why is your answer to part (a) just an estimate?

....

(1 mark)

(c) Which is the modal group?

....

(1 mark)

(d) In which group is the median time?

....

(1 mark)

(e) If ten people from the first group left, what would happen to the mean time and why?

....

(1 mark)

4 A building society offers you interest at a rate of 4% for the first year and 9% for the second. A second building society offers you a rate of 6.6% fixed over two years.

Which building society gives you the best overall rate? Show all your working.

....

....

....

(3 marks)

5 The mean of twelve numbers is 5 and the mode is 7. Ten of the numbers are show in the table.

1	5	7	2	3	
6	7	9	8	2	

(a) Fill in the two missing numbers.

....

(2 marks)

(b) Calculate the median of the twelve numbers.

....

(2 marks)

Range and Quartiles

Finding the range is about as easy as it gets. Quartiles are just that little bit harder — but more useful.

The *Range* — How far the Data *Spreads*

To find the range of a set of data you just work out the difference between the highest and the lowest number.

Example: Find the range of these numbers: 7, 12, 5, 4, 3, 7, 5, 11, 6, 4, 9

Answer: Highest number – Lowest number = 12 – 3
The range is 9. It's a really simple way of giving you an idea of the spread of data.

However...
Outliers will seriously distort the range as it's calculated using only the highest and lowest values.

Finding the *Quartiles* is a bit More Tricky

Quartiles divide the data into four equal groups. They're known as the lower quartile, Q_1, the median, Q_2 and the upper quartile, Q_3.
If you put the data in ascending order, the quartiles are 25% (¼), 50% (½) and 75% (¾) of the way through the list.

If you get non-integer values for $(n + 1) \div 4$ or $3(n + 1) \div 4$, round up.
If you get a non-integer value for $(n + 1) \div 2$, use the two values either side.

METHOD:

1) Put the data in ascending order.
2) Work out where the quartiles come in the list using the following formulas:

Q_1 position number = $(n + 1) \div 4$
Q_2 position number = $2(n + 1) \div 4$
Q_3 position number = $3(n + 1) \div 4$

E.g. using the same set of data as before:

Step 1: 3 4 4 5 5 6 7 7 9 11 12

Step 2: $n = 11$ so Q_1 position no. = $(11 + 1) \div 4 = 3$
Q_2 position no. = $2(11 + 1) \div 4 = 6$
Q_3 position no. = $3(11 + 1) \div 4 = 9$

3 4 4 5 5 6 7 7 9 11 12
Q_1 (under 3rd value), Q_2 (under 6th value), Q_3 (under 9th value)
position 1 (3) ... position 11 (12)

3) So, the lower quartile $Q_1 = 4$, the median $Q_2 = 6$ and the upper quartile $Q_3 = 9$.

You can use more groups to give you a more flexible view of the spread of data.

1) Deciles, D_1 to D_9 divide the data into ten equal groups.
2) Percentiles, P_1 to P_{99}, divide the data into one hundred equal groups.

$Q_2 = D_5 = P_{50}$, all of which represent the median.

The formulas to work out the positions of deciles and percentiles are really similar to the ones for working out quartiles: D_1 position no. = $(n + 1) \div 10$, D_2 position no. = $2(n + 1) \div 10$, ...
P_1 position no. = $(n + 1) \div 100$, P_2 position no. = $2(n + 1) \div 100$, ...

The range is easy — the quartiles take a bit more work...

If you know how to find the median, you've already got your second quartile. It's just adapting the method you know already to find the first and the third. If you can't find the median — back to p.71 with you...

Interquartile and Interpercentile Range

The range doesn't necessarily tell you a great deal about a data set — the interquartile and interpercentile ranges can be a lot more useful.

Interquartile *means "Between Quartiles"*

The interquartile range is the difference between the upper quartile and the lower quartile.

Example: Find the interquartile range of the data from p.77:

3 4 4 5 5 6 7 7 9 11 12

Answer: Upper quartile = 9 Lower quartile = 4 Interquartile range = 9 – 4 = 5

So, you know how to find the interquartile range for non-grouped data, but with grouped data it's a bit trickier. You'll have the same problems finding the quartiles as you had getting the median...

Grouped Data — Estimate *the Interquartile Range Using a* ***Graph***

If you have grouped data, you can only estimate the interquartile range. One way of doing this is to estimate the quartiles using a similar method to the 'estimating the median' method on p.73.

An easier way, though, is to find values for your upper and lower quartiles by drawing a cumulative frequency curve. If you can't remember how to draw one have a look at p.51.

Interquartile Range — The ***Cumulative Frequency Method***

Step 1: **Draw your cumulative frequency curve.**

Step 2: **Draw horizontal lines from the 25% and 75% marks on the y-axis to the cumulative frequency curve, then read off the corresponding x-values. These are Q_1 and Q_3 respectively.**

Step 3: **Calculate the difference between your upper and lower quartiles to give the interquartile range — i.e. $Q_3 - Q_1$.**

You can also use this method to estimate the median.

See opposite for an example.

You can estimate interpercentile ranges in much the same way. Just draw your lines across from, say, the 10% and 90% marks on the y-axis — then read off the values P_{10} and P_{90} on the x-axis.

The P_{90} to P_{10} percentile range is then $P_{90} - P_{10}$.

Three Important Details *About* ***Ranges***

1) The interquartile range tells you the range of the middle 50% of the data — where most of the activity's going on — so it's often more useful than the range itself.
2) Small percentile ranges let you see what's going on in smaller areas of the data. This is most useful when the data's irregular, or isn't symmetrical about the mean (skewed).
3) The P_{90} to P_{10} percentile range gives a more realistic idea of the spread of data than the range does. It gives the range of the middle 80% of the data, ignoring any outliers.

Two more ranges — useful tools for measuring spread...

Interpercentile ranges are extra useful because you can tailor them to suit your data. Once you've worked out how to get the P_{90} to P_{10} percentile range it's only a small adjustment to get lots of others.

Interquartile and Interpercentile Range

You've learned the methods from the previous page — here's how to put them to good use.

Example

The table shows the time taken for each of 200 people to solve a puzzle:

If you don't understand this table — better check out 'Cumulative Frequency' again (see p.48).

Time (mins)	Frequency	Cumulative Frequency
$0 \leq t < 5$	8	8
$5 \leq t < 10$	30	38
$10 \leq t < 15$	66	104
$15 \leq t < 20$	58	162
$20 \leq t < 25$	26	188
$25 \leq t < 30$	12	200

Find the **Interquartile Range** for the Data:

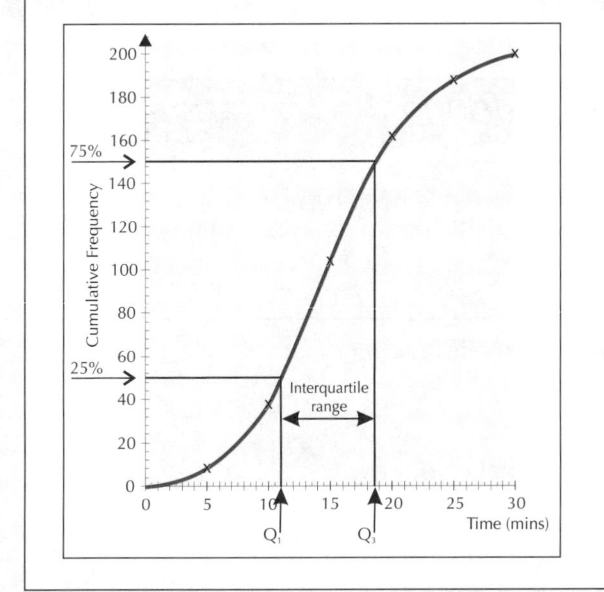

1) Here's the cumulative frequency curve for the above table.
2) Draw your lines across from the 25% and 75% marks on the y-axis — these correspond to x-values of 11 and 18.5 respectively. So $Q_1 = 11$ and $Q_3 = 18.5$.
3) So, interquartile range
   $= Q_3 - Q_1$
   $= 18.5 - 11$
   $= \underline{7.5}$

Find the P_{90} to P_{10} **Percentile Range** for the Data:

Using the same curve:

1) For the P_{90} to P_{10} percentile range, draw your lines from the 90% and 10% marks on the y-axis to the curve. This gives you the x-values — $P_{90} = 23$ and $P_{10} = 7.5$.
2) So, P_{90} to P_{10} Percentile range
   $= P_{90} - P_{10}$
   $= 23 - 7.5$
   $= \underline{15.5}$

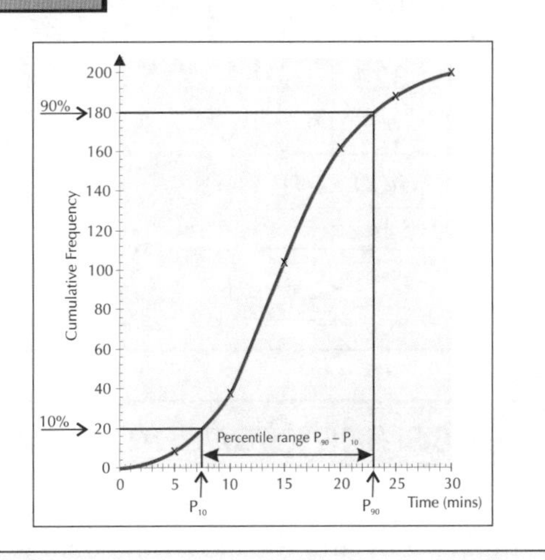

First plot your curve — then read off your values...

There's loads of stuff you'll need to have mastered before you get this. If grouped frequencies, cumulative frequency curves or quartile and percentile positions are troubling you — go back and re-read those pages.

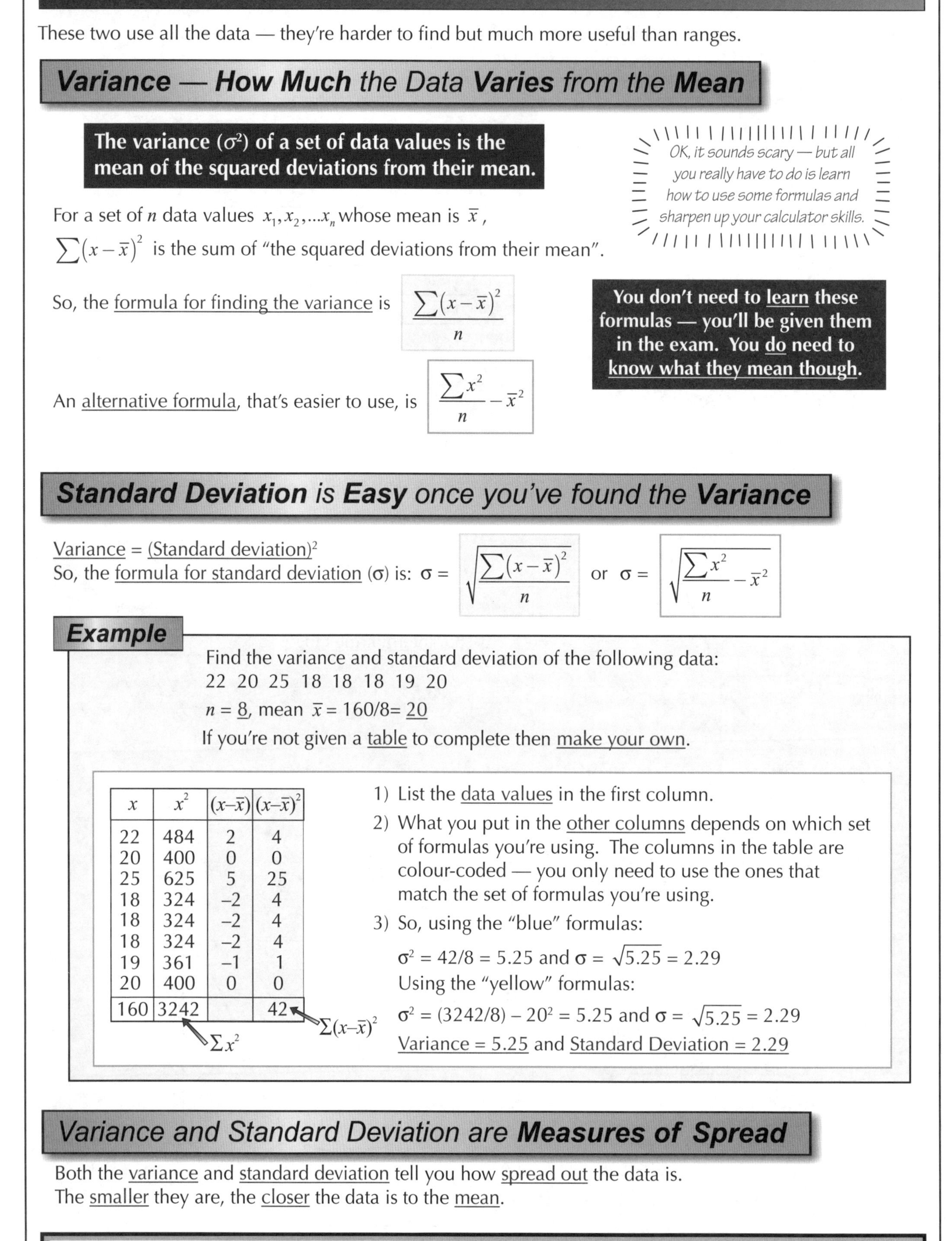

Variance and Standard Deviation

These two use all the data — they're harder to find but much more useful than ranges.

Variance — How Much the Data Varies from the Mean

The variance (σ^2) of a set of data values is the mean of the squared deviations from their mean.

OK, it sounds scary — but all you really have to do is learn how to use some formulas and sharpen up your calculator skills.

For a set of n data values $x_1, x_2, ... x_n$ whose mean is $\bar{x}$,

$\sum(x-\bar{x})^2$ is the sum of "the squared deviations from their mean".

So, the formula for finding the variance is $\frac{\sum(x-\bar{x})^2}{n}$

An alternative formula, that's easier to use, is $\frac{\sum x^2}{n} - \bar{x}^2$

You don't need to learn these formulas — you'll be given them in the exam. You do need to know what they mean though.

Standard Deviation is Easy once you've found the Variance

Variance = (Standard deviation)^2

So, the formula for standard deviation (σ) is: $\sigma = \sqrt{\frac{\sum(x-\bar{x})^2}{n}}$ or $\sigma = \sqrt{\frac{\sum x^2}{n} - \bar{x}^2}$

Example

Find the variance and standard deviation of the following data:

22 20 25 18 18 18 19 20

$n = 8$, mean $\bar{x} = 160/8 = 20$

If you're not given a table to complete then make your own.

x	x^2	$(x-\bar{x})$	$(x-\bar{x})^2$
22	484	2	4
20	400	0	0
25	625	5	25
18	324	−2	4
18	324	−2	4
18	324	−2	4
19	361	−1	1
20	400	0	0
160	3242		42

$\sum x^2$ (= 3242), $\sum(x-\bar{x})^2$ (= 42)

1) List the data values in the first column.
2) What you put in the other columns depends on which set of formulas you're using. The columns in the table are colour-coded — you only need to use the ones that match the set of formulas you're using.
3) So, using the "blue" formulas:

   $\sigma^2 = 42/8 = 5.25$ and $\sigma = \sqrt{5.25} = 2.29$

   Using the "yellow" formulas:

   $\sigma^2 = (3242/8) - 20^2 = 5.25$ and $\sigma = \sqrt{5.25} = 2.29$

   Variance = 5.25 and Standard Deviation = 2.29

Variance and Standard Deviation are Measures of Spread

Both the variance and standard deviation tell you how spread out the data is.

The smaller they are, the closer the data is to the mean.

Use variance and standard deviation to find the spread of your data...

If you know the variance you pretty much know the standard deviation. Get to know how to use one of the two sets of formulas really well — but don't get them confused or you'll be in all sorts of bother.

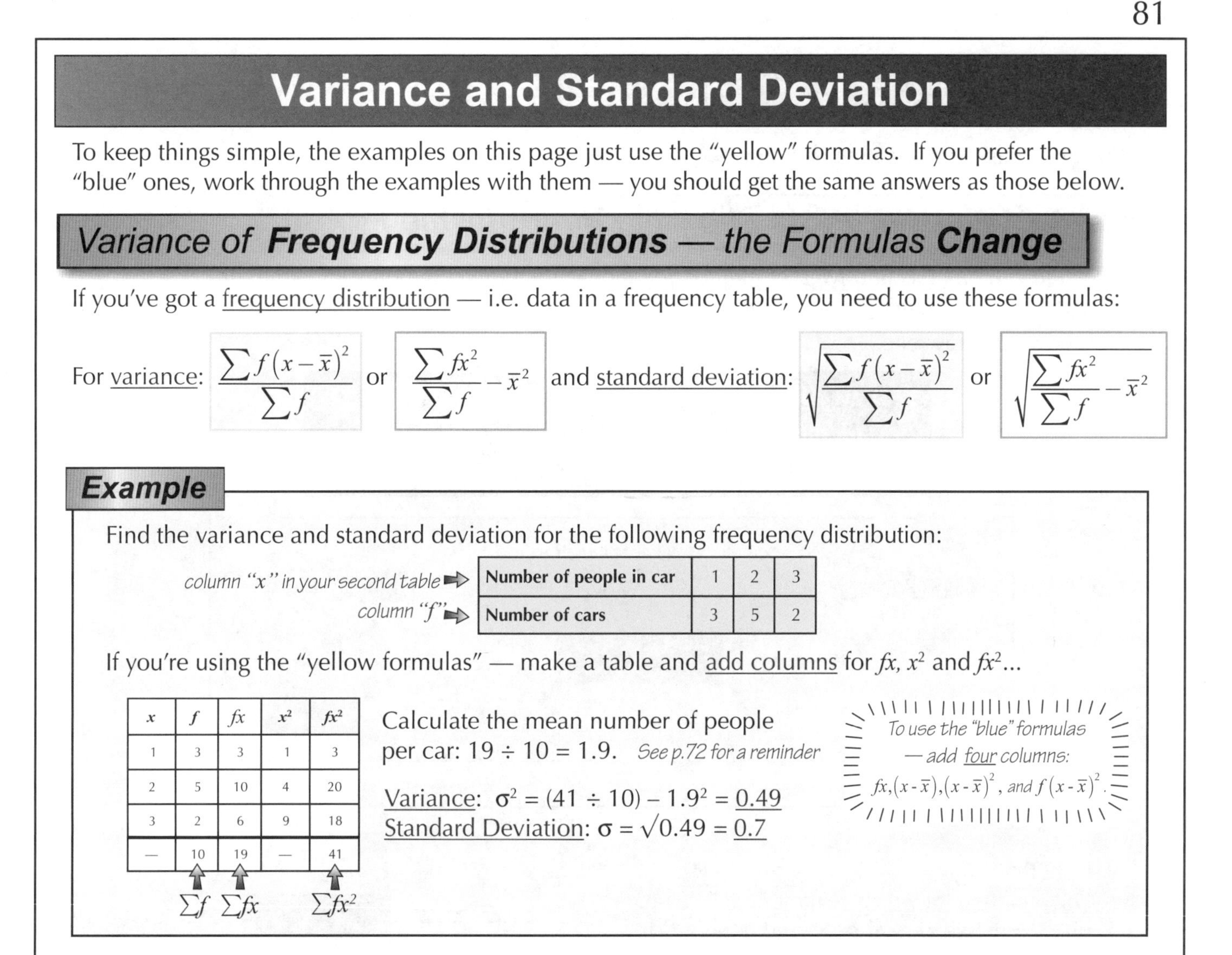

Variance and Standard Deviation

To keep things simple, the examples on this page just use the "yellow" formulas. If you prefer the "blue" ones, work through the examples with them — you should get the same answers as those below.

Variance of **Frequency Distributions** — the Formulas **Change**

If you've got a frequency distribution — i.e. data in a frequency table, you need to use these formulas:

For variance: $\dfrac{\sum f(x-\bar{x})^2}{\sum f}$ or $\dfrac{\sum fx^2}{\sum f} - \bar{x}^2$ and standard deviation: $\sqrt{\dfrac{\sum f(x-\bar{x})^2}{\sum f}}$ or $\sqrt{\dfrac{\sum fx^2}{\sum f} - \bar{x}^2}$

Example

Find the variance and standard deviation for the following frequency distribution:

column "x" in your second table ➡	Number of people in car	1	2	3
column "f" ➡	Number of cars	3	5	2

If you're using the "yellow formulas" — make a table and add columns for fx, x^2 and fx^2...

x	f	fx	x^2	fx^2
1	3	3	1	3
2	5	10	4	20
3	2	6	9	18
—	10	19	—	41
	$\sum f$	$\sum fx$		$\sum fx^2$

Calculate the mean number of people per car: $19 \div 10 = 1.9$. *See p.72 for a reminder*

Variance: $\sigma^2 = (41 \div 10) - 1.9^2 = 0.49$
Standard Deviation: $\sigma = \sqrt{0.49} = 0.7$

To use the "blue" formulas — add four columns: $fx, (x-\bar{x}), (x-\bar{x})^2$, and $f(x-\bar{x})^2$.

For **Grouped** Frequency Distributions x is the **Midpoint**

When you've got a grouped frequency distribution you can only make estimates for the variance and standard deviation. You do this by taking the midpoint of the group as your x value.

Example

Find the variance and standard deviation for the following grouped frequency distribution:

Height (cm)	$50 < x \le 75$	$75 < x \le 100$	$100 < x \le 125$	$125 < x \le 150$	$150 < x \le 175$
Frequency	7	18	42	25	8

x	f	fx	x^2	fx^2
62.5	7	437.5	3906.25	27 343.75
87.5	18	1575	7656.25	137 812.5
112.5	42	4725	12 656.25	531 562.5
137.5	25	3437.5	18 906.25	472 656.25
162.5	8	1300	26 406.25	211 250
—	100	11 475	—	1 380 625
	$\sum f$	$\sum fx$		$\sum fx^2$

Again, you make a table with three extra columns — but now the 'x' column contains the midpoints rather than the actual data values.

Calculating the mean...
$11\,475 \div 100 = 114.75$.

So, $\sigma^2 = (1\,380\,625 \div 100) - 114.75^2 = 638.68...$
$\sigma = \sqrt{638.68...} = 25.27...$

So, to 1 d.p.:
Variance = 638.7 cm^2 and Standard Deviation = 25.3 cm

Grouped frequency distributions — pick one set of formulas to learn...

It's all too easy to make a slip with these methods — so pick your favourite formula and practise using it.

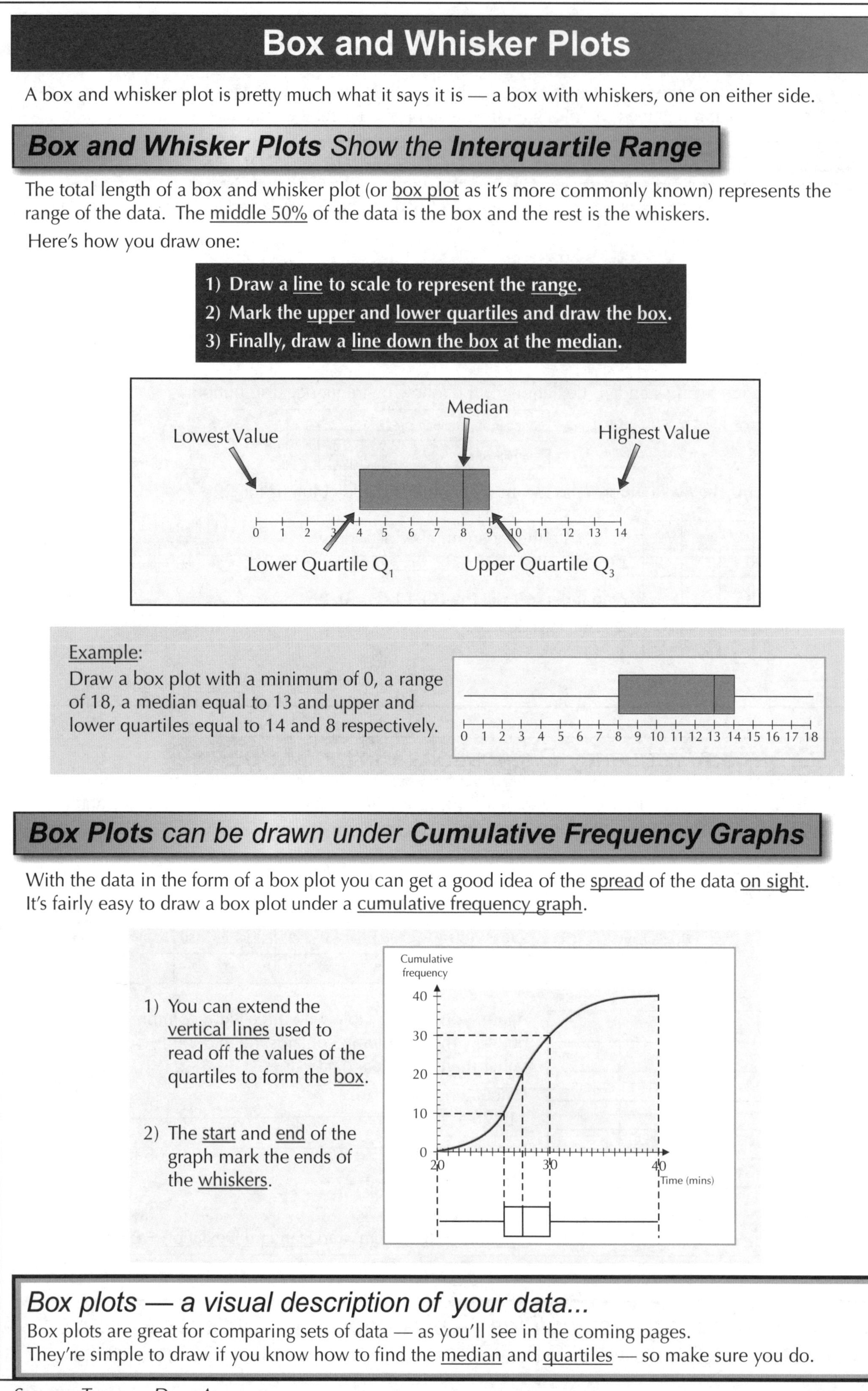

Box and Whisker Plots

A box and whisker plot is pretty much what it says it is — a box with whiskers, one on either side.

Box and Whisker Plots *Show the* ***Interquartile Range***

The total length of a box and whisker plot (or box plot as it's more commonly known) represents the range of the data. The middle 50% of the data is the box and the rest is the whiskers.

Here's how you draw one:

1) Draw a line to scale to represent the range.
2) Mark the upper and lower quartiles and draw the box.
3) Finally, draw a line down the box at the median.

Example:
Draw a box plot with a minimum of 0, a range of 18, a median equal to 13 and upper and lower quartiles equal to 14 and 8 respectively.

Box Plots *can be drawn under* ***Cumulative Frequency Graphs***

With the data in the form of a box plot you can get a good idea of the spread of the data on sight. It's fairly easy to draw a box plot under a cumulative frequency graph.

1) You can extend the vertical lines used to read off the values of the quartiles to form the box.

2) The start and end of the graph mark the ends of the whiskers.

Box plots — a visual description of your data...

Box plots are great for comparing sets of data — as you'll see in the coming pages.
They're simple to draw if you know how to find the median and quartiles — so make sure you do.

Box and Whisker Plots

Box plots are also useful in identifying outliers. Honestly, I won't hear a bad word said about them...

Outliers are Values a Long Way from the Mean

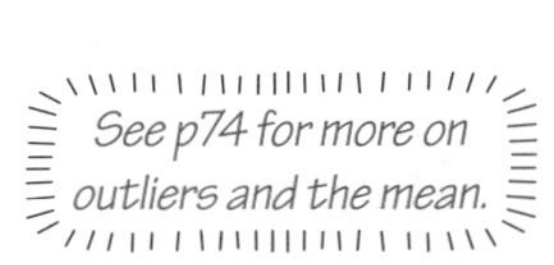
See p74 for more on outliers and the mean.

Outliers are values that are out on their own, a long way from the mean.
These can distort an otherwise reasonable set of data — so you need to identify them.

The usual way to identify outliers is to look for any values that are more than one and a half times the interquartile range away from the upper or lower quartiles.

In other words —

Outliers are values $> Q_3 + 1.5(Q_3 - Q_1)$
or values $< Q_1 - 1.5(Q_3 - Q_1)$

If you Find any Outliers — Shorten your Whiskers

A box plot helps you find the outliers because the range of the data and the upper and lower quartiles are there for you to see.

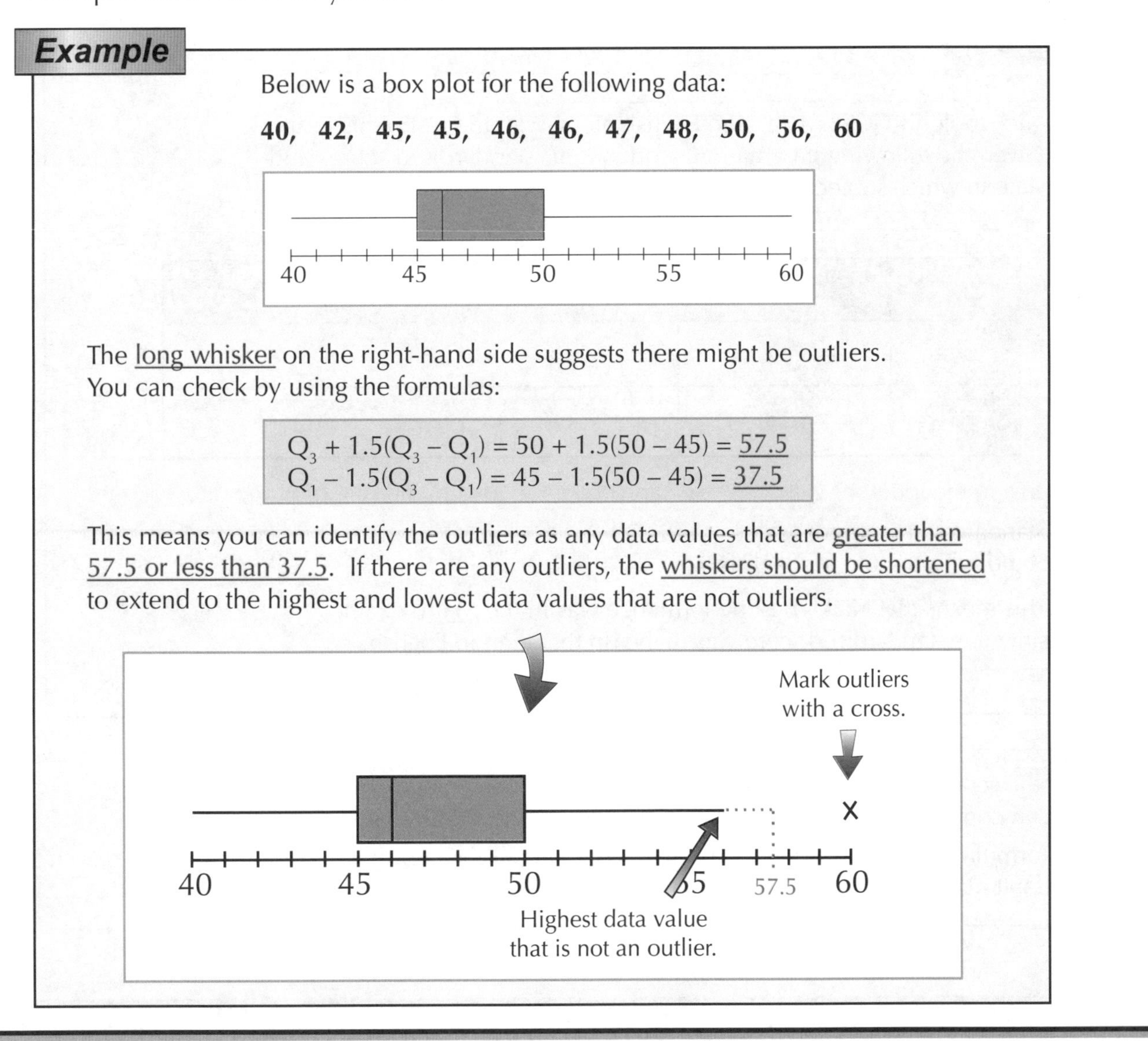

Example

Below is a box plot for the following data:

40, 42, 45, 45, 46, 46, 47, 48, 50, 56, 60

The long whisker on the right-hand side suggests there might be outliers.
You can check by using the formulas:

$Q_3 + 1.5(Q_3 - Q_1) = 50 + 1.5(50 - 45) = \underline{57.5}$
$Q_1 - 1.5(Q_3 - Q_1) = 45 - 1.5(50 - 45) = \underline{37.5}$

This means you can identify the outliers as any data values that are greater than 57.5 or less than 37.5. If there are any outliers, the whiskers should be shortened to extend to the highest and lowest data values that are not outliers.

Box plots can help you pick out the outliers...

A box plot with the whiskers shortened to the highest and lowest values that aren't outliers will give a better picture of the spread of your data. Don't forget your crosses though — outliers are data too...

Standardised Scores

Standardised scores are used to compare values from different sets of data — when the sets of data are of different size and spread.

Formula for Finding the **Standardised Score**

You can't compare individual values from two different data sets directly, e.g. you couldn't compare a mark from an easier exam with one from a more difficult paper. You need to standardise them first.

$$\text{standardised score} = \frac{\text{value} - \text{mean}}{\text{standard deviation}}$$

1) Any value equal to the mean has a standardised score of zero — you can see that from the formula — so zero is an average score.
2) Anything above zero is better than average and anything negative is below average.

Example

Nick took his GCSE Maths and English along with the rest of his year. Given the following information, work out his standardised scores and state in which subject he did the best.

Subject	Score	Mean	Standard Deviation
Maths	60%	70%	1.8
English	65%	72%	1.2

Standardised score for Maths = (60 – 70) ÷ 1.8 = –5.6
Standardised score for English = (65 – 72) ÷ 1.2 = –5.8

This means that Nick's best performance was in the Maths exam, since his standardised score was higher in that than in English.

1) Both the scores in this example are out of 100 (i.e. a percentage), but they don't have to be. You can compare a score out of 50 with one out of, say, 7842 — it makes no difference.
2) This formula only strictly applies if both sets of data follow a normal distribution (p.55). You don't really need to worry about that though.

Comparing data — first standardise your scores...

This page takes some bits and pieces you've learnt already and puts them together in one easy-to-use formula. As long as you know how to calculate the mean and standard deviation, this should be quite an easy — and dare I say handy — addition to your stats arsenal.

Comparing Data Sets

Averages and measures of spread can be combined to compare different sets of data.

Comparing Data Sets — Which Measure is Most **Useful**?

The following sets of data show the percentage results (in ascending order) for 20 students in French and English:

French	31	35	39	40	43	43	45	47	47	48
	51	55	59	62	65	65	68	71	72	78
English	37	38	42	42	43	45	48	49	50	51
	51	57	58	59	59	60	61	61	64	65

The table and box plots below show some comparisons between the two sets of data.

	French	English
Mean	53.2	52
Median	49.5	51
Mode	43, 47, 65	42, 51, 59, 61
Range	47	28
Upper Quartile	65	59.5
Lower Quartile	43	44
Interquartile Range	22	15.5
Standard Deviation	13.19	8.60

1) The box plots show that the results for English were much closer together, having a smaller range.
2) The standard deviations also show this, but that's all they show. Unlike the box plot, they don't give you any idea of the actual values.
3) The mean and median are always useful to give you a quick average or central location of the data. The mode, in this case, is not much use at all.

It Can be Useful to **Compare Individual Values**

Standardised scores let you compare standards of performance.

Example: Compare the top marks in French and English.
Standardised top score for French = (78 – 53.2) ÷ 13.19 = 1.88
Standardised top score for English = (65 – 52) ÷ 8.6 = 1.51

These results show that the top score for French was better than that in English — it was better in relation to the other students' performances.

Different measures say different things about a data set...

This page is about applying what you know — taking sets of data and analysing them with the methods you've learnt. It's not just about applying the formulas — but thinking about what they tell you.

Warm-Up and Worked Exam Questions

Right, knuckle down to these warm-up questions before you have a crack at the fiendish exam questions.

Warm-Up Questions

1) What is the range of the numbers 1, 2, 3, ... , 100?
2) What is the upper quartile of the first seven whole numbers, 1, 2, ... , 7?
3) If the variance of a set of numbers is 11.5, what is the standard deviation?
4) The mean of the following data is 73. Find the variance: 74, 82, 61, 75, 68, 78, 73.
5) The interquartile range of a set of data is 20, the lower quartile is 50, the data ranges from 20 to 80 and the median is 55. Draw a box and whisker plot to show this information.
6) In his history exam, Dave got 80%. If the mean was 58% and the standard deviation was 4.4%, what was his standardised score?

Worked Exam Questions

Make sure you go through these worked questions carefully until you can work out quartiles, variance and standard deviation in your sleep. Examiners just love asking about them.

1 The weights of a dozen eggs are recorded below.

102 g	110 g	105 g	102 g	114 g	103 g
103 g	101 g	106 g	101 g	104 g	105 g

(a) What is the range of weights of eggs?

114 – 101 = 13 g

(1 mark)

(b) Find the median, upper and lower quartiles and the interquartile range of the data.

Median position = $(n + 1) \div 2 = 6.5^{th}$ value, so median = 103.5 g **(1 mark)**

Q_3 position = $3(n + 1) \div 4 = 9.75^{th} = 10^{th}$ value, so Q_3 = 106 g **(1 mark)**

Q_1 position = $(n + 1) \div 4 = 3.25^{th} = 4^{th}$ value, so Q_1 = 102 g **(1 mark)**

Interquartile range = $Q_3 - Q_1$ = 106 – 102 = 4 g **(1 mark)**

(4 marks)

(c) Identify any outliers. Show your working.

$Q_3 + 1.5(4) = 106 + 6 = 112$. $Q_1 - 1.5(4) = 102 - 6 = 96$. 114 is the only outlier, as it is the only data value greater than 112 or less than 96.

(2 marks for correct answer with working, otherwise 1 mark for 112 or 96.) *(2 marks)*

(d) Draw a box and whisker plot for this data.

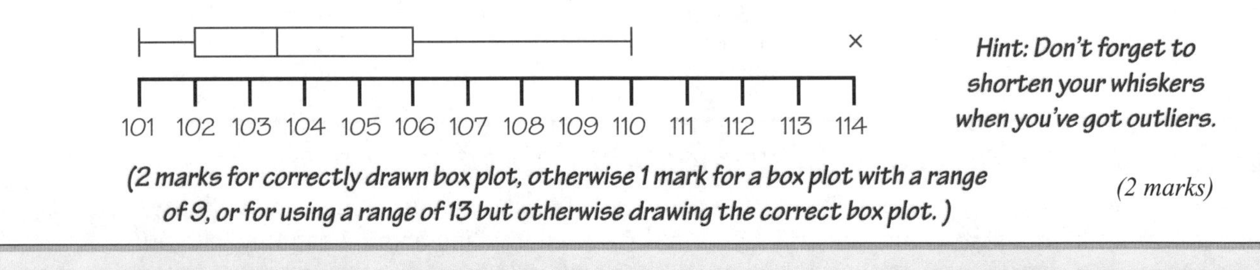

(2 marks for correctly drawn box plot, otherwise 1 mark for a box plot with a range of 9, or for using a range of 13 but otherwise drawing the correct box plot.) *(2 marks)*

Worked Exam Questions

Worked Exam Questions

2 25 holidaymakers out crab-fishing were asked how many crabs they had caught in the last hour. The results are shown in this table:

Number of crabs (x)	0	1	2	3	4	5	6
Number of holidaymakers (f)	3	2	5	6	6	2	1
fx^2	0	2	20	54	96	50	36

Calculate the variance and standard deviation for this data, given that the mean is 2.8.

$\sum fx^2 = 2 + 20 + 54 + 96 + 50 + 36 = 258$

$Variance = \left(\sum fx^2 \div \sum f\right) - \bar{x}^2 = (258 \div 25) - 2.8^2 = 2.48$

$Standard\ Deviation = \sqrt{Variance} = 1.57$

(3 marks for both correct, otherwise 2 marks for the correct method but with an error in working, or 1 mark for using the variance formula.) *(3 marks)*

3 120 people were asked how long, on average, they spend reading the Sunday newspaper. The cumulative frequency graph below shows the results.

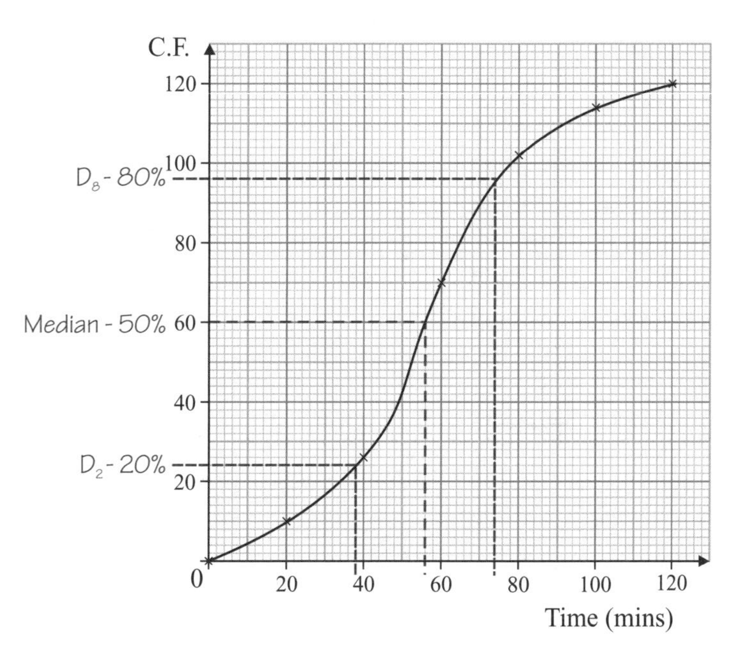

(a) Use the graph to estimate the median time taken reading the Sunday newspaper.

56 minutes

(1 mark)

(b) Estimate the D_8 to D_2 range for this data.

$D_8 = 74$ and $D_2 = 38$

D_8 to D_2 range = 74 - 38 = 36

(2 marks for correct answer, otherwise 1 mark for D_8 or D_2.) *(2 marks)*

Exam Questions

4 The following table shows the number of tins of baked beans consumed by certain families in one month.

Number of tins (n)	$0 \leq n < 5$	$5 \leq n < 10$	$10 \leq n < 15$	$15 \leq n < 20$	$20 \leq n < 25$	$25 \leq n < 30$
Frequency	5	24	38	19	12	2
Cumulative Frequency						

(a) Complete the table to show cumulative frequency.

(1 mark)

(b) Draw a cumulative frequency curve for this data on the grid below.

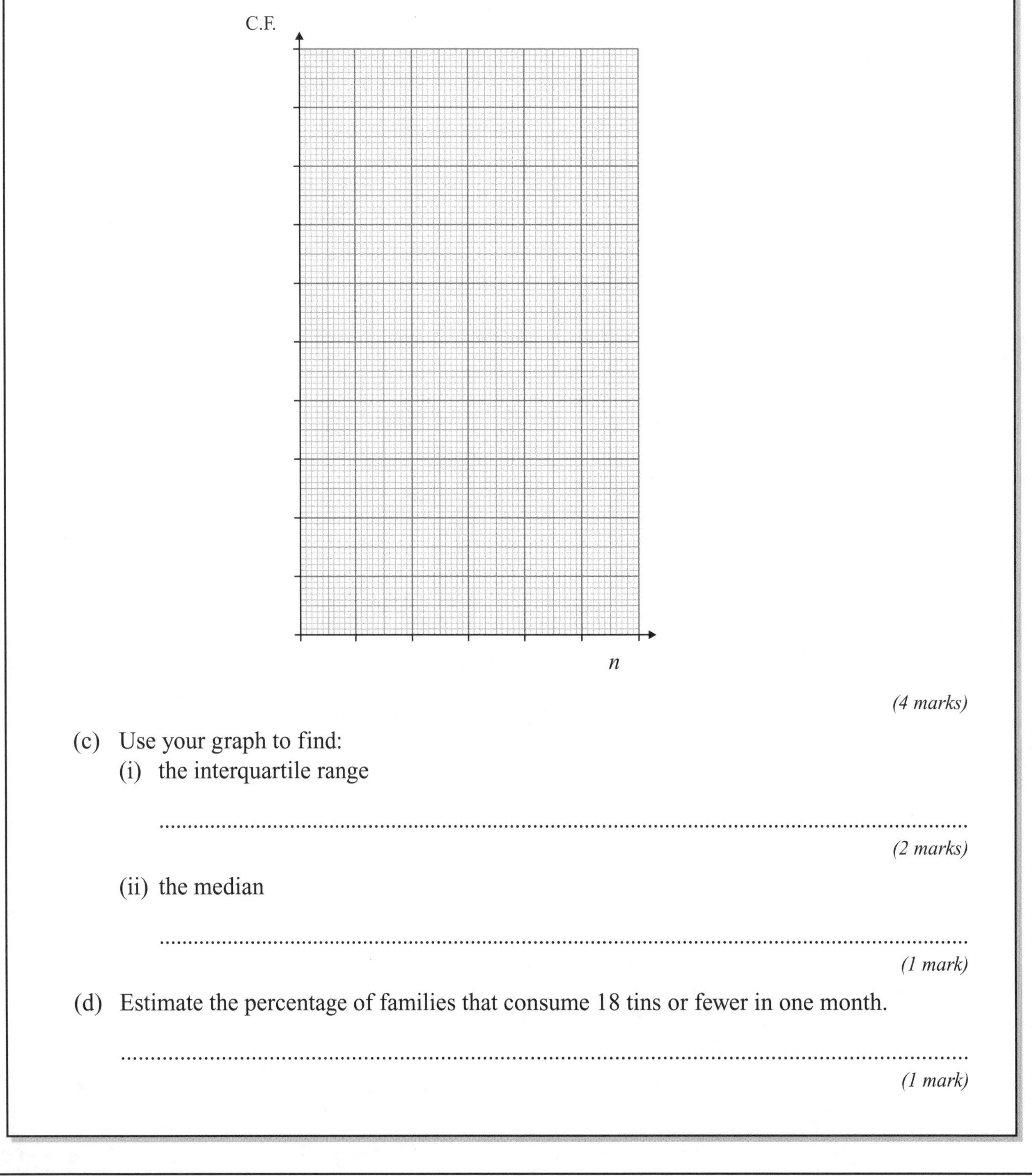

(4 marks)

(c) Use your graph to find:
(i) the interquartile range

....

(2 marks)

(ii) the median

....

(1 mark)

(d) Estimate the percentage of families that consume 18 tins or fewer in one month.

....

(1 mark)

Exam Questions

5 Twenty competitors took part in an ice dance competition. They had to perform two dances — one compulsory and one freestyle. A maximum score of 50 was possible for each dance. The results for the compulsory dance are shown below:

Compulsory Score	26 - 30	31 - 35	36 - 40	41 - 45	46 - 50
Frequency	2	5	8	4	1

The mean compulsory score is 37.25.

(a) Find the variance and standard deviation of the scores.

(3 marks)

The mean and standard deviation of the freestyle scores are 41.7 and 3.2 respectively. The scores awarded to two of the competitors, Nathan and Zac, are shown in the table below.

	Nathan	Zac
Compulsory	43	40
Freestyle	41	44

(b) (i) Using part (a) and the information above, calculate Zac's standardised compulsory and freestyle scores. Add these scores together to find his total standardised score.

(3 marks)

(ii) Who gave the best overall performance, Nathan or Zac? Show your working.

(3 marks)

6 The following box plots summarise the GCSE French results for students of two schools — Abbeyknock and Blakeney.

Abbeyknock

% 0 10 20 30 40 50 60 70 80 90 100

Blakeney

(a) Give two ways in which the performances of the schools are similar.

(2 marks)

(b) Which school had the better results? Give a reason for your answer.

(1 mark)

Summary Statistics

Index numbers are all about measuring change. Different types are used in different situations.

Simple Index Numbers — Just Percentages Really

Index numbers are usually used to compare price changes over time.
The values are compared to the values in a particular year — known as the base year.

$$\text{Index number} = \frac{\text{value}}{\text{value in base year}} \times 100$$

The value in the base year always has an index of 100 (meaning 100%).

Example: The table below shows the price of a house over three years. 2001 is the base year. Find the index number for 2003.

Year	2001	2002	2003
House Price	£148 000	£167 000	£174 000

Index number for 2003 = $\frac{174\,000}{148\,000} \times 100 = 117.6$

Chain Base Numbers are Index Numbers from Year to Year

Chain base numbers are index numbers which show how values change from year to year.
They always use the previous year as the base year.

Weighted Index Numbers Take Proportions Into Account

For example, a dried fruit mixture contains apricots and prunes in the ratio 5:2. If the price of apricots or prunes goes up, then so will the price of the mixture. BUT... a rise in the price of apricots will have more effect on the price of the mixture than a rise in the price of prunes.

Weighted index numbers take the difference in importance into account. And there's a lovely formula for it too —

$$\text{Weighted index number} = \frac{\sum(\text{index number} \times \text{weight})}{\sum \text{weights}}$$

Example:
Every year a school holds a cheese and wine party and always buys the same amount of cheese and wine — 5 kg of cheese and 10 cases of wine.
Using the table on the right, calculate the weighted index number for 2003 using 2000 as the base year.

	2000	2003	Weight
Cost of Cheese (per kg)	£3.40	£3.70	5
Cost of Wine (per case)	£42	£39	10

Cheese index number × weight = $\left(\frac{3.7}{3.4} \times 100\right) \times 5 = 544.12$ Wine index number × weight = $\left(\frac{39}{42} \times 100\right) \times 10 = 928.57$

So, the weighted index number = $\frac{544.12 + 928.57}{5 + 10} = 98.18$ (2 d.p.)

The Retail Price Index (RPI) is a Weighted Index

It shows changes in the cost of living for an average person or family. Every month, the prices of loads of items (the same ones each month) are combined to get a weighted index number.
The weightings are chosen to show the spending habits of an average family.
As stuff gets more expensive, this index number gets higher and higher.

Learn what index numbers mean — and how to work them out...

A couple of formulas here for you to get to know well — cover the page and write them both down.

Summary Statistics

Crude rates are the most basic way of measuring the levels of things like births and deaths.

Crude Rates Tell You How Many In Every 1000

Crude death rates are the number of deaths per thousand of the population.
Crude birth rates are the number of births per thousand of the population.

To calculate crude rates, you need to use the following formula:

The Formula

$$\text{Crude birth or death rate} = \frac{\text{number of births or deaths}}{\text{total population}} \times 1000$$

You can use this formula to calculate other types of crude rate too — for example, crime rates, unemployment rates etc.

Examples

1. Bodbury has a population of 142 000. There were 3270 deaths there last year. What was the crude death rate in Bodbury last year?

$$\text{Crude death rate} = \frac{3270}{142\,000} \times 1000 = \underline{23.03}$$

This means that last year there were about 23 deaths for every 1000 people in Bodbury. This is okay as a rough guide to the death rate in Bodbury alone, but is not much use for comparing it with different areas. One town may be full of retirement homes — more elderly residents means the death rate is bound to be higher.

2. Allfit has a population of 220 000. Last year there were 6141 births there. What was the crude birth rate in Allfit last year?

$$\text{Crude birth rate} = \frac{6141}{220\,000} \times 1000 = \underline{27.91}$$

This means that there were about 28 births for every 1000 people in Allfit. Again though, this doesn't take into account the size of different age groups in the town and so can't really be used to compare places.

Crude rates — a simple method but not great for comparisons...

Crude rates are really simple, but they're a little, well... crude. You'll find more subtle ways of measuring this kind of stuff on the next page — but you'll need to learn this formula first.

Summary Statistics

Standardised rates take the age groups of people living in an area into consideration.
This means you can compare rates in different places fairly.

***Standardised Rates** are More **Useful** than Crude Rates*

There's a formula for this too. You use something called the standard population — this is the number of people in each age group over the whole country (usually given as a percentage), which you can get from census data.

First, work out the crude rate for each age group individually. Then put your values into this formula:

$$\text{Standardised rate} = \frac{\sum(\text{crude rate for age group} \times \text{standard population for age group})}{\sum(\text{standard population})}$$

Example

The number of deaths in Bodbury and Allfit last year are recorded in the table.
Calculate the standardised death rate in both places.

	Bodbury		Allfit		Standard Population
Age Group	Population	No. of Deaths	Population	No. of Deaths	
< 40	72,000	180	83,000	160	42
40 - 60	41,000	360	47,000	340	34
> 60	29,000	2,730	90,000	6,200	24

The standardised death rate in Bodbury

$$= \frac{\left(\frac{180 \times 1000}{72\,000} \times 42\right) + \left(\frac{360 \times 1000}{41000} \times 34\right) + \left(\frac{2730 \times 1000}{29\,000} \times 24\right)}{42 + 34 + 24} = \frac{105 + 298.537 + 2259.310}{100} = \underline{26.63}$$

The standardised death rate in Allfit

$$= \frac{\left(\frac{160 \times 1000}{83\,000} \times 42\right) + \left(\frac{340 \times 1000}{47\,000} \times 34\right) + \left(\frac{6200 \times 1000}{90\,000} \times 24\right)}{42 + 34 + 24} = \frac{80.964 + 245.957 + 1653.333}{100} = \underline{19.80}$$

This tells you that the standardised death rate in Allfit is lower than that in Bodbury (even though the crude death rate is higher there) so it would seem that the people of Allfit are generally healthier.

Standardised rates — the less crude rate...

Standardised rates are another of those methods for making statistics more useful.
They're pretty handy and easy to do — once you've learned the formula and how to use it.

Warm-Up and Worked Exam Questions

Here are some more warm-ups to test you on the last few pages, and so soon after the last set too...

Warm-Up Questions

1) In 2006, 250 g of butter cost £0.68. In 2008 the same amount of butter cost £1.12. Using 2006 as the base year, calculate the index number for 2008.
2) Last year there were 52 000 people living in Rhyskworth. If 400 people from Rhyskworth died that year, what was the crude death rate?
3) A car was worth £17 500 in 2006, £15 000 in 2007 and £11 000 in 2008. What was its chain base number in 2008?
4) 512 babies were born in Nutwood in 2007 and 107 babies were born in Greendale in the same year. Why could you not conclude that the birth rate was higher in Nutwood than in Greendale?
5) The RPI is used to show changes in the cost of living. What does RPI stand for?

Worked Exam Questions

This set of questions is all about getting the hang of index numbers and rates. These worked examples show you how to get yourself some marks.

1 The escalating price of a luxury food hamper is shown in the table below.

Year	2005	2006	2007	2008
Price (£)	420	435	478	510

(a) Using 2005 as the base year, calculate the index number for 2008.

$(510 \div 420) \times 100 = 121.4$

(1 mark)

(b) What is the chain base number for 2008?

$(510 \div 478) \times 100 = 106.7$

(1 mark)

2 A smoothie is made using milk, bananas and strawberries in the ratio 5:2:1. The cost of the ingredients in 2007 and 2008 is shown in the table below.

	2007	2008	Weight
Milk (per part)	20p	24p	5
Bananas (per part)	22p	26p	2
Strawberries (per part)	30p	38p	1

(a) Complete the table.

(1 mark)

(b) Using 2007 as the base year, calculate the weighted index number for 2008.

Milk index = $(24 \div 20) \times 100 = 120$, index $\times 5 = 600$

Banana index = $(26 \div 22) \times 100 = 118.18...$, index $\times 2 = 236.4$

Strawberry index = $(38 \div 30) \times 100 = 126.66...$, index $\times 1 = 126.7$

Weighted Index Number = $(600 + 236.4 + 126.7) \div (5 + 2 + 1) = 120.4$

(4 marks for correct answer, otherwise 1 mark for using the correct method for a weighted index and 1 mark each for up to two correct index numbers.)

(4 marks)

Exam Questions

3 The number of deaths in two towns, Mudgrave and Ollington, last year are shown in the table.

	Mudgrave		Ollington		Standard Population
Age Group	Population	Number of deaths	Population	Number of deaths	
< 40	57 000	120	80 000	100	42%
40 - 60	30 000	320	49 000	500	
> 60	44 000	5260	86 000	8050	24%

(a) Complete the table.

(1 mark)

(b) Calculate the crude death rate for Mudgrave.

....

....

(2 marks)

(c) Calculate the standardised death rates for both towns, showing your working.
Explain which town seems to have the healthier population.

....

....

....

....

....

(6 marks)

4 A company uses two lengths of steel and 60 rivets to make an aircraft part.
The costs (in £) of the materials in 2007 and 2008 are shown in the table below.

Year	2007	2008	Weight
Length of steel	275.00	350.00	
10 rivets	12.00	15.00	

(a) Complete the table.

(1 mark)

(b) Using 2007 as the base year, what is the weighted index number for 2008?

....

....

....

(4 marks)

Time Series and Predictions

Time series use data taken over a period of time at equal intervals to show trends.

A Trend Line is Used for Making Predictions

Example: The following data shows the unemployment figures (in thousands) for Idleville averaged over each six-month period from January 2000 till December 2003.

	2000	2001	2002	2003
Jan - Jun	78	97	103	114
Jul - Dec	84	76	92	99

This data can be plotted on a time series graph:

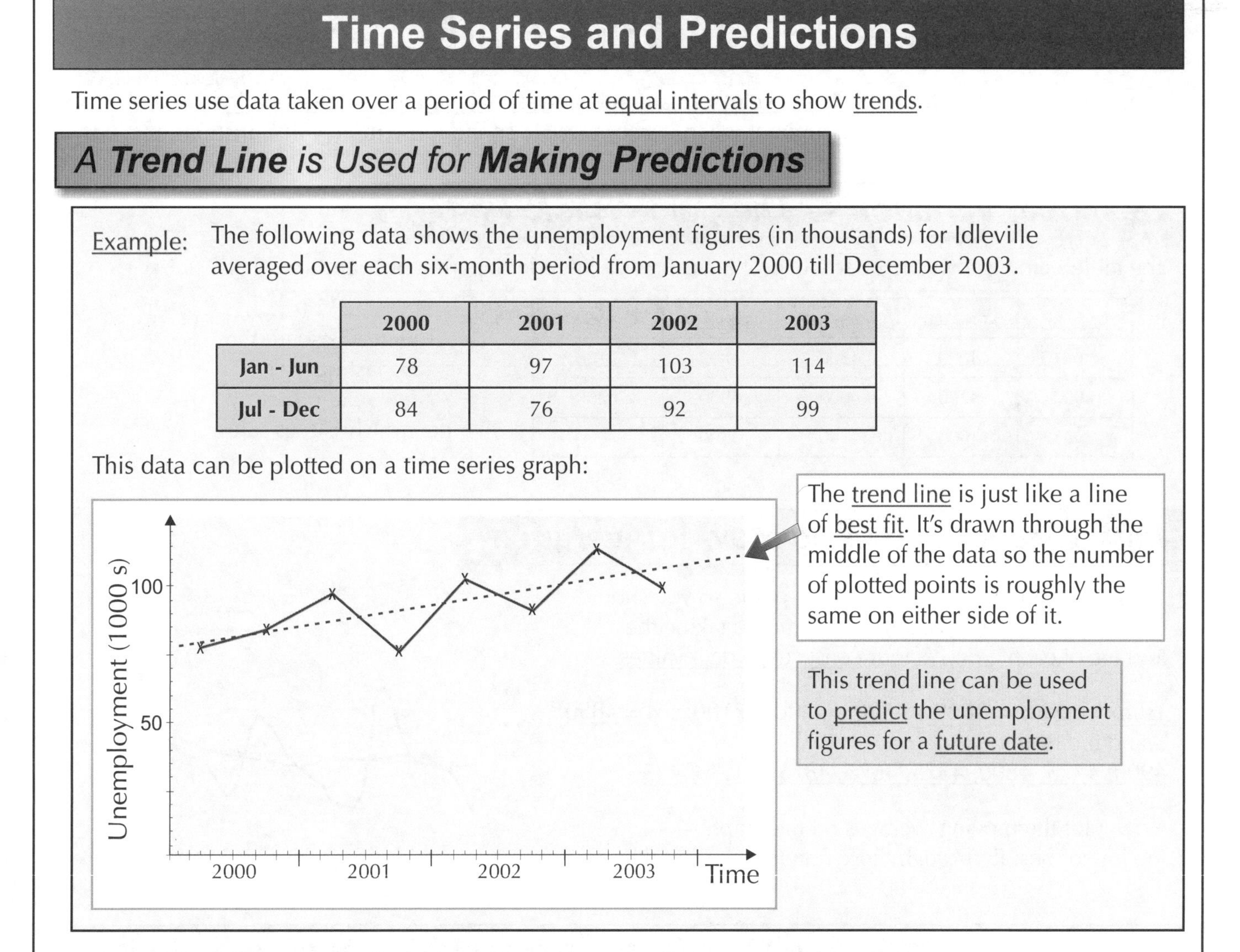

The trend line is just like a line of best fit. It's drawn through the middle of the data so the number of plotted points is roughly the same on either side of it.

This trend line can be used to predict the unemployment figures for a future date.

Moving Averages give a More Accurate Prediction

A moving average "smooths out" fluctuations in the data and lets you work out, a lot more precisely, where the trend line should go.

The data values from the example on unemployment figures are shown in this table.
The values have been arranged in a line to make it easier to see how the moving average works.

2000	2001	2002	2003
78, 84	97, 76	103, 92	114, 99

1st average = (78 + 84 + 97 + 76) ÷ 4 = 83.75

2nd average = (84 + 97 + 76 + 103) ÷ 4 = 90

1) This example is using a 4-point moving average. That means taking the average of each group of four consecutive data values. i.e. you start by taking the average of 78, 84, 97 and 76.
2) You then move along one and average the next group of values, i.e. 84, 97, 76 and 103 — and so on through the data.
3) By plotting these moving averages you can see more clearly where the trend line needs to go — see the next page for an example.

Take the time to learn about time series...

Open up a newspaper and you'll often bump into a time series graph. Make sure you can calculate moving averages — they're a favourite with examiners. There's more on time series on the next page...

More on Time Series

Some time series graphs fluctuate in cycles. This is called seasonal variation or seasonality. More ice creams are sold in the summer when it's hot, people spend more money at Christmas, etc.

Seasonal Variation — The Same **Basic Pattern**

The table below shows the quarterly profits (in £) for a lingerie department over three years.

	Jan - Mar	Apr - Jun	Jul - Sep	Oct - Dec
2001	3000	4500	4800	7100
2002	3200	4000	4900	6200
2003	3600	4800	5500	7800

The profits soared in the last quarter of each year, probably due to Christmas sales.

Plot a **Trend Line** using **Moving Averages**

The pattern repeats after every fourth point, so you should use a 4-point moving average. That means taking the average of each group of four consecutive data values.

1st moving av. = (3000 + 4500 + 4800 + 7100) ÷ 4 = 4850
...and the rest:
4900, 4775, 4800, 4575, 4675, 4875, 5025, 5425.

Now, plot the moving averages on the graph — the line of best fit through these points is the trend line.

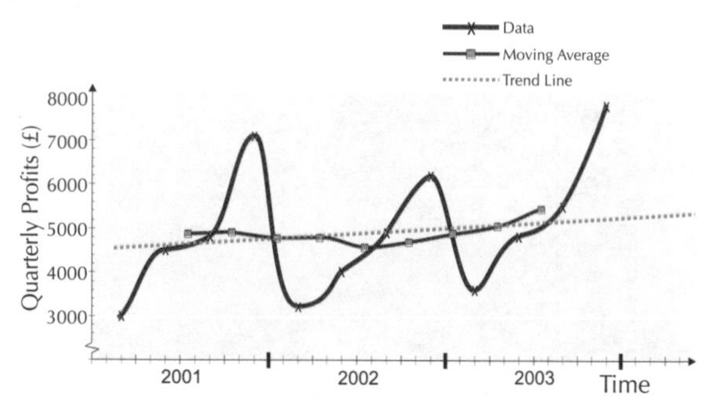

Seasonal Effect — The Gap Between **Real Value** and **Trend Line**

The difference between a real value and the value taken from the trend line is known as the seasonal effect.

TREND LINE value (read this off the graph)

E.g. The seasonal effect for the 4th quarter in 2001 is £7100 – £4700 = £2400

REAL value

SEASONAL EFFECT

The average seasonal effect is the mean of all the seasonal effects for the same point in each cycle. In the example, the average seasonal effect could be calculated for each quarter.

So, the average seasonal effect for the 1st quarter is:

[(3000 – 4500) + (3200 – 4800) + (3600 – 5000)] ÷ 3 = –£1500

You can use this average to make more accurate predictions.

The predicted sales profit is the value taken from the trend line plus the average seasonal effect.

So, the predicted sales profit for the 1st quarter in 2004 is £5250 – £1500 = £3750

Seasonal variation — how the time of year affects your data...

Choose your size of moving average based on how often the pattern repeats itself. Make sure you understand what's meant by the 'seasonal effect' and that you're happy about calculating the average.

Quality Assurance

People can make mistakes, and machinery can stop working properly. Quality assurance is about making sure that certain measured values stay as close as possible to target values.

Quality Assurance is Making Sure Products Turn out Okay

QUALITY ASSURANCE METHOD:
1) Take a small sample from the production line at regular intervals.
2) Measure each product and find an average measurement for the whole sample. This is usually the mean or median — but it depends on what you're checking.
3) Plot the averages against the time the samples were taken.
4) Look for any trends or outliers that suggest something's wrong.
5) If all's not well, stop production and do something about it.

Example

A protractor manufacturer wants to be sure that his instruments are made accurately.
1) He takes ten protractors each hour and uses them to measure a known angle of 40°. He finds the average of each group of ten.
2) He plots each average against the time he took the sample.
3) All the averages are within one degree of the target value. There's nothing to suggest that anything is wrong.
4) No need to do anything — all seems to be okay.

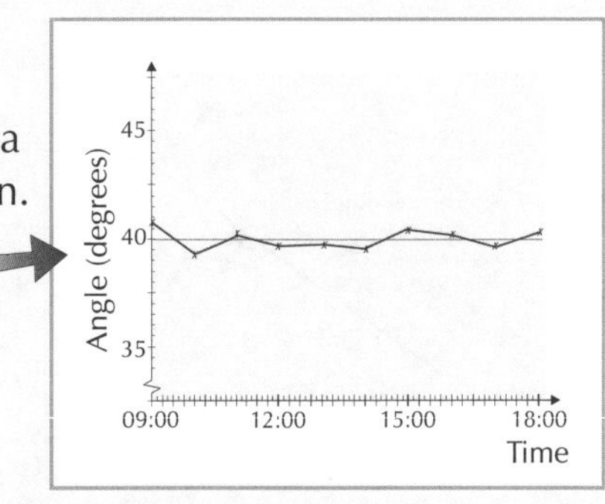

Quality Assurance Graphs — When Something is Wrong

The graphs below show other possible results from the protractor factory.

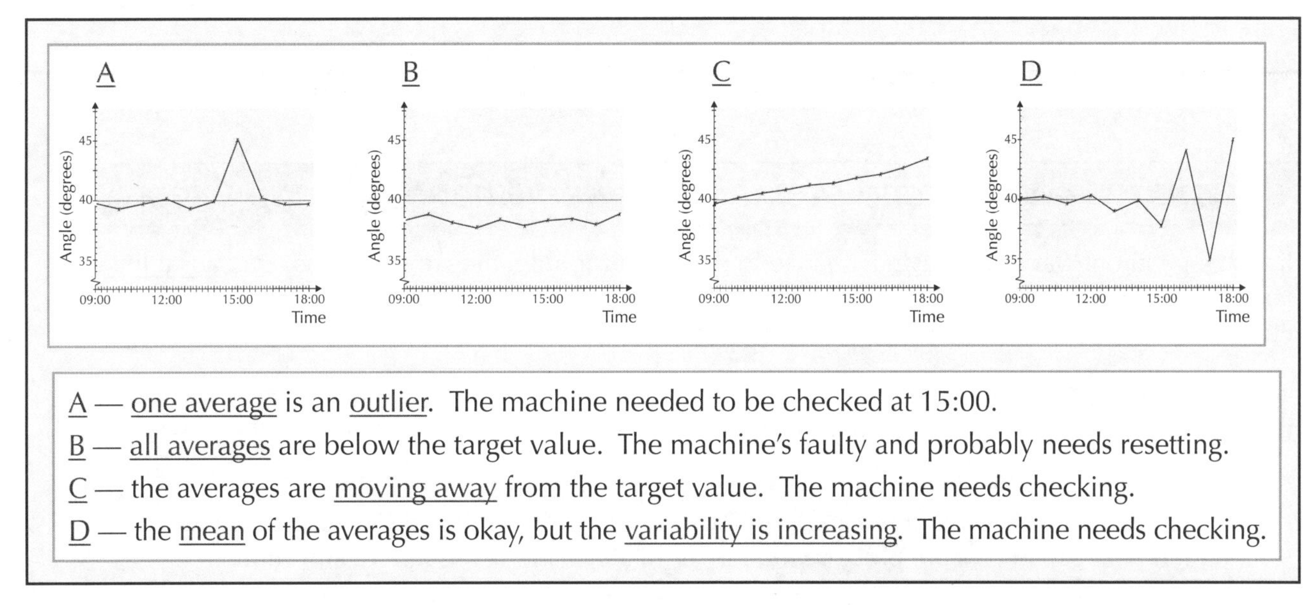

A — one average is an outlier. The machine needed to be checked at 15:00.
B — all averages are below the target value. The machine's faulty and probably needs resetting.
C — the averages are moving away from the target value. The machine needs checking.
D — the mean of the averages is okay, but the variability is increasing. The machine needs checking.

Quality Assurance graphs — recognise when something is wrong...

There aren't any tricky formulas to learn on this page. Quality assurance questions usually just mean thinking carefully about what the graph is telling you — so make sure you understand the examples.

Correlation

You might want to find out whether or not two variables are related in any way — e.g. are GCSE Statistics exam marks related to the amount of revision a person does? Hmmmmm...

Scatter Diagrams *Show Whether Two Variables are Related*

Scatter diagrams are graphs with two variables plotted against each other (bivariate data).

When you're drawing a scatter diagram:

1) **The scale doesn't have to be the same on both axes, so pick 'easy to use' scales for both axes. Try not to use a scale that leaves you guessing where to plot a point.**
2) **Plot the points carefully (a sharp pencil helps). Check that the number of plotted points equals the number of pairs of variables.**

Correlation *— Can you See a Line Forming?*

Drawing "lines of best fit" can help you see the correlation *(see p.100).*

Correlation is just a fancy term for how closely related two things are.

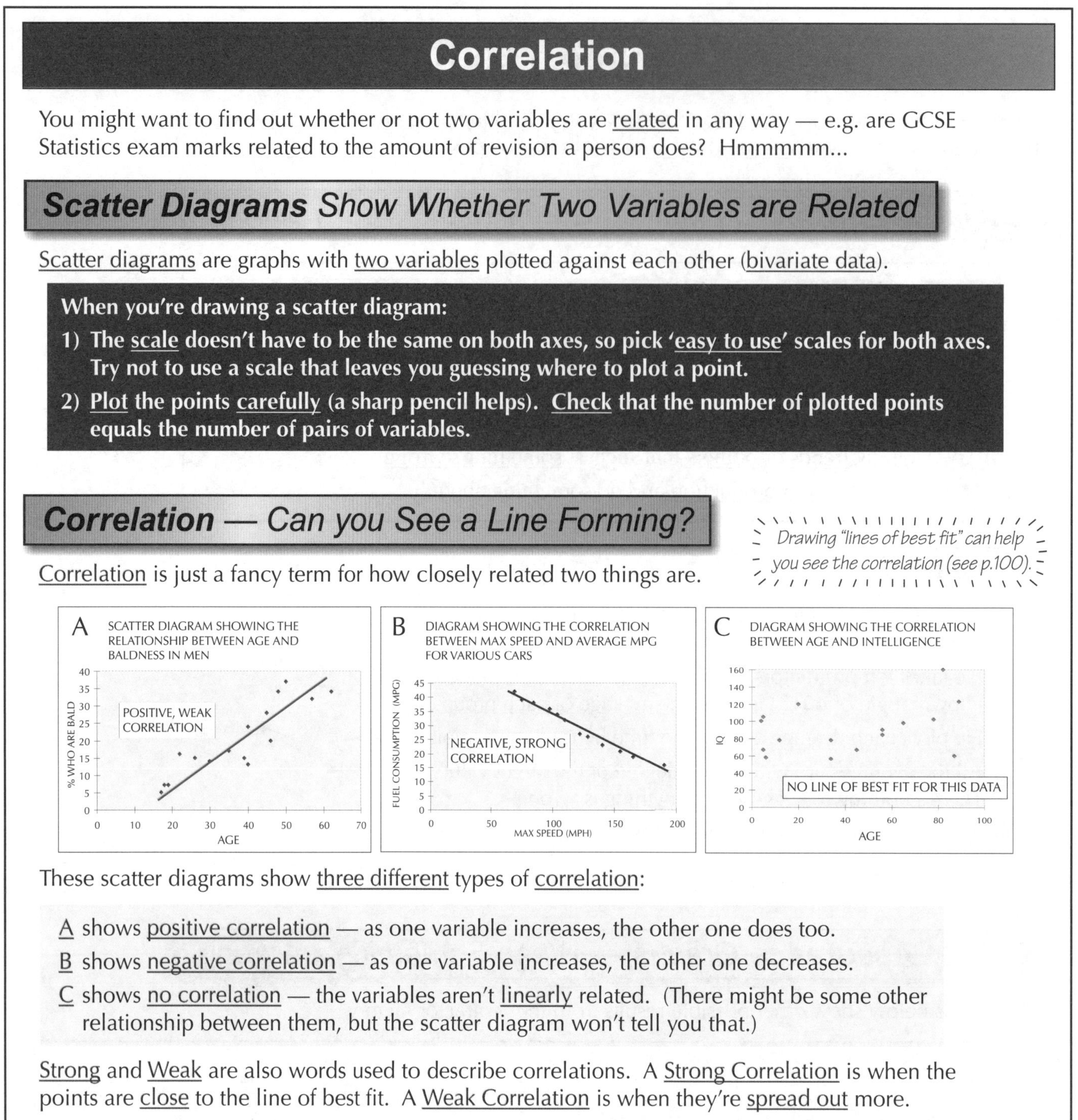

These scatter diagrams show three different types of correlation:

A shows positive correlation — as one variable increases, the other one does too.
B shows negative correlation — as one variable increases, the other one decreases.
C shows no correlation — the variables aren't linearly related. (There might be some other relationship between them, but the scatter diagram won't tell you that.)

Strong and Weak are also words used to describe correlations. A Strong Correlation is when the points are close to the line of best fit. A Weak Correlation is when they're spread out more.

Causality *— When one Variable* **Causes** *Changes in the Other*

If a change in one variable causes a change in the other variable, they're said to have a causal link. For example, a rise in the temperature outside could cause an increase in ice cream sales. However, an increase in ice cream sales wouldn't cause the weather to improve — unfortunately.

You have to be very careful with causality, though. Just because there's a correlation between two things, it doesn't necessarily mean there's a causal link — there could be a third factor involved.

For example, the number of pairs of sunglasses sold per week in a particular town is positively correlated with the amount of algae in a local pond. Neither one causes the other, though. Both of these increases are probably due to an increase in the amount of sunshine.

Remember — correlation and causality aren't the same...

This is something that's quite easy to slip up on — so be extra careful when answering questions on correlation. Don't jump to conclusions — even if the correlation is very strong.

Spearman's Rank Correlation Coefficient

Spearman's rank correlation coefficient, often shortened to r_s (bit less of a mouthful), measures how closely related two sets of data are. It only works for data that can be ranked into place order, (highest to lowest or first to last) — e.g. exam marks and the number of hours spent revising.

There's a **Four-Step** Method for finding r_s

1) Rank both sets of data. For each set, give the highest value a rank of 1, the next highest a rank of 2, and so on.
2) Find the difference in rank (d) between the two values in each data pair.
3) Count the number of data pairs, n.
4) Use the following formula to find r_s:

$$r_s = 1 - \frac{6\sum d^2}{n(n^2-1)}$$

This is on your formula sheet, so you don't need to learn it.

Example

Two judges awarded marks to high-board divers from six different countries as follows:

	Aus	Bul	Ch	Den	Est	Fra
Judge Judy	5.7	4.9	6.0	6.3	5.9	5.5
Judge Justin	5.8	5.2	5.8	6.0	6.1	5.6

Rank the marks and find d for each country:

	Aus	Bul	Ch	Den	Est	Fra
Judge Judy	4	6	2	1	3	5
Judge Justin	3.5	6	3.5	2	1	5
d	0.5	0	1.5	1	2	0
d^2	0.25	0	2.25	1	4	0

Judge Justin gave Austria and China the same mark, so they get the same rank — they share ranks 3 and 4 between them.

There are 6 data pairs, so $n = 6$.

$\sum d^2 = 0.25 + 0 + 2.25 + 1 + 4 + 0 = 7.5$

So, $r_s = 1 - \frac{6 \times 7.5}{6(6^2-1)} = 1 - \frac{45}{210} = 0.786$ (to 3 d.p.)

r_s is Always Between –1 and 1

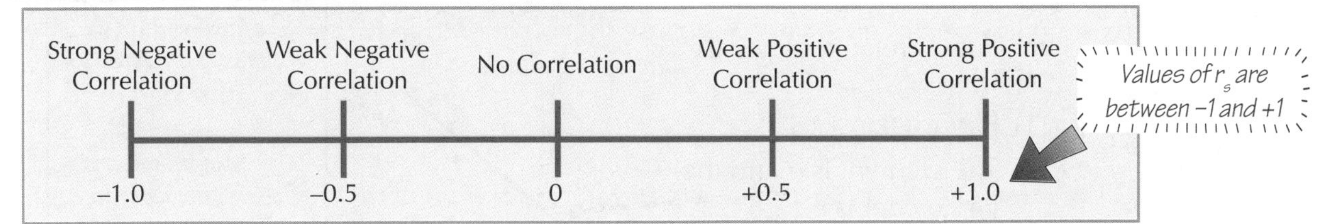

In the example, the Spearman's rank correlation coefficient is quite close to 1. This means that the two judges were pretty much in agreement about the relative performance of the six divers.

Spearman's rank correlation coefficient — in just four steps...

This is another measure that becomes more manageable if you add a few extra rows to your table. In the example, there's a row each for d and d^2. You don't have to — but it makes mistakes less likely.

Working with Scatter Diagrams

If a scatter diagram shows correlation, you can draw a line of best fit.

Line of Best Fit — A Straight Line Through the Data

1) The line of best fit should run right through the middle of the plotted points, ideally through the mean of both variables, and so that it is close to as many points as possible.
2) You should end up with roughly the same number of plotted points on either side of the line.
3) The closer the points are to the line, the stronger the correlation.

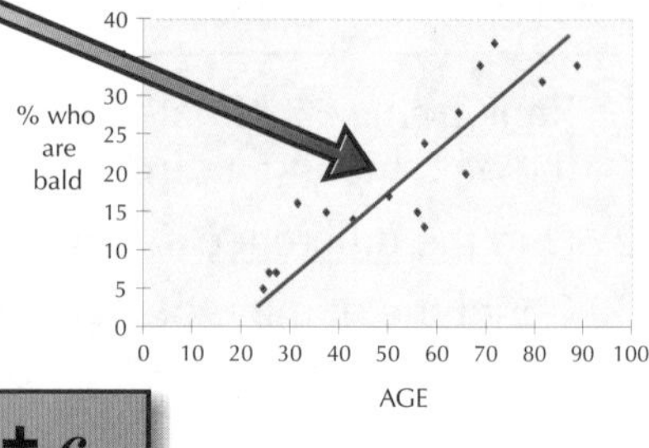

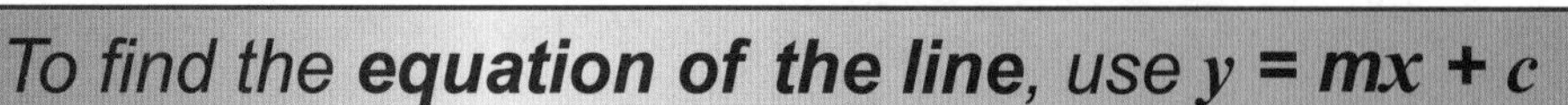

To find the equation of the line, use $y = mx + c$

The equation of the line of best fit can be written in the form $y = mx + c$, where 'm' is the gradient and 'c' is the y-intercept (where the line crosses the y-axis).

EXAMPLE: It is widely believed in Somerset that anyone who can throw a cricket ball a long way should be able to throw a Wellington boot just as well. 20 people tested this theory and the results were plotted on a scatter diagram.

1) First, find the gradient...
   Pick two points on the line, the further apart the better.
   In this case (0, 0) and (30, 20) look good.
   Gradient, m, is "the change in y" over "the change in x"
   So, $m = 20/30 = 2/3$
2) Next, find the y-intercept, c...
   $c = 0$, because the line passes through the origin.
3) So the equation of the line is $y = (2/3)x$.

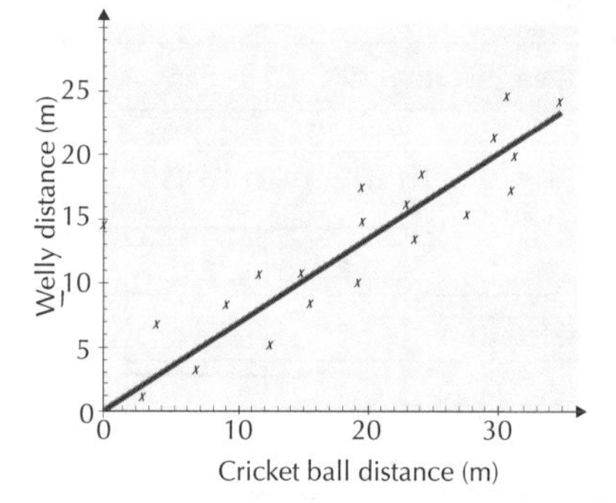

Now you can estimate how far someone will be able to throw a welly based on how far they can throw a cricket ball (or vice versa) using the equation. So, if you can throw a cricket ball 45 m, you should be able to throw a welly $(2/3) \times 45 = 30$ m.

Non-Linear Data Lies on a Curve

If the line of best fit through the points on a graph is a curve, the relationship is non-linear. You can sometimes make this into a nice straight-line graph (which is a lot easier to analyse) by plotting y against an expression with x in (rather than just x). You'll be told in the exam what expression to use.

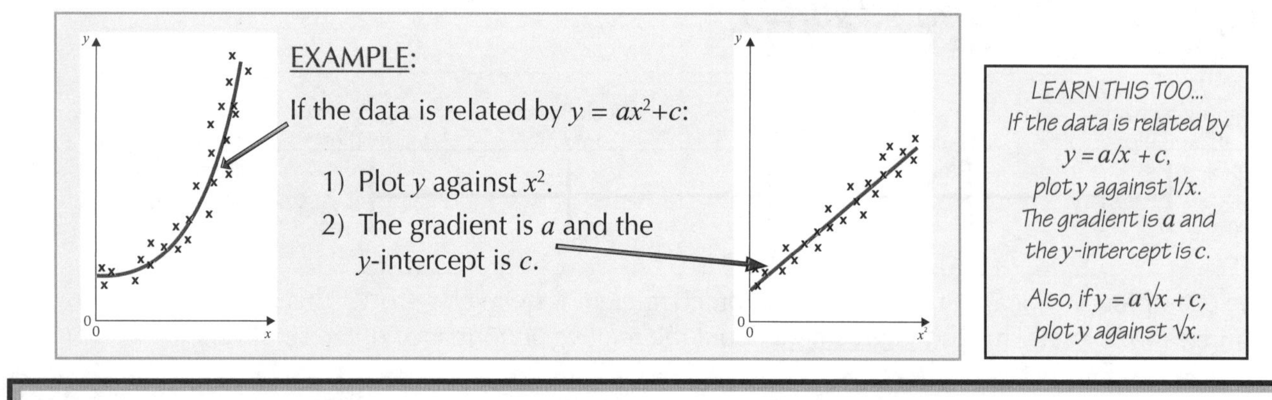

EXAMPLE:

If the data is related by $y = ax^2 + c$:

1) Plot y against x^2.
2) The gradient is a and the y-intercept is c.

LEARN THIS TOO...
If the data is related by $y = a/x + c$, plot y against $1/x$. The gradient is a and the y-intercept is c.

Also, if $y = a\sqrt{x} + c$, plot y against $\sqrt{x}$.

Ruler, sharp pencil and a steady hand — for a better line of best fit...

Finding the equation of your line of best fit is useful for making estimates about the data.
And you should recognise the '$y = mx + c$' method from 'normal' maths. Excellent.

Interpolation and Extrapolation

You can use the line of best fit on a scatter diagram to predict unknown values, using either interpolation or extrapolation — scary words but they're not too bad really...

Use *Interpolation* to Find Values *Within your Data Set*

Interpolation is the method you use to find a value that lies between two known values.

EXAMPLE: This scatter diagram shows the chest and waist sizes of ten men.

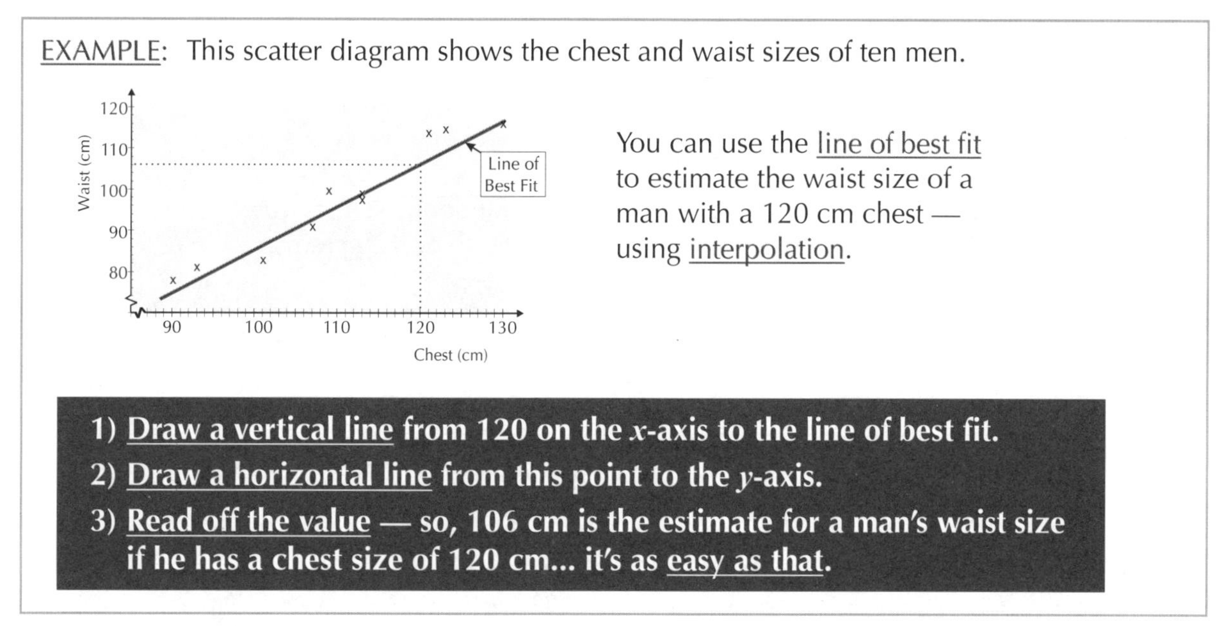

You can use the line of best fit to estimate the waist size of a man with a 120 cm chest — using interpolation.

1) Draw a vertical line from 120 on the x-axis to the line of best fit.
2) Draw a horizontal line from this point to the y-axis.
3) Read off the value — so, 106 cm is the estimate for a man's waist size if he has a chest size of 120 cm... it's as easy as that.

Interpolation tends to give fairly reliable results — so long as you get the line of best fit right.

Extrapolation Looks *Beyond* the Sampled Data

You can also make predictions outside the plotted data — and this is called extrapolation. There are two ways to do this:

1) Extend the line of best fit, then find the values you're after just like you did for interpolation.
2) Better still, use the equation of the line (see p.100).

EXAMPLE: The equation for the line of best fit in the example above is $y = 1.1x - 26$.
To estimate the waist size (y) for a man with a chest size (x) of 140 cm, just stick your value of x into the equation...

$$y = 1.1(140) - 26 = 128 \text{ cm}$$

So, you would expect a man with a 140 cm chest to have about a 128 cm waist.

You Need to be Very *Careful* with *Extrapolation*

When you extrapolate, you're going into unknown territory. You have no idea what happens to the link between your variables once you go outside your data set, so you're just guessing. The graph might curve, or level off, or turn into a series of small furry animals... okay, that last one's unlikely — but the point is that you don't know.

So, it's a good plan not to try and extrapolate too far from what you do know.

Interpolation and extrapolation — get to know the difference...

In terms of method these two are largely the same — reading a value off your line of best fit, or using the line's equation. However, as extrapolation goes beyond your data it can become a bit dodgy.

Estimation of Population

A population is a whole set of things being measured — it doesn't just mean the number of people living somewhere. So, make sure you learn what this term means...

*Make **Estimates** about a Population **Using Samples***

Populations can sometimes be very large — often too big to be counted (e.g. the number of fish in the sea). To make estimates about a population (e.g. size, the mean, etc.) you need to use an appropriate sample that represents the whole population.

Example

A market gardener has a field of 500 potato plants. He randomly selects 30 plants from different areas and finds the mean weight of a potato to be 120 grams.

From this sample, the gardener can estimate that the mean weight of each potato in his crop is 120 g.

He also counts the number of potatoes in his sample and finds that each plant produces an average of 9 potatoes.

2 Using this estimate he can estimate the total population of his potato crop. Estimated total number in crop = 9 × 500 = 4500 potatoes.

This method's fine, but you need to know how many units (e.g. plants) there are in the whole population — and sometimes you don't have this much information.
A different way of estimating a population size is by the method of capture and recapture (see p.32)...

***Opinion Polls** Tell You What People Think*

Many organisations (e.g. governments, advertising agencies, etc.) find it very useful to know what people are thinking. They do this by asking the opinions of a selected sample of people, which are then used to represent the whole population — this is called an opinion poll.

Example

A food manufacturer carried out an opinion poll of 1000 people to find out the nation's favourite flavour of crisps.
Six hundred people said their favourite flavour was Chilli Cheese.

The manufacturer used this result to estimate that Chilli Cheese is the favourite flavour of crisp for 60% of the population of Britain.

The bigger the sample, the more accurate the result. You wouldn't be able to form much of an opinion on what music the population of your town liked if you only asked 10 people — this sample size would be too small.

The bigger the sample — the more accurate the estimate...

The methods on this page aren't the trickiest in statistics — what is difficult is making sure that your sample is properly representative. Any doubts — have another read of Section One...

Warm-Up and Worked Exam Questions

If you can breeze through these, you're ready for exam questions. If not — time to revise the section.

Warm-Up Questions

1) Bernard's Bike Store's quarterly sales of their most expensive bicycle over three years are recorded below. Calculate the first four values of a four-point moving average.

Year	1999				2000				2001			
Quarter	1	2	3	4	1	2	3	4	1	2	3	4
Sales	4	6	9	7	5	7	12	10	4	5	7	5

2) Describe the type of correlation you would expect between each pair of variables below.
(a) Hours of sunshine per day and sales of sun-block skin protection.
(b) Hours of sunshine per day and sales of bread.
(c) Hours of sunshine per day and sales of umbrellas.

3) Five competitors in a talent show have been ranked according to the scores given by two judges:

Competitor	a	b	c	d	e
Judge A Rank	5	3	1	4	2
Judge B Rank	4	1	2	5	3

Calculate the value of Spearman's rank correlation coefficient.

4) Brockshire Badger Project have drawn a graph of the badger population in their area during their decade of work. The line of best fit goes through '78 badgers' for their sixth year and '74 badgers' for the year they began (year zero).
Calculate the equation of the line and estimate badger numbers for their ninth year.

5) A company employs 1500 people. 50 randomly selected employees are asked what motivates them most about their job — 20 say it's their wages. Estimate the number of employees in the whole company whose main motivation is their wages.

Worked Exam Questions

Time series and correlation are the big topics here. These exam questions will give you a good idea of the kind of thing to expect in the exam.

1 A meteorology station records temperature, T (°C), to an accuracy of one tenth of a degree at the same time on consecutive days.

Day	1	2	3	4	5
T (°C)	5.4	6.2	4.0	4.8	x

The first three-point moving average is 5.2 °C.

(a) Calculate the next three-point moving average.

$(6.2 + 4.0 + 4.8) \div 3 = 15 \div 3 = 5.0$ °C

(1 mark)

(b) Find the temperature, x, on Day 5 if the third three-point moving average is 4.8 °C.

$(4.0 + 4.8 + x) \div 3 = 4.8$ **(1 mark for setting up appropriate equation)**

$8.8 + x = 4.8 \times 3$

$x = 5.6$ °C **(2 marks for the correct answer, otherwise 1 mark as shown.)**

(2 marks)

Worked Exam Questions

Worked Exam Questions

2 At a certain factory, copper wire is manufactured with an intended diameter of 4 mm. Once every ten minutes, a light beam measures the diameter, d (mm), of the wire produced to the nearest 0.01 mm. Only wire that satisfies 3.96 mm $\leq d \leq$ 4.04 mm is acceptable.

A graph of the diameters recorded during the first hour of production is shown below.

The next four recordings of the diameter were 3.98 mm, 3.96 mm, 3.97 mm and 3.96 mm.

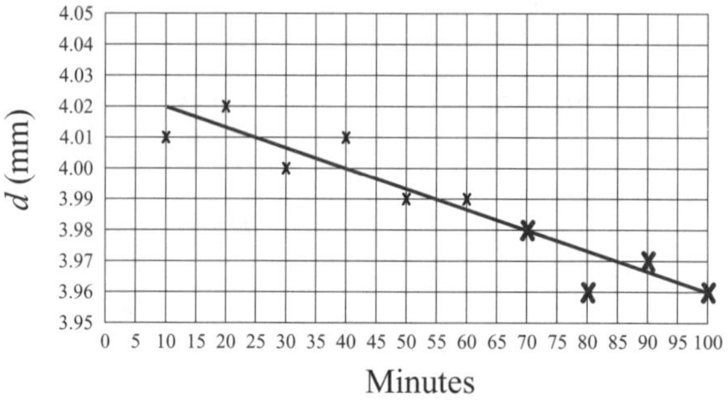

(a) Plot the additional data on the graph.

(1 mark)

The mean time of recordings is 55 minutes. The mean diameter recorded is 3.989 mm.

(b) Draw a line of best fit on the graph.

(1 mark for a line through the mean and 1 mark for a line roughly passing through middle of points.) *(2 marks)*

(c) Comment on the graph with reference to the production process.

Production should be stopped because the trend is away from the intended diameter.

(1 mark)

3 The members of Scoresdale Sports Club go out each weekend to try different sports. One week they went karting at a local circuit and each recorded their fastest lap times. The next week they went to a dry ski slope and noted their fastest times on a slalom course.

(a) Complete the rank column for Week 2.

(1 mark)

	Week 1 t (sec)	Week 2 t (sec)	Week 1 rank	Week 2 rank	d	d^2
Anna	56	65	3	5	2	4
Becca	62	62	4	4	0	0
Chaz	51	60	1	3	2	4
Dave	80	58	5	1	4	16
Eric	53	59	2	2	0	0

(b) Calculate the Spearman's rank correlation coefficient for Week 1 against Week 2. You may use the blank columns for your working.

$r_s = 1 - [6\sum d^2 \div n(n^2 - 1)]$, and $\sum d^2 = 24$

So, $r_s = 1 - [(6 \times 24) \div 5(25 - 1)] = -0.2$

(4 marks for the correct answer, otherwise 1 mark for the correct d column, 1 mark for $\sum d^2$ and 1 mark for substituting in the correct formula.)

(4 marks)

(c) Use your answer to part (b) to comment on the relationship between the times for the two sports.

Weak negative correlation — i.e. close to no link between the karting and skiing times.

(1 mark)

Exam Questions

4 A drilling ship measures the temperature, t (°C), at various depths, d (km), below the seabed as it drills into the Earth's crust. The table below shows these measurements.

d (km)	1.2	1.5	2.1	2.3	3.1	3.3	3.5	3.8
t (°C)	18	24	30	36	40	46	46	48

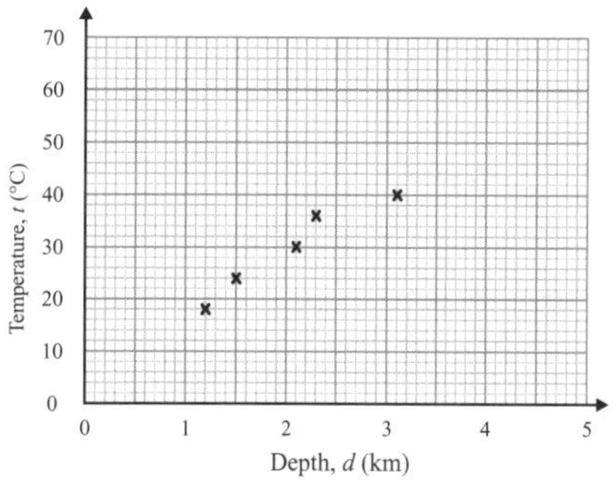

(a) Plot the last three points in the table on the scatter diagram.

Temperature, t (°C)
70
60
50
40
30
20
10
0
0 1 2 3 4 5
Depth, d (km)

(1 mark)

(b) Describe the relationship between depth below seabed and temperature.

....

(1 mark)

(c) The mean depth of measurements in the table is 2.6 km. Find the mean temperature recorded.

....

(1 mark)

(d) Using your answer to part (c), draw a line of best fit on the graph.

(2 marks)

(e) Use your line of best fit to estimate:

(i) The temperature at a depth of 1.9 km below the seabed. ....

(1 mark)

(ii) The temperature on the seabed. Comment on the reliability of your answer.

....

(2 marks)

5 Eight dancers in a competition perform a single dance. Two judges award a mark out of 10 to each dancer, with higher marks given for better performances.

Dancer	A	B	C	D	E	F	G	H
Judge 1	8	6	10	9	5	7	4	8
Judge 2	6	7	9	10	5	6	4	8

(a) Work out Spearman's rank correlation coefficient for the judges' scores. You may extend the table for your working.

....

....

(4 marks)

(b) Describe the correlation found in part (a).

....

(1 mark)

(c) A third judge has scored the same dancers doing the same dance. Spearman's rank correlation coefficient for Judge 2 and Judge 3 is 1.0 exactly. Based on this information alone, what can be said about Judge 3's opinion of Dancer F's performance?

....

(1 mark)

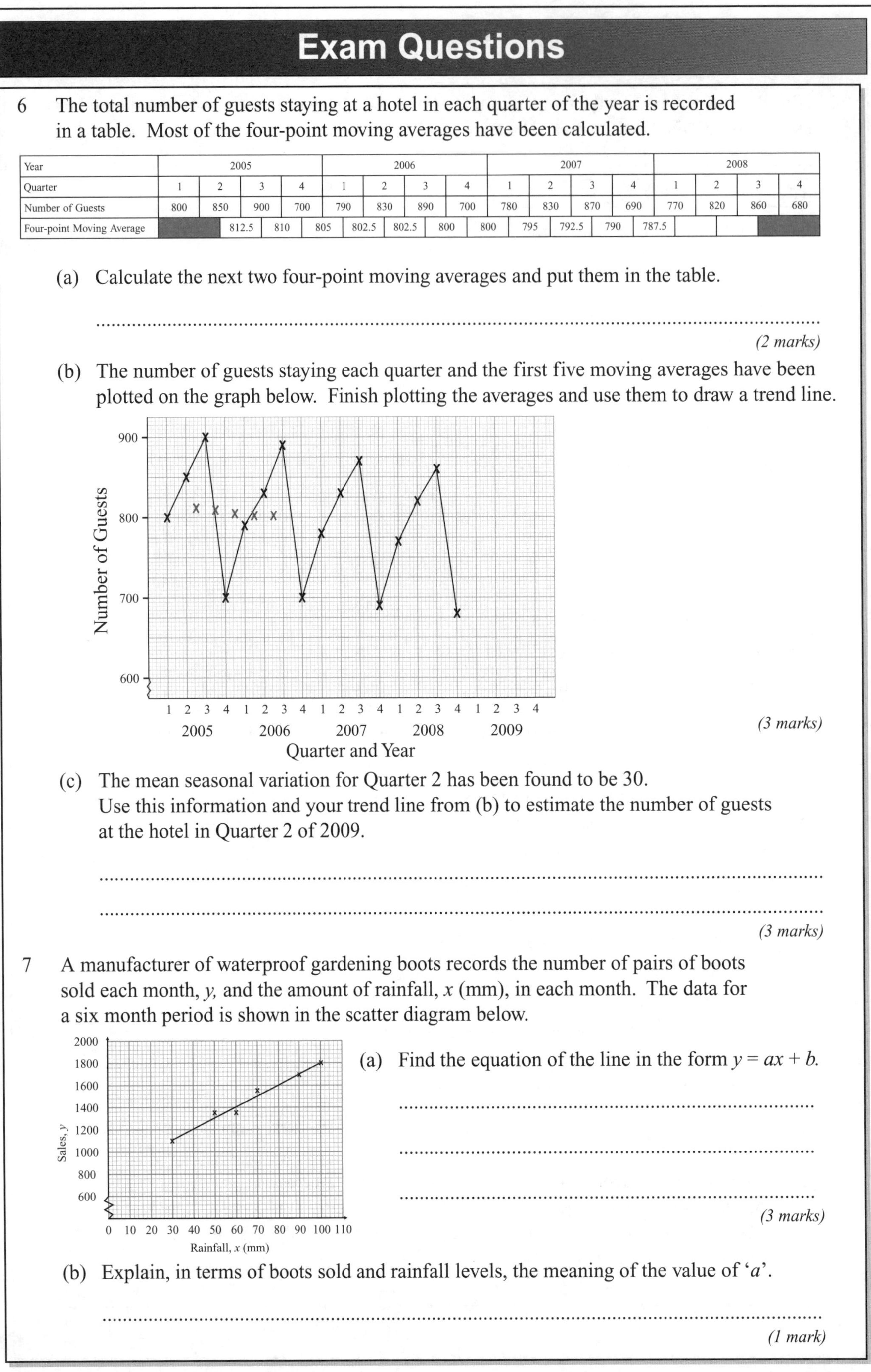

Exam Questions

6 The total number of guests staying at a hotel in each quarter of the year is recorded in a table. Most of the four-point moving averages have been calculated.

Year	2005				2006				2007				2008			
Quarter	1	2	3	4	1	2	3	4	1	2	3	4	1	2	3	4
Number of Guests	800	850	900	700	790	830	890	700	780	830	870	690	770	820	860	680
Four-point Moving Average		812.5	810	805	802.5	802.5	800	800	795	792.5	790	787.5				

(a) Calculate the next two four-point moving averages and put them in the table.

....

(2 marks)

(b) The number of guests staying each quarter and the first five moving averages have been plotted on the graph below. Finish plotting the averages and use them to draw a trend line.

(3 marks)

(c) The mean seasonal variation for Quarter 2 has been found to be 30.
Use this information and your trend line from (b) to estimate the number of guests at the hotel in Quarter 2 of 2009.

....

....

(3 marks)

7 A manufacturer of waterproof gardening boots records the number of pairs of boots sold each month, y, and the amount of rainfall, x (mm), in each month. The data for a six month period is shown in the scatter diagram below.

(a) Find the equation of the line in the form $y = ax + b$.

....

....

....

(3 marks)

(b) Explain, in terms of boots sold and rainfall levels, the meaning of the value of 'a'.

....

(1 mark)

Revision Summary for Section Three

Here's the really fun page. The inevitable list of straight-down-the-middle questions to test how much you know. Remember — these questions will sort out, faster than anything else, exactly what you know and what you don't. And that's what revision is all about, don't forget: finding out what you don't know and then learning it until you do. Enjoy.

Keep learning the basic facts until you know them

1) What is another term for 'mean'?
2) How do you work out the mean?
3) What is the median?
4) What is the modal number of days in a month?
5) If coursework and exam results are combined to give an overall result, what kind of mean is generally required?
6) What method could you use for finding the mean of large numbers?
7) What does $\sum$ stand for in a formula?
8) What kind of frequency distribution table would you use for continuous data?
9) For what kind of data is the mode likely to be a meaningful average?
10) Give one advantage of finding the mean over the median or mode.
11) How do you find the geometric mean?
12) What is the range of a set of data?
13) How would you work out the position of the lower quartile of a set of data?
14) How do you calculate the interquartile range?
15) How would you estimate the upper quartile from a cumulative frequency curve?
16) What is the standard deviation a measure of?
17) Write down the formula for finding the variance of a grouped frequency distribution.
18) What do you need to know to draw a box plot?
19) What is an outlier?
20) How do you find a standardised score?
21) What is the index number of a base year?
22) What is the difference between simple and chain base index numbers?
23) What is a crude rate?
24) What is the formula for finding a standardised birth/death rate?
25) What kind of moving average would you use for quarterly bills?
26) How do you find the seasonal effect?
27) What is the purpose of quality assurance?
28) What is the name of the graph used for bivariate data?
29) What is causality?
30) What range of values can Spearman's rank correlation coefficient take?
31) What does a rank correlation coefficient of zero mean?
32) Where should a line of best fit be drawn?
33) What does the m represent in $y = mx + c$?
34) What is the difference between interpolation and extrapolation?
35) A light bulb manufacturer wants to test the lifetime of its bulbs, so it finds the mean lifetime of a sample of 200 bulbs. Why is this sample mean only an estimate of the population mean?
36) What is an opinion poll?

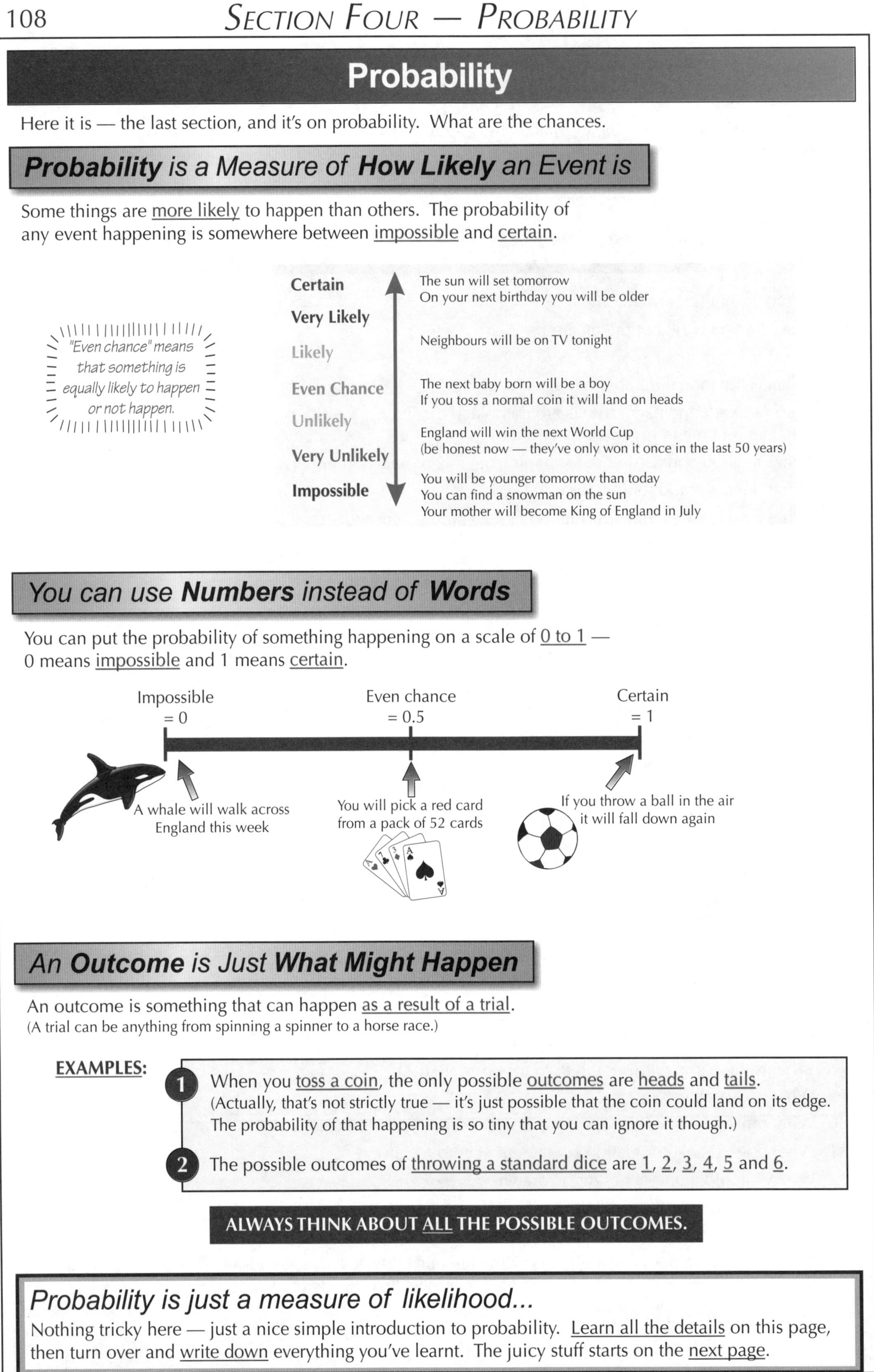

Probability

Here it is — the last section, and it's on probability. What are the chances.

Probability *is a Measure of* ***How Likely*** *an Event is*

Some things are more likely to happen than others. The probability of any event happening is somewhere between impossible and certain.

You can use ***Numbers*** *instead of* ***Words***

You can put the probability of something happening on a scale of 0 to 1 — 0 means impossible and 1 means certain.

An ***Outcome*** *is Just* ***What Might Happen***

An outcome is something that can happen as a result of a trial.
(A trial can be anything from spinning a spinner to a horse race.)

EXAMPLES:

1. When you toss a coin, the only possible outcomes are heads and tails. (Actually, that's not strictly true — it's just possible that the coin could land on its edge. The probability of that happening is so tiny that you can ignore it though.)
2. The possible outcomes of throwing a standard dice are 1, 2, 3, 4, 5 and 6.

ALWAYS THINK ABOUT ALL THE POSSIBLE OUTCOMES.

Probability is just a measure of likelihood...

Nothing tricky here — just a nice simple introduction to probability. Learn all the details on this page, then turn over and write down everything you've learnt. The juicy stuff starts on the next page.

Probability

This page has some definitions and an important formula to learn. Make sure you read it carefully...

You can find *Probabilities of Events* using a *Formula*

Remember that the possible results of a trial are called outcomes.
An event is a description that matches a set of possible outcomes.

EXAMPLE:
When throwing a normal six-sided dice, the outcomes are the numbers 1, 2, 3, 4, 5 and 6.
There are loads of possible events. Here are just three:

Event A: Throwing a 1
Event B: Throwing an even number
Event C: Throwing a number less than 5

There is only one outcome that matches Event A — the number 1.
There are three outcomes that match Event B — the numbers 2, 4 and 6.
There are four outcomes that match Event C — any of the numbers 1, 2, 3 or 4.

If outcomes of a trial have the same chance of happening, they are called equally likely outcomes.
If all the possible outcomes are equally likely, you can use the following formula to find probabilities:

$$\text{P(event)} = \frac{\text{number of outcomes matching event}}{\text{total number of outcomes}}$$

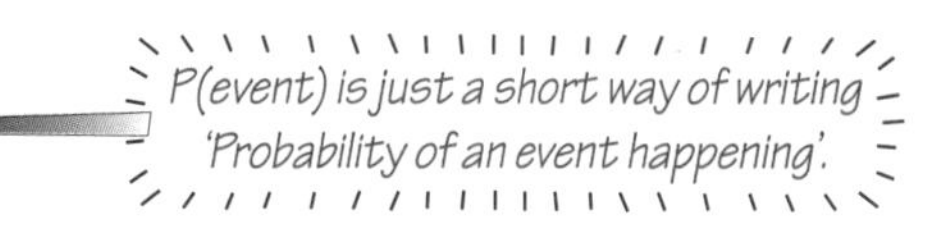

Don't worry if this is all a bit confusing — it'll become clear when you work through this example:

Example

Calculate the probabilities of landing on green and landing on orange when spinning this spinner:

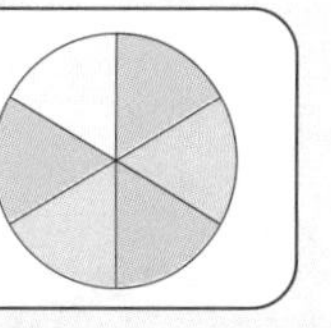

If you spin this spinner, there are six possible outcomes because there are six sections it might land on — 3 orange, 1 yellow, 1 green and 1 purple. Each section on the spinner is equally sized so there is the same chance of landing on each section. So there are six equally likely outcomes — one giving the event "green" and three giving the event "orange". Using the formula:

The probability of landing on green is:

$$\text{P(green)} = \frac{\text{The number of green sections}}{\text{The total number of sections}} = \frac{1}{6}$$

The probability of landing on orange is:

$$\text{P(orange)} = \frac{\text{The number of orange sections}}{\text{The total number of sections}} = \frac{3}{6} = \frac{1}{2}$$

The event "landing on orange" is much more likely to occur than the event "landing on green" because there are more outcomes that match this event.

Probabilities *Always* add up to *One*

For the above example, the probability of getting:

green is $\frac{1}{6}$
yellow is $\frac{1}{6}$
purple is $\frac{1}{6}$
orange is $\frac{3}{6}$

$\frac{1}{6} + \frac{1}{6} + \frac{1}{6} + \frac{3}{6} = \frac{6}{6} = 1$

Learn how to calculate simple probabilities using the formula...

Whew, there's some confusing stuff on this page. Make sure you know what the difference between an outcome and an event is. And remember that the formula only works for equally likely outcomes.

Probability

Bacon, odds and sinking yachts — that's the stuff of probability.

Probabilities Can Be Written as **Odds**

Odds are the ratio of the number of favourable outcomes to the number of unfavourable outcomes.

Example

Four names are put in a hat. The person whose name is drawn will win a year's supply of bacon.

The odds of each person winning are 1:3.
The odds of each of them not winning are 3:1.

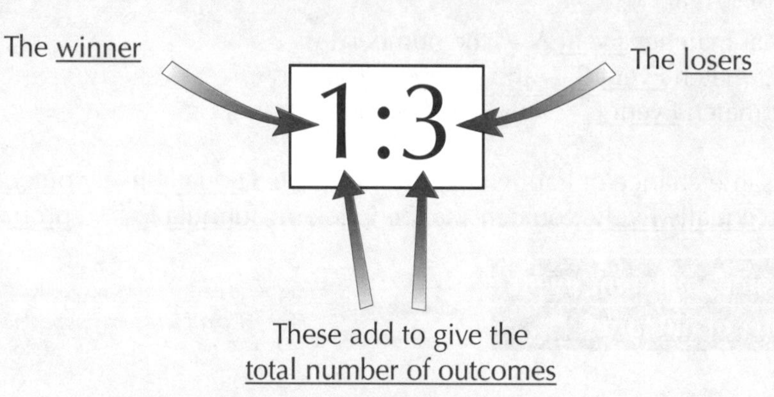

Note — odds are not the same as probabilities.
There are 4 outcomes in total, so P(wins bacon) = $\frac{1}{4}$, not $\frac{1}{3}$.

Probabilities Are Used To **Assess Risk**

Insurance companies use probabilities to decide how likely you are to make a claim.
This is risk assessment. They'll use this information to decide how much to charge you.

Example

If you want insurance against your yacht sinking, the insurance company will look at how many yachts like yours sink each year and compare it to the total number of yachts like yours.

$$\text{Estimated probability of your yacht sinking} = \frac{\text{number of yachts that sink}}{\text{total number of yachts}}$$

They'll also take into account the amount of money they'll need to pay out if your yacht does sink.

Probability — it's a risky business...

Learn how to write simple probabilities as odds and make sure you understand the example of risk assessment. Then turn over and write it all down. Nobody ever said Statistics would be fun all the time.

Sample Space

Things are pretty straightforward when you've only got one event to worry about.
It's when you get <u>two or more</u> events happening that life starts to get stressful.

A Sample Space is a List of All Possible Outcomes

1) If you throw a normal dice, there are <u>6 possible outcomes</u>.

2) If you spin a spinner with 3 sections, there are <u>3 possible outcomes</u>.

3) Throwing the dice <u>and</u> spinning the spinner gives <u>18 (6×3) different combinations</u> altogether (since any number on the dice could come up with any colour on the spinner).

4) A <u>list</u> of these 18 outcomes is called a <u>sample space</u>. Luckily, there are some easy ways to work out what these outcomes can be.

❶ *Use a **Sample Space Diagram** to List all the Outcomes*

A <u>sample space diagram</u> is basically a posh name for a <u>table</u>. If you use one, you're less likely to miss out any outcomes.

This table uses <u>columns</u> for the spinner outcomes and <u>rows</u> for the dice. It doesn't matter which way round you do it though.

	Red	Orange	Yellow
1	1R	1O	1Y
2	2R	2O	2Y
3	3R	3O	3Y
4	4R	4O	4Y
5	5R	5O	5Y
6	6R	6O	6Y

❷ *Cartesian Grids are Graphs of Sample Space Diagrams*

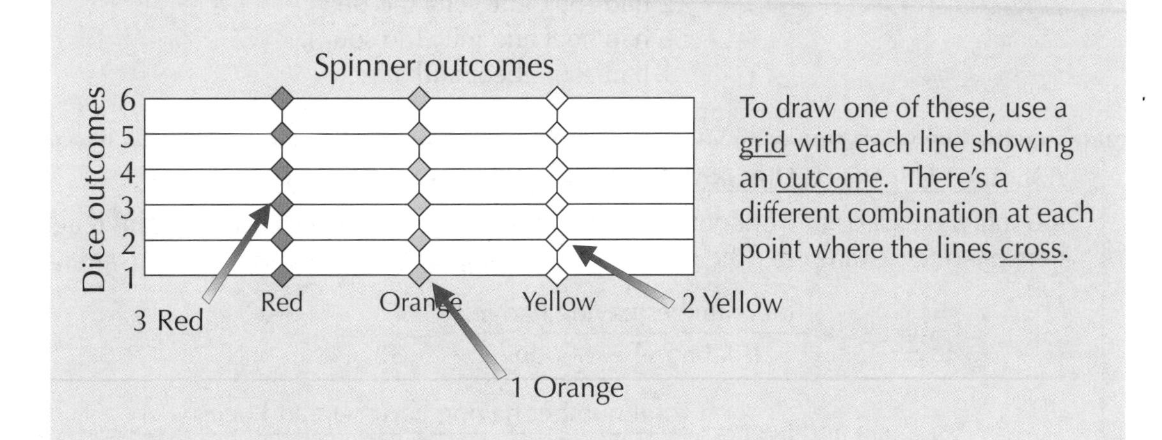

To draw one of these, use a <u>grid</u> with each line showing an <u>outcome</u>. There's a different combination at each point where the lines <u>cross</u>.

Learn these two sample space diagrams...

<u>Sample space diagrams</u> are nice, tidy ways of showing <u>all the possible outcomes</u> when you've got two or more things happening. You should be able to draw <u>both</u> types of diagram on this page.

Sample Space and Venn Diagrams

Here is a third way of showing a sample space...

A **Venn Diagram** Shows a **Sample Space** Too

Example

The Venn diagram below has spaces for every combination of items from the menu.

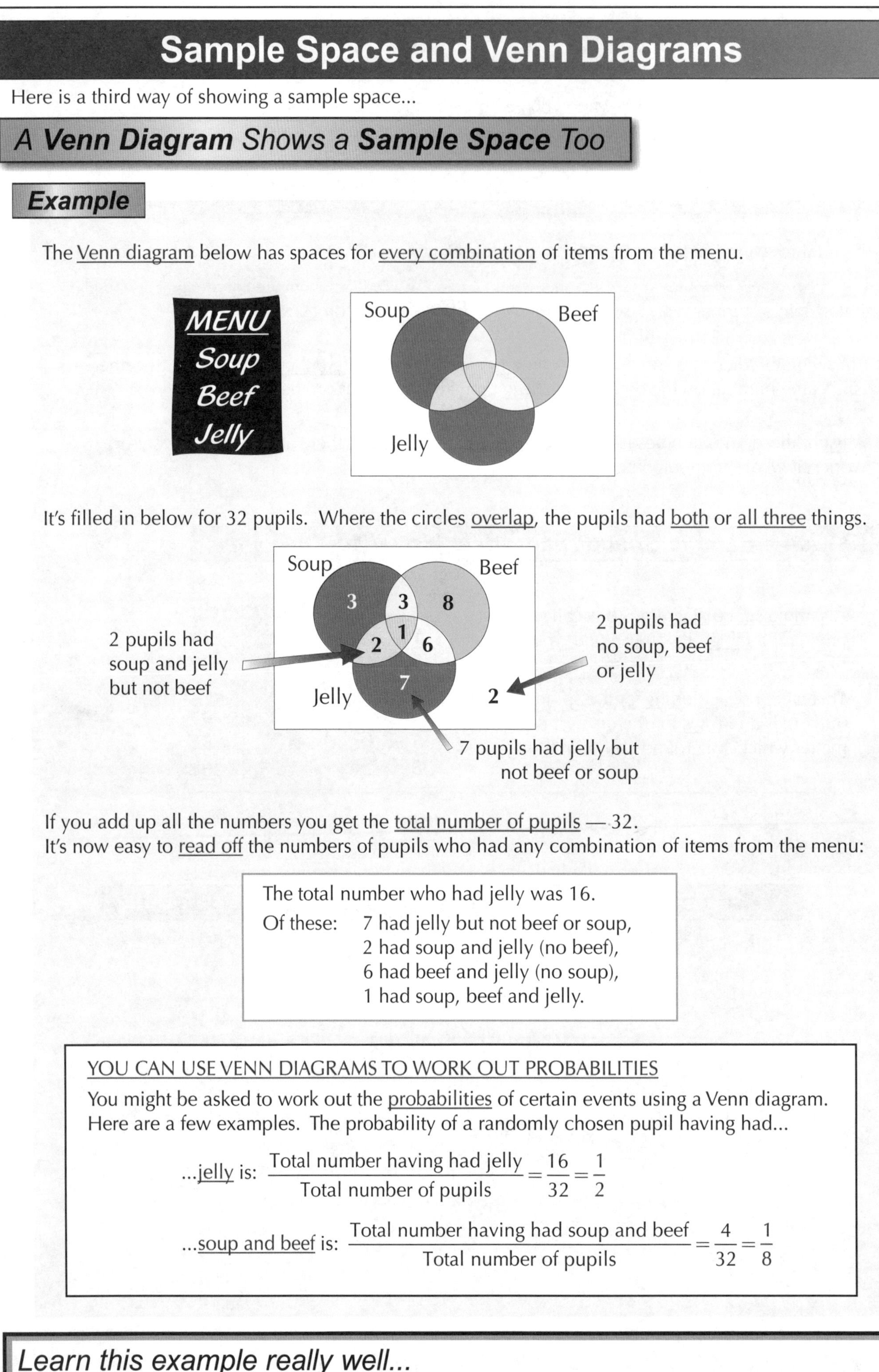

It's filled in below for 32 pupils. Where the circles overlap, the pupils had both or all three things.

If you add up all the numbers you get the total number of pupils — 32.
It's now easy to read off the numbers of pupils who had any combination of items from the menu:

The total number who had jelly was 16.

Of these: 7 had jelly but not beef or soup,
2 had soup and jelly (no beef),
6 had beef and jelly (no soup),
1 had soup, beef and jelly.

YOU CAN USE VENN DIAGRAMS TO WORK OUT PROBABILITIES

You might be asked to work out the probabilities of certain events using a Venn diagram.
Here are a few examples. The probability of a randomly chosen pupil having had...

...jelly is: $\dfrac{\text{Total number having had jelly}}{\text{Total number of pupils}} = \dfrac{16}{32} = \dfrac{1}{2}$

...soup and beef is: $\dfrac{\text{Total number having had soup and beef}}{\text{Total number of pupils}} = \dfrac{4}{32} = \dfrac{1}{8}$

Learn this example really well...

The overlapping bits of Venn diagrams make them really useful for showing events happening together. You should be able to draw and read Venn diagrams and use them to find probabilities. Mmmm, jelly...

Expected and Actual Frequencies

Just like the Spanish inquisition — what you actually get might be different from what you expect...

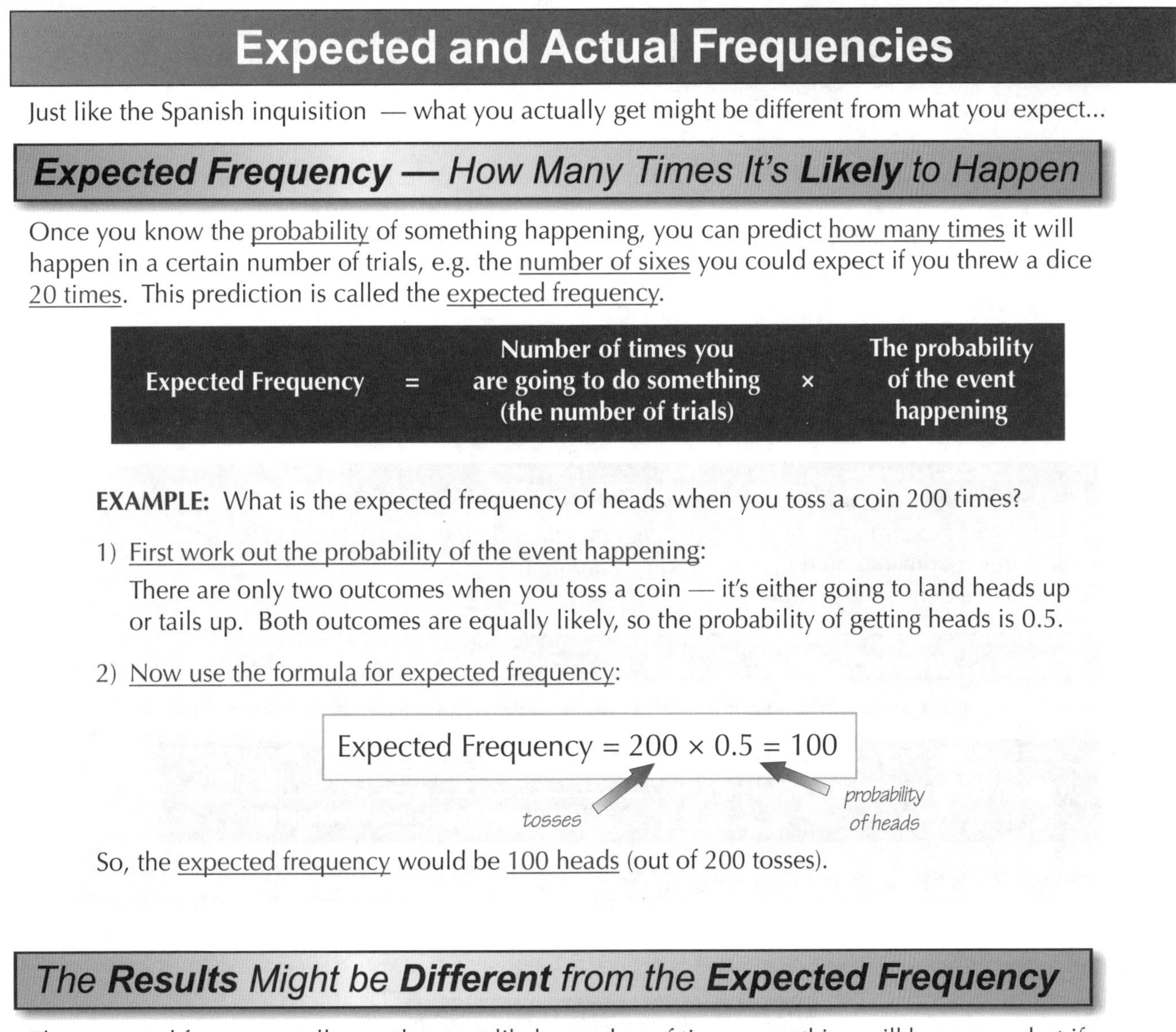

*Expected Frequency — How Many Times It's **Likely** to Happen*

Once you know the probability of something happening, you can predict how many times it will happen in a certain number of trials, e.g. the number of sixes you could expect if you threw a dice 20 times. This prediction is called the expected frequency.

Expected Frequency = Number of times you are going to do something (the number of trials) × The probability of the event happening

EXAMPLE: What is the expected frequency of heads when you toss a coin 200 times?

1) First work out the probability of the event happening:
   There are only two outcomes when you toss a coin — it's either going to land heads up or tails up. Both outcomes are equally likely, so the probability of getting heads is 0.5.

2) Now use the formula for expected frequency:

$$\text{Expected Frequency} = 200 \times 0.5 = 100$$

tosses (200) *probability of heads* (0.5)

So, the expected frequency would be 100 heads (out of 200 tosses).

*The **Results** Might be **Different** from the **Expected Frequency***

The expected frequency tells you the most likely number of times something will happen — but if you test it you'll probably get slightly different results. Often the easiest way to compare your actual results with the predicted results (i.e. the expected frequencies) is to draw a graph.

EXAMPLE: You are asked to investigate how the expected frequency of each number on a standard dice compares to the actual frequencies you get when you throw a dice 60 times.

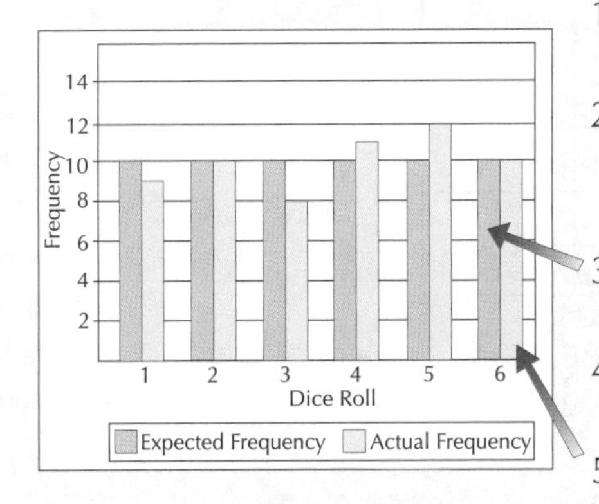

1) There are six sides on the dice and each is equally likely to come up, so the probability of getting each number is $\frac{1}{6}$.
2) If you throw the dice 60 times, the expected frequency of each number is $\frac{1}{6} \times 60 = 10$
   (i.e. in your test you expect to get each number 10 times).
3) Draw columns on the graph to show these expected frequencies.
4) Throw the dice 60 times and record the actual number of times each number is thrown.
5) Draw these actual frequencies on the graph.

The actual frequencies are quite close to the expected frequencies, but not exactly the same.

The Expected and Actual frequencies are unlikely to be the same...

Learn the definition of expected frequency and that nice big formula for working it out. Make sure you understand what's going on in both of the examples on this page and you'll have no worries.

Relative Frequency

This is a way of working out probabilities when the outcomes aren't equally likely...

Fair or Biased?

The probability of rolling a 3 on a dice is $1/6$ — you know that each of the six numbers is equally likely to be rolled and there's only one 3.

However this only works if it's a fair dice. If the dice is a bit wonky (the technical term is "biased") then each number won't have an equal chance of being rolled. That's where relative frequency comes in — you can use it to estimate probabilities when things might be wonky.

Do the Experiment Again and Again and Again

You need to do an experiment over and over again and then do a quick calculation.
(Remember, an experiment could just mean rolling a dice.)
Usually the results of these experiments will be written in a table.

There's a Formula for Relative Frequency

Once you have the results of the experiments, you can put them into this handy formula:

$$\text{Probability of something happening} = \frac{\text{Number of times it happens in experiment}}{\text{Number of trials in experiment}}$$

You can work out the relative frequency as a fraction but usually decimals are best for comparing relative frequencies.

The important thing to remember is:

The more trials there are, the more accurate the probability will be.

Example

So, back to the suspected wonky dice. What is the probability of rolling a 3?

Number of times the dice was rolled	10	20	50	100
Number of 3s rolled	3	7	19	37
Relative frequency	$\frac{3}{10} = 0.3$	$\frac{7}{20} = 0.35$	$\frac{19}{50} = 0.38$	$\frac{37}{100} = 0.37$

So, what's the probability? We've got four possible answers, but the most reliable one is the one worked out using the greatest number of dice rolls.
This makes the probability of rolling a 3 on this dice 0.37.

And since for a fair, unbiased dice, the probability of rolling a three is $1/6$ (about 0.17), then our dice is probably biased.

Relative frequency — a handy way of estimating probabilities...

Okay, lots of things to learn on this page. Make sure you know what 'biased' means, learn that lovely formula for working out relative frequency and remember that more trials increases the accuracy.

Warm-Up and Worked Exam Questions

I don't care if you say they're just for double checking, you're not going to be able to sneak a coin, two dice and a bag full of differently coloured geese into the exam...

Warm-Up Questions

1) A fair coin is tossed three times. How many possible outcomes are there?

2) Two fair spinners are shown.

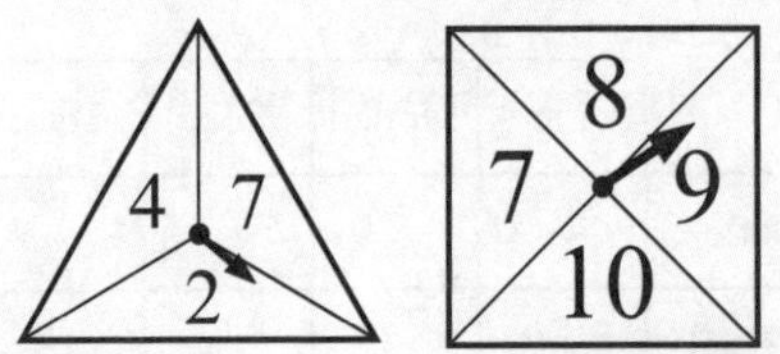

Both spinners are spun once and the results are added together.
Draw a sample space showing all twelve possible outcomes.

What is the probability of the total being an odd number?
What is the probability of the total being a square number?

3) If you roll a normal dice 42 times, how many times would you expect to get a 5?

Worked Exam Questions

Probability can be deceptively tricky — so make sure you totally understand these worked questions...

1 In order to drive legally on Britain's roads drivers need to have both a driving licence and insurance. One day a police officer at a checkpoint randomly stops a large number of drivers. The police officer finds that, of the people stopped, 14% have no insurance, 8% have no driving licence and 2% have no driving licence and also no insurance.

(a) Complete the Venn diagram to show this information.

No driving licence | No insurance
6% | 2% | 12%
80%

The intersection is 2%

Just no licence: $8 - 2 = 6\%$

Just no insurance: $14 - 2 = 12\%$

So, $100 - 2 - 6 - 12 = 80\%$ have both

(1 mark for 6, 2, 12 correctly placed, 1 mark for 80 outside circles.) *(2 marks)*

(b) Find the probability, as a fraction, that a driver stopped in this survey is driving illegally.

$$\frac{6+2+12}{100} = \frac{1}{5}$$

(3 marks for correct answer, otherwise 1 mark for 6 + 2 + 12 or 20% seen, and 1 mark for fraction with denominator 100.)

(3 marks)

(c) The following day the police stop 275 drivers. How many drivers can the police expect to find that have a driving licence but no insurance?

From the survey, P(driving licence but no insurance) = 0.12 **(This is the 'relative frequency.')**

$0.12 \times 275 = 33$ **(2 marks for correct answer, otherwise 1 mark for '0.12'.)**

(2 marks)

Exam Questions

2 A pizza delivery company employs 40 people to deliver pizzas to customers.
Employees each use one of three methods of transport.
Some employees deliver by car, others use a moped and the remainder deliver on foot.

30% of all employees deliver on foot.

Of the female employees $\frac{1}{3}$ use a car. Of those employees delivering on foot $\frac{1}{3}$ are male.

(a) Complete the table to show all the information.

....

....

....

	Car	Moped	Foot	Total
Male				
Female				15
Total	20			40

(3 marks)

(b) The manager selects a delivery person at random.
Calculate the probability that the person chosen:

(i) is female and delivers on foot

....

(1 mark)

(ii) is not a car user given that they are male

....

(2 marks)

(iii) is a moped user or male, or both

....

(2 marks)

3 Sam and Rory have made a hexagonal spinner out of card. They have numbered each of the sectors on the card from 1 to 6, as shown. They aren't sure whether the spinner is a regular hexagon or not. In an attempt to find out, they spin it 50 times and record how often they score each number.

Spinner score	1	2	3	4	5	6
Frequency	10	8	8	8	7	9

(a) Sam says that the spinner is *not* a regular hexagon because it is biased to land on '1'.
Explain why Sam may be right that the spinner is biased.

....

(1 mark)

(b) Rory says that it may be a perfectly fair spinner. Give two reasons why he may be right.

....

....

(2 marks)

Probability Laws

This page deals with "either/or" probabilities and there are two lovely laws to learn.

Mutually Exclusive Events Can't Happen Together

When two events can't happen at the same time, they are mutually exclusive. You can use the addition law to find the probability of either one or the other of these events happening.

P(A or B) = P(A) + P(B)

The probability of A or B is equal to the probability of A plus the probability of B.

EXAMPLE: You throw a dice once. What's the probability of rolling a 2 or a multiple of 3?

The probability of rolling a 2 is $1/6$

The probability of rolling a multiple of 3 is $2/6$ (because you can throw a 3 or a 6).

The events are mutually exclusive, so P(getting a 2 or a multiple of 3) = $\frac{1}{6} + \frac{2}{6} = \frac{3}{6} = \frac{1}{2}$

If you have more than two mutually exclusive events, you do pretty much the same thing.
You always just add the probabilities of each event to find the probability of any one of them happening.
For example, for four mutually exclusive events: P(A or B or C or D) = P(A) + P(B) + P(C) + P(D)

Use The *General Addition Law* for *Non*-Mutually Exclusive Events

You need to use this when more than one event can happen together. You don't want to count the overlap twice, so you have to take it away — simple as that.

P(A or B) = P(A) + P(B) – P(A and B)

EXAMPLE: You throw a dice. What's the probability of rolling a multiple of 2 or a multiple of 3?

The probability of throwing a multiple of 2 is $3/6$ because you could get a 2, 4 or 6.

The probability of throwing a multiple of 3 is $2/6$ because you could get a 3 or 6.

Rolling a six has been counted twice (since it's a multiple of 2 and a multiple of 3), so you need to take away the probability of rolling a six ($1/6$).

So, P(getting a multiple of 2 or a multiple of 3) = $\frac{3}{6} + \frac{2}{6} - \frac{1}{6} = \frac{4}{6} = \frac{2}{3}$

Exhaustive Events — at least *One* of them *Must Happen*

Events are exhaustive if together they include all the possible outcomes — so at least one of the events must happen.

EXAMPLE: You draw a card randomly from a standard pack of 52 playing cards. What's the probability of picking a spade, a heart, a diamond or a club?

Here, the four events are "picking a spade", "picking a heart", "picking a diamond" and "picking a club". There are no other possibilities, so the probability of one of the four events happening must be 1.

Two important laws to learn here...

Lots of juicy facts to get your teeth into on this page. It's really important that you learn those two addition laws. Then you just use them in the exam and you get marks — how great is that?

Probability Laws

Now we move on to probabilities with "and" in them, and another law for you...

*Independent Events are **Unconnected***

Two events are independent if one has no effect on the other.

Example

You toss a coin and then pick a card from a pack.
What's the probability of the coin showing heads and the card being a heart?

It doesn't matter which way the coin lands — it won't affect the card you pick out of the pack, so the two events are independent. The possible results are shown in this sample space diagram:

	Clubs	**Diamonds**	**Hearts**	**Spades**
Heads	H, C	H, D	H, H	H, S
Tails	T, C	T, D	T, H	T, S

There are 8 possible outcomes, so the probability of getting any one of the outcomes is $1/8$.
So P(hearts and heads) = $1/8$.

You don't have to draw a sample space diagram and count outcomes each time, though. There's a quicker way of calculating the probability of two independent events happening — all you need to do is to multiply the probabilities of each event together.

It's called the Rule of Independent Events:

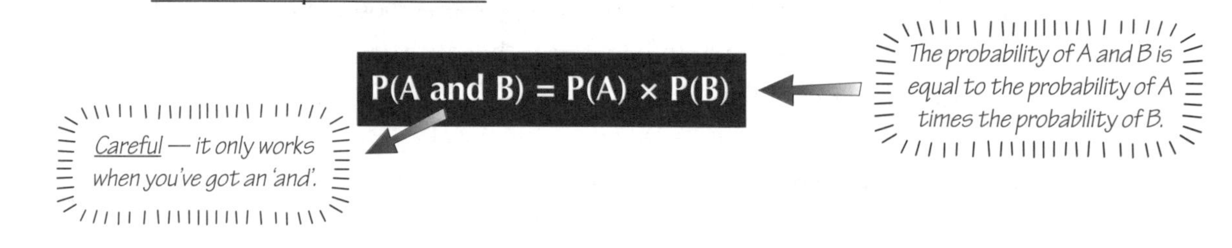

So the above example can be worked out by saying:
"The probability of picking a heart is $1/4$, and the probability of the coin showing heads is $1/2$.
So P(hearts and heads) = $\frac{1}{4} \times \frac{1}{2} = \frac{1}{8}$."

It doesn't matter how many events there are as long as they're independent — you just keep multiplying to find out the probability of them all happening. So, if there are four, the Rule of Independent Events would look like this: P(A and B and C and D) = P(A) × P(B) × P(C) × P(D)

Independent events have no effect on each other...

Another really important law for you to learn here. Make sure you know what it means and where you can use it. I don't know about you, but this kind of stuff gets me out of bed in the morning.

Probability Laws

Sometimes two or more events are connected...

Conditional Probability is a Bit Different

Sometimes the probability of the second event depends on the outcome of the first.
E.g. pulling coloured balls out of a sack without replacing them.

This is called Conditional Probability and to tackle it you need to use the General Multiplication Law:

P(A and B) = P(A) × P(B given that A occurs)

This means the probability of B happening, assuming that A has happened. You might see this phrase shortened to P(B|A).

A Couple of Examples of Conditional Probability

The easiest way to understand conditional probability is to look at some examples:

Example 1

A basket of fruit contains 2 apples and 4 pears. If two fruits are picked out at random, what's the probability that they're both pears?

The chance of picking out a pear first is $^4/_6$. You then have only 5 pieces of fruit left in the basket. The probability of picking out a pear, given that you have already picked a pear is $^3/_5$.

So the probability of picking out two pears is: $\frac{4}{6} \times \frac{3}{5} = \frac{12}{30} = \frac{2}{5}$

Example 2

In a lottery draw there are 49 balls, numbered 1–49.
What is the probability that the first two balls drawn out will both have a value less than 10?

Of the 49 balls, 9 have a value less than 10, so the probability that the first ball drawn is less than 10 is $^9/_{49}$.
Now there are only 48 balls left in the draw. The probability that the second ball drawn is less than 10, given that the first ball was less than 10 is $^8/_{48}$.

So the probability of picking out two numbers less than 10 is: $\frac{9}{49} \times \frac{8}{48} = \frac{72}{2352} = \frac{3}{98}$

Make sure you learn all the laws from the last three pages...

Right, I'll say it one more time: learn all of these laws. It's just easy marks in the exam. Remember — conditional probabilities are different so make sure you use the right formula when working them out.

Tree Diagrams

Tree Diagrams are an easy way of making sure you don't make a mistake when you're using the multiplication laws on pages 118 and 119. They're bound to come in useful in the exam.

For Probability Questions Use a Tree Diagram

Here's how tree diagrams work, in general...

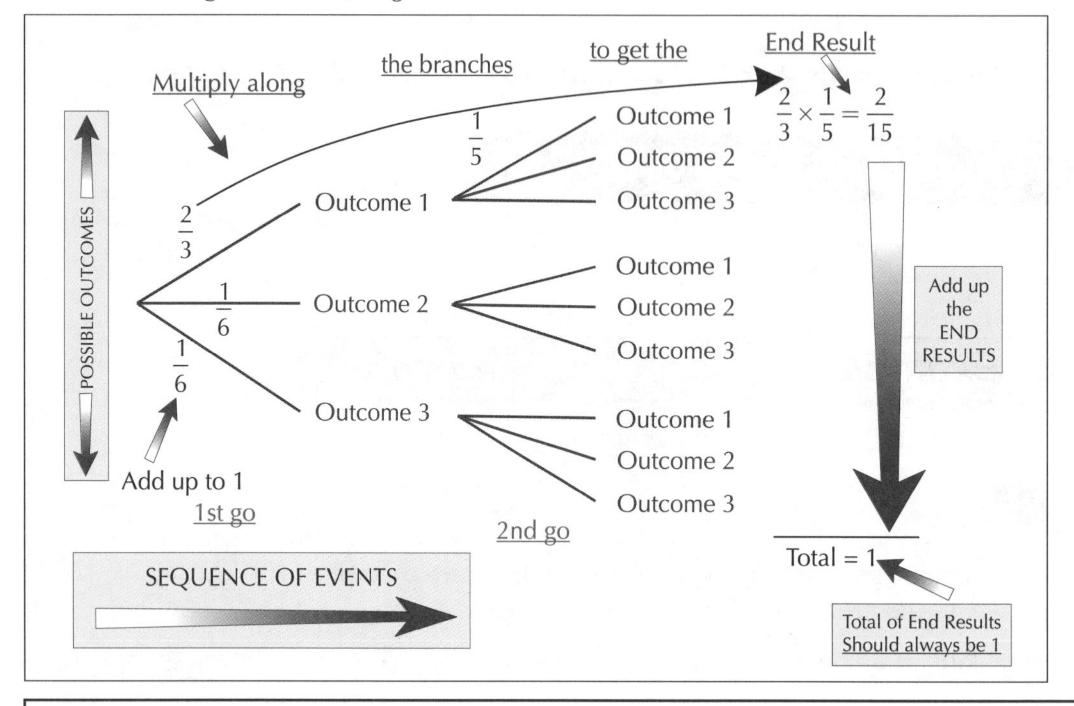

1) Always multiply along the branches (as shown) to get the end results.
2) On any set of branches which all meet at a point, the probabilities must always add up to 1.
3) Check that your diagram is correct by making sure the end results add up to one.
4) To answer any question, simply add up the relevant end results (see below).

EXAMPLE: There are five coloured balls in a bag. Three balls are blue and two are green. One ball is drawn out of the bag at random and its colour recorded. It is put back into the bag and another ball is drawn out. What is the probability that both balls will be the same colour?

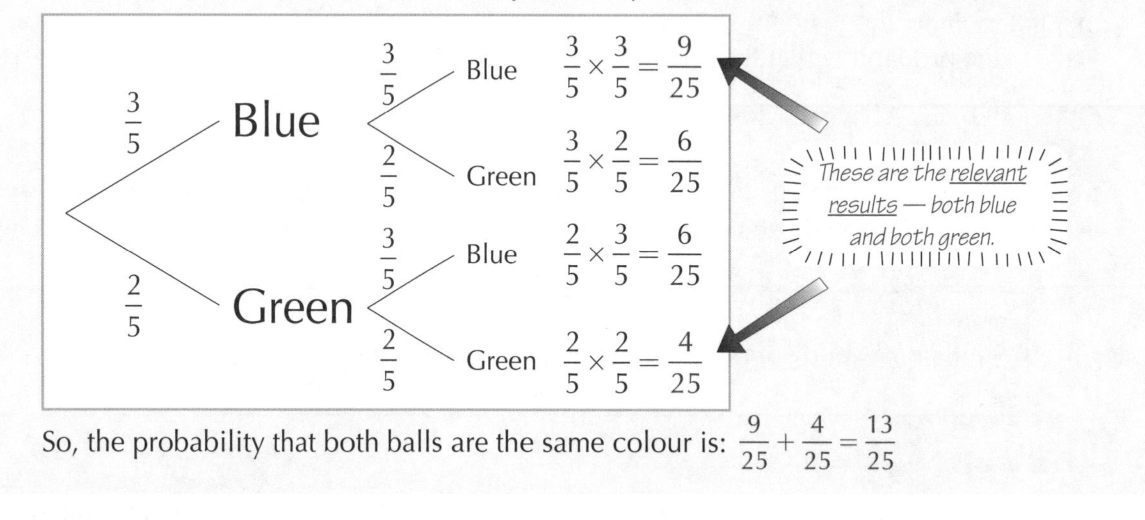

So, the probability that both balls are the same colour is: $\frac{9}{25} + \frac{4}{25} = \frac{13}{25}$

Tree diagrams are really important...

The tree diagram is the top toy when it comes to probability questions. Even if the question doesn't specifically ask for a tree diagram you should draw one straight away so you know what's going on.

Tree Diagrams

Here are some more examples of how tree diagrams can be used...

A couple of ***Likely*** *Tree Diagram* ***Questions***

This example shows you how a tree diagram can be used to find conditional probabilities.

EXAMPLE: A card is picked at random from a pack. Without replacing the first card, a second card is picked. What is the probability that both cards are aces?

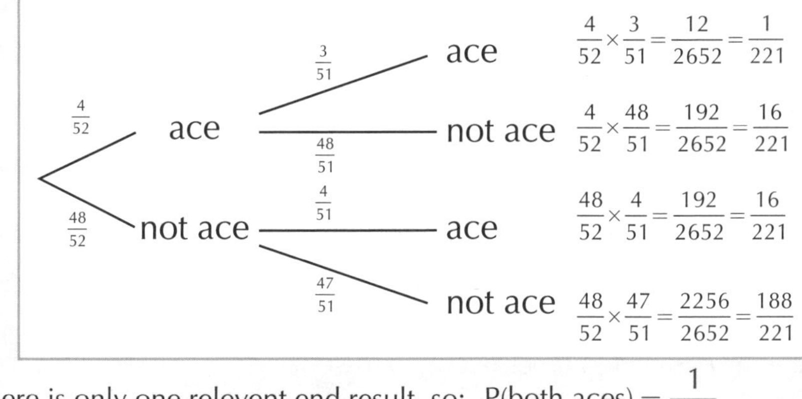

There is only one relevent end result, so: P(both aces) $= \frac{1}{221}$

This example shows you how the information in a question can be transformed into a tree diagram.

EXAMPLE: A skier is twice as likely to fall on used snow as on freshly fallen snow. On freshly fallen snow, she falls on one tenth of her runs down the slope. Snow is likely to fall every other day at the ski slope. What's the chance of the skier falling on her first run of a given day?

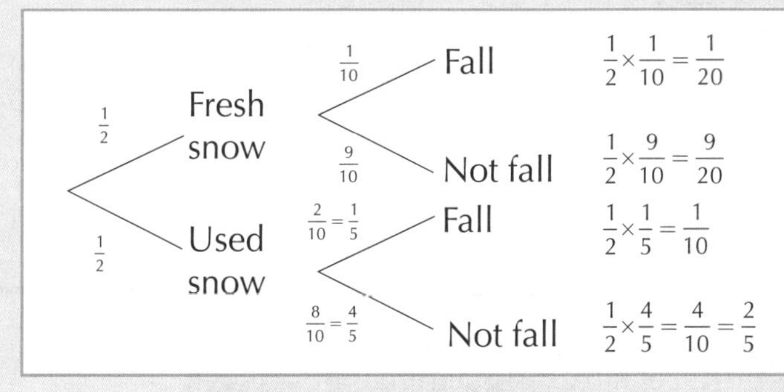

Once the tree diagram is drawn, all you need to do to answer the question is select the relevant end results and then add them together:

$$\text{P(falling)} = \frac{1}{20} + \frac{1}{10} = \frac{3}{20}$$

*P(**at least 1**) = 1 – P(**none**)*

EXAMPLE: "A woman has four children. Find the probability that at least one of them is a girl, assuming that boys and girls are equally likely."

"At least one girl" means "1 girl", "2 girls", "3 girls" or "4 girls", which could take a while to work out. It's easier to work out P(no girls) and subtract the answer from 1.

P(no girls) = P(boy) × P(boy) × P(boy) × P(boy) = $\frac{1}{2} \times \frac{1}{2} \times \frac{1}{2} \times \frac{1}{2} = \frac{1}{16}$

So, P(at least one girl) = $1 - \frac{1}{16} = \frac{15}{16}$.

See how useful tree diagrams are...

The first two examples on this page show how tree diagrams can save the day. It takes a bit of thinking to decide how to do the diagram and which results you need. Once you've done that it's plain sailing.

Discrete Probability Distributions

Here we go — the last page of the last section, and it's a beauty...

Discrete Uniform Distribution — Equal Chances

If everything is fair and you randomly pull a card from one suit of a pack, you have an equal chance of getting an ace, 2, 3, 4, 5, 6, 7, 8, 9, 10, jack, queen or king. In each case the probability is 1/13.

If there are only a certain number of equally likely outcomes, you have a discrete uniform distribution.

A graph of the probability of each outcome looks like this:

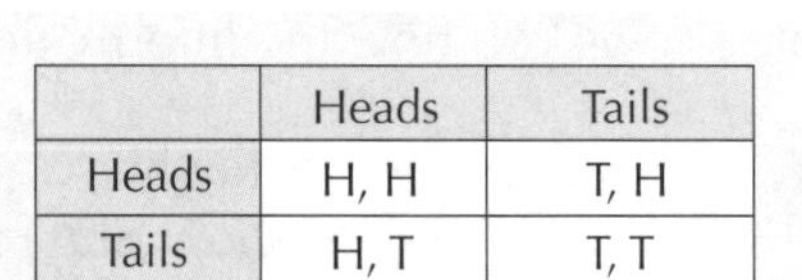

You get a discrete uniform distribution when the probability of each outcome is equal.

Binomial Distribution — Two Mutually Exclusive Outcomes

Some trials only have two possible outcomes, e.g. toss a coin and it will only be heads or tails. When this is true, you can use the binomial distribution to work out the probability of a certain overall outcome from n trials, e.g. a coin landing on heads 4 times out of 10 tosses.

Imagine you're tossing a fair coin. Call the probability of getting heads p and the probability of not getting heads (i.e. getting tails) q. Heads and tails are equally likely, so $p = 0.5$ and $q = 0.5$.

If you toss the coin twice (i.e. you carry out 2 trials) there are 4 outcomes altogether (but 2 of these (T, H and H, T) are really the same, so there are actually only 3 different combinations).

	Heads	Tails
Heads	H, H	T, H
Tails	H, T	T, T

The probabilities of the outcomes from these two trials are:

$P(H,H) = p \times p = p^2$, $P(H,T) = p \times q = pq$, $P(T,H) = q \times p = pq$, $P(T,T) = q \times q = q^2$.

Add these together and you get... $p^2 + 2pq + q^2$ ...which is the expansion of $(p + q)^2$.

The probability of getting two heads. The probability of getting one head and one tail.

For three tosses the result is: $p^3 + 3p^2q + 3pq^2 + q^3$ which is the expansion of $(p + q)^3$.

So, the probability of getting 2 heads and a tail is $3p^2q = 3(0.5)^2(0.5) = 0.375$

For n trials, the probabilities of the outcomes are given by the expansion of $(p + q)^n$.

You can quickly work out the expansions using Pascal's Triangle — e.g. the expansion of $(p + q)^6$ is

$$p^6 + 6p^5q + 15p^4q^2 + 20p^3q^3 + 15p^2q^4 + 6pq^5 + q^6$$

Number of Trials	Coefficients in the expansion of $(p + q)^n$	Number of Different Combinations
1	1 1	2
2	1 2 1	3
3	1 3 3 1	4
4	1 4 6 4 1	5
5	1 5 10 10 5 1	6
6	1 6 15 20 15 6 1	7
etc		etc

Each number is the sum of the two numbers above it.

You can use the binomial distribution to calculate probabilities if:

1) There are just two mutually exclusive outcomes from each trial (e.g. heads or tails).
2) The probabilities don't change from one trial to the next [e.g. P(heads) is always 0.5].
3) Each trial is independent of the one before it.

Learn these two probability distributions...

The stuff on this page is all pretty tricky, so go through it carefully. Make sure you learn all the details, then turn over and scribble down everything you've learned. Now have a crack at these questions...

Warm-Up and Worked Exam Questions

These warm-up questions should raise your temperature nicely.
The one on conditional probability is particularly spicy.

Warm-Up Questions

1) Trevor has a packet of mixed sweets. Half the sweets are milk chocolates, a quarter are liquorice, an eighth are flying saucers and an eighth are pear drops. Trevor doesn't like flying saucers or liquorice. He takes out a sweet at random.
   Find the probability that he won't like it.
2) Two bags contain solid shapes. The first bag contains 2 cubes and 3 spheres. The second bag contains 3 cubes and 4 spheres.
   One solid shape is taken at random from each bag. Find the probability of selecting two cubes.
3) A bag contains 3 red balls and 2 yellow balls. A ball is taken out of the bag at random and its colour recorded before it is replaced. Then a second ball is picked at random.
   Draw a tree diagram to show all the possible outcomes. Find the probability that the two balls taken out are the same colour.
4) A card is drawn at random from a shuffled pack and is not replaced. A second card is then drawn.
   What is the probability that the first is a diamond and the second card is red?
5) The probability of rain on any given day of a three-day Bank Holiday weekend is $\frac{1}{4}$. Calculate the probability of there being rain on exactly two days of the Bank Holiday weekend. You may use $(p + q)^3 = p^3 + 3p^2q + 3pq^2 + q^3$.

Worked Exam Questions

Imagine a world in which a confused and tired examiner has mistakenly left the answers written on the exam paper. Dream no longer...

1 A cricket match is scheduled to be played over a weekend. The probability that play will have to be stopped on Saturday due to poor weather conditions is 0.3. The probability that play will have to be stopped on Sunday is 0.4.

(a) Draw a tree diagram to show this information.

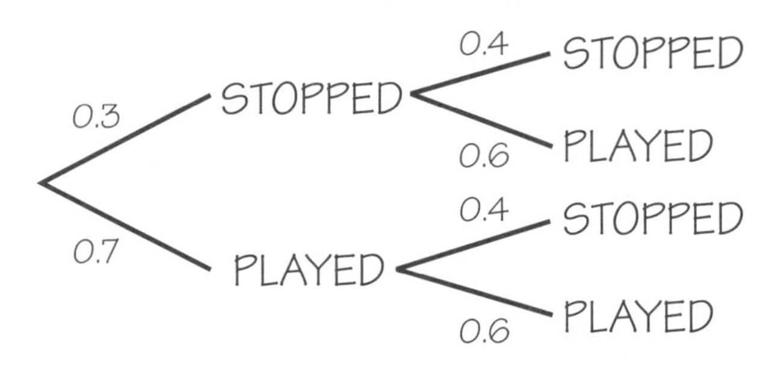

(2 marks for a correct diagram, minus 1 mark for each error in probabilities.)

(2 marks)

(b) Find the probability that play is stopped on both days.

$P(SS) = 0.3 \times 0.4 = 0.12$ *(2 marks for correct answer, otherwise 1 mark for correct method.)*

(2 marks)

(c) Find the probability that play is stopped on exactly 1 day.

$P(SP) + P(PS) = (0.3 \times 0.6) + (0.7 \times 0.4) = 0.18 + 0.28 = 0.46$

(2 marks for correct answer, otherwise 1 mark for correct method.) *(2 marks)*

Exam Questions

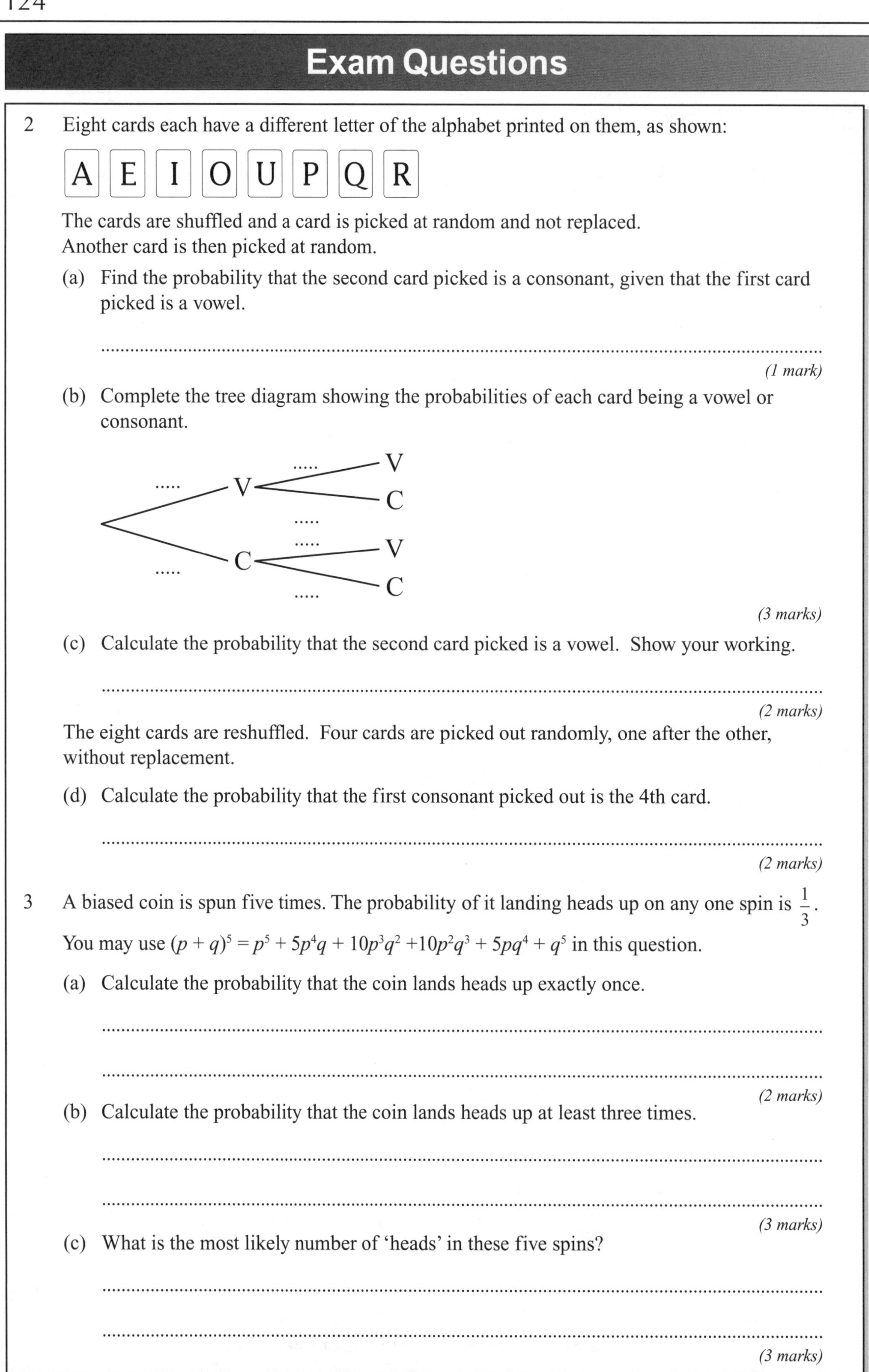

2 Eight cards each have a different letter of the alphabet printed on them, as shown:

A E I O U P Q R

The cards are shuffled and a card is picked at random and not replaced.
Another card is then picked at random.

(a) Find the probability that the second card picked is a consonant, given that the first card picked is a vowel.

....

(1 mark)

(b) Complete the tree diagram showing the probabilities of each card being a vowel or consonant.

..... V V
..... C
..... C V
..... C

(3 marks)

(c) Calculate the probability that the second card picked is a vowel. Show your working.

....

(2 marks)

The eight cards are reshuffled. Four cards are picked out randomly, one after the other, without replacement.

(d) Calculate the probability that the first consonant picked out is the 4th card.

....

(2 marks)

3 A biased coin is spun five times. The probability of it landing heads up on any one spin is $\frac{1}{3}$.

You may use $(p + q)^5 = p^5 + 5p^4q + 10p^3q^2 + 10p^2q^3 + 5pq^4 + q^5$ in this question.

(a) Calculate the probability that the coin lands heads up exactly once.

....

....

(2 marks)

(b) Calculate the probability that the coin lands heads up at least three times.

....

....

(3 marks)

(c) What is the most likely number of 'heads' in these five spins?

....

....

(3 marks)

Revision Summary for Section Four

Well, it's quite probable that you've had enough of probability by now. Don't despair — you've nearly reached the end of the section. Just a few questions to go. Keep going through them until the probability of you getting one of them wrong is zero. If you can answer all these, you stand a very good chance of doing well in the exam.

Keep learning the basic facts until you know them

1) What is the numerical probability of an event which:
   a) is certain
   b) is impossible
   c) has an even chance?
2) Give a brief definition of the word "outcome".
3) Complete the probability formula for equally likely outcomes, P(event) = ...
4) What is the difference between probability and odds?
5) How are probabilities used by insurance companies?
6) What is a sample space?
7) Name three ways of showing a sample space.
8) How do you work out expected frequency?
9) Will your actual results always match the expected frequency?
10) What's a good way of comparing actual results with the expected frequencies?
11) Write down the formula for relative frequency.
12) What are mutually exclusive events?
13) What is meant by exhaustive events?
14) What is the law that can be used to work out the probability of any one of a number of mutually exclusive events happening? Write out this law.
15) What similar law should be used for events that aren't mutually exclusive? Write out this law.
16) Give an example of two events that are independent.
17) Write out the Rule of Independent Events.
18) Give a brief description of conditional probability.
19) What law can be used to find the probability of two events happening, when the second event is conditional on the first? Write out this law.
20) Write a list of everything you need to include when drawing a tree diagram.
21) What's a useful way of tackling "at least" questions?
22) When do you get a discrete uniform distribution?
23) How can you easily find the coefficients of a binomial expansion?
24) Write out the binomial expansion in terms of p and q if there are 7 trials.

Practice Exam

Once you've been through all the questions in this book, you should feel pretty confident about the exam. As final preparation, here is a practice exam to really get you set for the real thing. Your actual exam paper will be out of slightly more or fewer marks depending on which syllabus you're doing. Either way, this paper is great practice. If you're doing Foundation then you won't have learnt every bit — but it's still good practice.

General Certificate of Secondary Education

GCSE Statistics

Time allowed: 2 hours 30 minutes

In addition to this paper you may need:
- A ruler.
- A protractor.
- A pair of compasses.
- An electronic calculator.

Instructions to candidates
- Answer the questions in the spaces provided.
- Do all rough work on the paper.
- Draw diagrams in pencil.

Information for candidates
- The marks available are given in brackets at the end of each question or part-question.
- There are 11 questions in this paper. There are no blank pages.
- You are expected to use a calculator where appropriate.

Advice to candidates
- Work steadily through the paper.
- Don't spend too long on one question.
- In calculations show clearly how you work out your answers.
- If you have time at the end, go back and check your answers.

GCSE Statistics Formula Sheet

Mean of a frequency distribution = $\dfrac{\sum fx}{\sum f}$

Mean of a grouped frequency distribution = $\dfrac{\sum fx}{\sum f}$, where x is the mid-interval value.

Standard deviation for a set of numbers $x_1, x_2, \ldots, x_n$ having a mean value of $\bar{x}$ is given by

$$\sqrt{\frac{\sum(x-\bar{x})^2}{n}} \text{ or } \sqrt{\frac{\sum x^2}{n} - \bar{x}^2}$$

Standard deviation for a frequency distribution is given by

$$\sqrt{\frac{\sum f(x-\bar{x})^2}{\sum f}} \text{ or } \sqrt{\frac{\sum fx^2}{\sum f} - \bar{x}^2}$$

The same formula applies to the standard deviation of a grouped frequency distribution where x is the mid-interval value.

Spearman's rank correlation coefficient = $1 - \dfrac{6\sum d^2}{n(n^2-1)}$

Leave blank

1 Rodney is considering opening a small restaurant in the village where he lives.

To find out the views of local people he delivers a questionnaire to every house in the village.

(a) Included in the questionnaire is a closed question asking for people's age.

(i) Explain what is meant by a *closed question*.

....

....

(1 mark)

(ii) Give one advantage of using a closed question for age.

....

....

(1 mark)

(b) Only 12% of the questionnaires are returned to Rodney.

How might Rodney have improved the response rate?

....

....

(1 mark)

(c) The returned questionnaires showed that some of his questions had been badly worded.

What should Rodney have done before he delivered his questionnaire to avoid this problem?

....

....

(1 mark)

(d) One of Rodney's questions was

"How often do you eat out at a pub or restaurant?"

Give two criticisms of this question.

Criticism 1 ....

....

(1 mark)

Criticism 2 ....

....

(1 mark)

AQA 2007

2 Danielle lives in a house which has a phone.
She also has a mobile phone.
Danielle receives 75% of all her calls on her mobile phone.

(a) (i) Complete the tree diagram to show the probabilities for the next two calls.
Assume that all calls are independent.

First call		Second call	
		....	Call on mobile
0.75	Call on mobile		
		....	Call on house phone
		....	Call on mobile
....	Call on house phone		
		....	Call on house phone

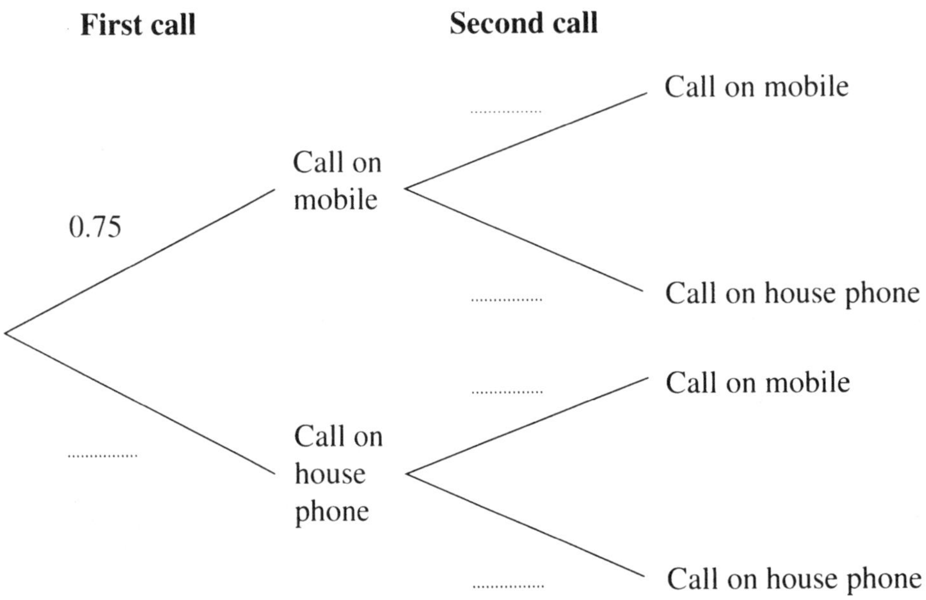

(3 marks)

(ii) Explain what is meant by the phrase in part (a)(i) that 'all calls are independent'.

....

....

(1 mark)

(b) Use the tree diagram to find the probability that the next two calls for Danielle are on her mobile phone.

....

....

Answer ....

(2 marks)

AQA 2007

Leave blank

Leave blank

3 The table shows the number of GCSE passes for 30 Year 11 students.

The gender of the students is also shown.

Student	Gender	Number of passes	Student	Gender	Number of passes
01	M	4	16	M	3
02	M	7	17	M	5
03	F	9	18	F	10
04	M	8	19	M	2
05	F	6	20	M	4
06	F	6	21	F	8
07	M	9	22	M	3
08	M	2	23	F	7
09	F	7	24	M	2
10	M	4	25	M	1
11	F	8	26	M	4
12	M	7	27	F	9
13	F	5	28	M	5
14	M	5	29	M	6
15	M	4	30	M	2

Here is a table of random numbers from 01 to 50.

Line 1	15	41	01	15	20	16
Line 2	32	22	33	30	19	08
Line 3	04	31	49	29	13	29
Line 4	14	23	37	11	24	29

Question 3 continues on page 5

(a) (i) Starting with the first number on Line 1 of the random number table and reading across from left to right, select a random sample of size eight.

Write your answers in the table.

Student number								
Gender								
Number of passes								

(3 marks)

(ii) Calculate the mean number of passes per student for this example.

....

Answer ....

(1 mark)

(b) (i) Starting with the first number on Line 3 of the random number table and reading from left to right, select a random sample of size six stratified by gender.

Write your answers in the table.

Student number						
Gender						
Number of passes						

....

....

(4 marks)

(ii) Calculate the mean number of passes per student for this sample.

....

Answer ....

(1 mark)

Leave blank

(c) Give a reason why the sampling method used in part (b)(i) is better than the sampling method used in part (a)(i).

....

....

....

(1 mark)

(d) After the examination period the students were given a questionnaire to complete.

One of the questions contained the following statement.

'Exams are getting easier'

.... ☐

.... ☐

.... ☐

.... ☐

.... ☐

(please tick a box)

Complete the response box headings.

(2 marks)

AQA 2007

4 The table shows the earnings each quarter from tourism to the UK, from the first quarter of the year 1999 to the second quarter of the year 2002.

	Earnings from tourism to the UK (in £ millions)			
Year	**Q1**	**Q2**	**Q3**	**Q4**
1999	2413	3064	4148	2874
2000	2315	3297	4284	2910
2001	2406	2815	3819	2265
2002	1901	2815		

(Data source: *National Statistics*)

The data is shown on the time series graph below.

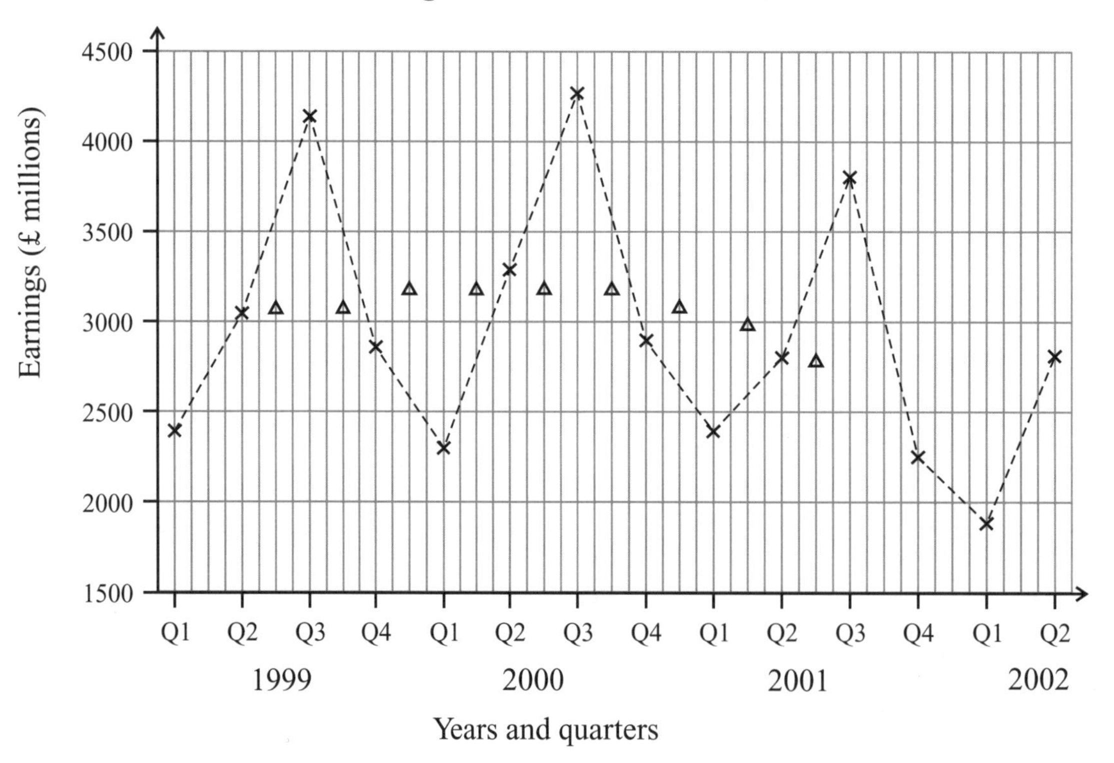

Leave blank

(a) In which quarter of each year was the greatest amount of money earned?

Answer ....

(1 mark)

(b) Give **one** reason why the earnings from tourism were higher in this quarter of each year.

....

....

(1 mark)

The first 9 four-quarterly moving averages, in £ millions, to two significant figures are:

3100 3100 3200 3200 3200 3200 3100 3000 2800

(c) Calculate the last **two** moving averages.

....

....

....

....

....

Answer £.................. million, £.................. million.

(2 marks)

(d) Plot the last **two** moving averages on the time series graph.

(1 mark)

(e) What can be inferred from the moving averages about the way the earnings from tourism changed for the years 1999 to 2002?

....

....

....

....

(2 marks)

EDEXCEL 2006

5 In a study on identical twins, the intelligence quotient (IQ) of 10 sets of twins was tested, and whether the twin was the first- or the second-born was recorded.

The results for the second-born twins are shown on the stem and leaf diagram below.

Second-born twins' IQ

Stem	Leaves
8	7 9
9	3 4 6 7
10	1 3
11	3
12	6

Key
8 | 7 = 87

(a) Find the median IQ of the second-born twins.

....

....

Answer ....

(1 mark)

(b) Find the lower and upper quartiles of the IQs of second-born twins.

....

....

....

....

Answer Lower quartile ....

Upper quartile ....

(2 marks)

(c) Show that 126 is **not** an outlier for the second-born twins' IQs.

....

....

....

....

....

(3 marks)

Leave blank

The IQs of the 10 first-born twins are shown as a box plot on the grid below.

(d) On the same grid draw a box plot for the IQs of the second-born twins.

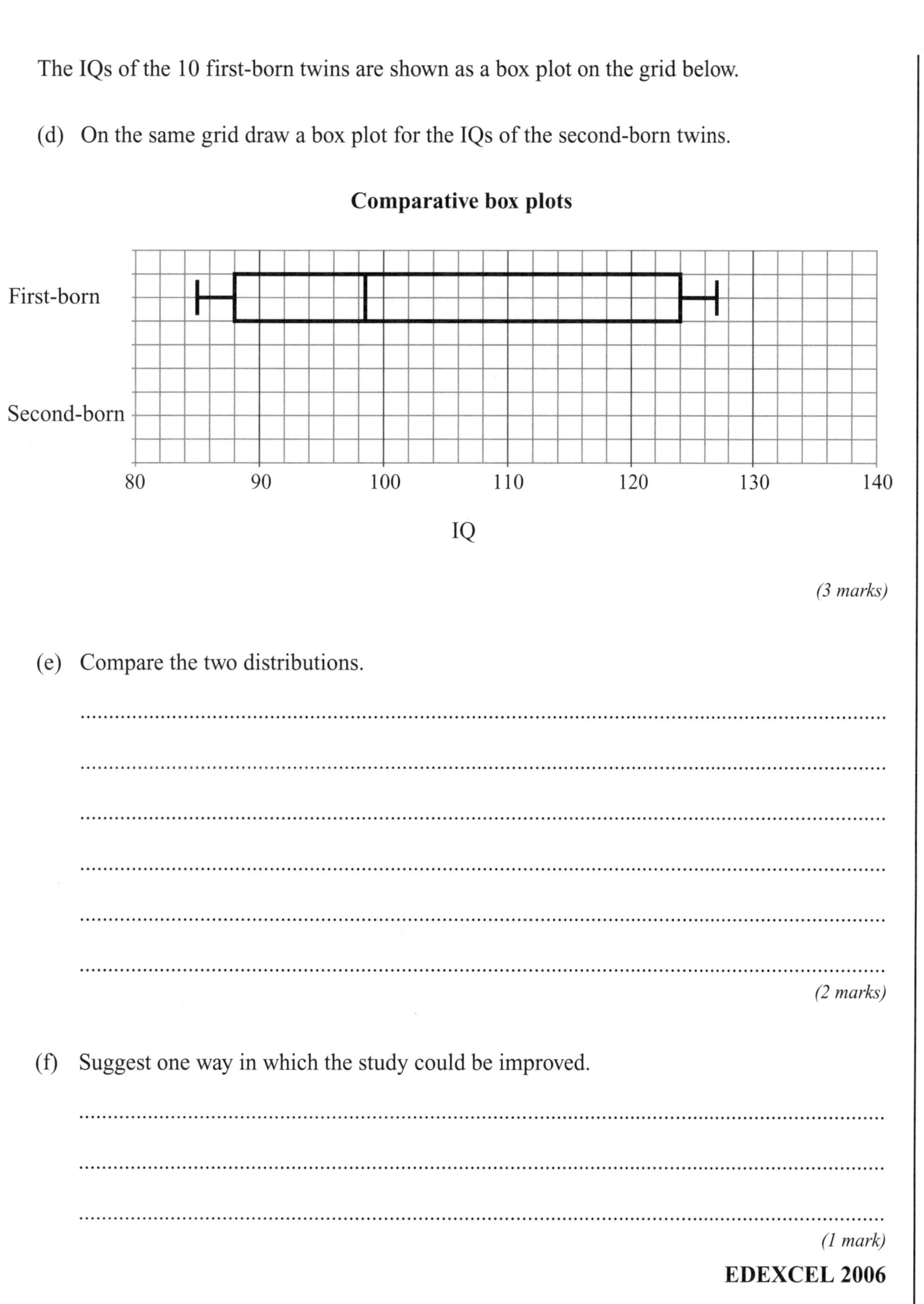

(3 marks)

(e) Compare the two distributions.

....

....

....

....

....

....

(2 marks)

(f) Suggest one way in which the study could be improved.

....

....

....

(1 mark)

EDEXCEL 2006

6 (a) A bank kept a daily record of the number of cheques with errors that were presented for payment.

Leave blank

The results from a random sample of 150 days are shown in the table.

Number of cheques with errors	Number of days
0	4
1	21
2	38
3	38
4	22
5	15
6	8
7	4

Calculate the mean, variance and standard deviation of the number of cheques per day with errors.

....

....

....

....

....

....

Answer Mean ....

Variance ....

Standard deviation ....

(5 marks)

Leave blank

(b) Another bank recorded the times taken to process an equal number of cheque errors at two of its branches, A and B.

The times taken in minutes, at each of the two branches were normally distributed with mean and standard deviation shown in the table.

	Mean (minutes)	Standard deviation (minutes)
Branch A	16.5	2.8
Branch B	14	4.5

To compare the performance of both branches it was agreed to standardise the times taken at each branch.

(i) What would be the standardised value for a cheque from Branch A taking 21 minutes to process?

....

....

....

Answer ....

(2 marks)

(ii) A cheque processed at Branch B had a standardised time of 2.4.

What was the actual processing time?

....

....

....

Answer .... minutes

(3 marks)

(iii) Between what limits would you expect approximately 99.9% of the cheque processing time for Branch A to lie?

....

....

....

Answer .... minutes

(3 marks)

AQA 2007

7 Alan works for the home delivery service of a large supermarket chain.

He has been asked by his manager to find out how long it takes to select and pack a sample of customer orders.

The table shows the results based on a sample of 75 orders.

Table 1

Time, t (minutes)	**Number of orders**
$0 \leqslant t < 3$	1
$3 \leqslant t < 6$	5
$6 \leqslant t < 9$	7
$9 \leqslant t < 12$	24
$12 \leqslant t < 15$	24
$15 \leqslant t < 18$	8
$18 \leqslant t < 21$	6

To simplify the data Alan regrouped the 75 values as follows:

Table 2

Time, t (minutes)	**Number of orders**
$0 \leqslant t < 6$	6
$6 \leqslant t < 10$	8
$10 \leqslant t < 11$	22
$11 \leqslant t < 14$	18
$14 \leqslant t < 21$	21

(a) Give two reasons why the first table is a better form of grouping than the second.

Reason 1 ....

....

Reason 2 ....

....

(2 marks)

(b) State the modal class(es) for the distributions in Tables 1 and 2.

Answer Table 1 ....

Table 2 ....

(2 marks)

Leave blank

(c) Use the data in **Table 2** to draw a histogram on the grid below.

....

....

....

....

....

(5 marks)

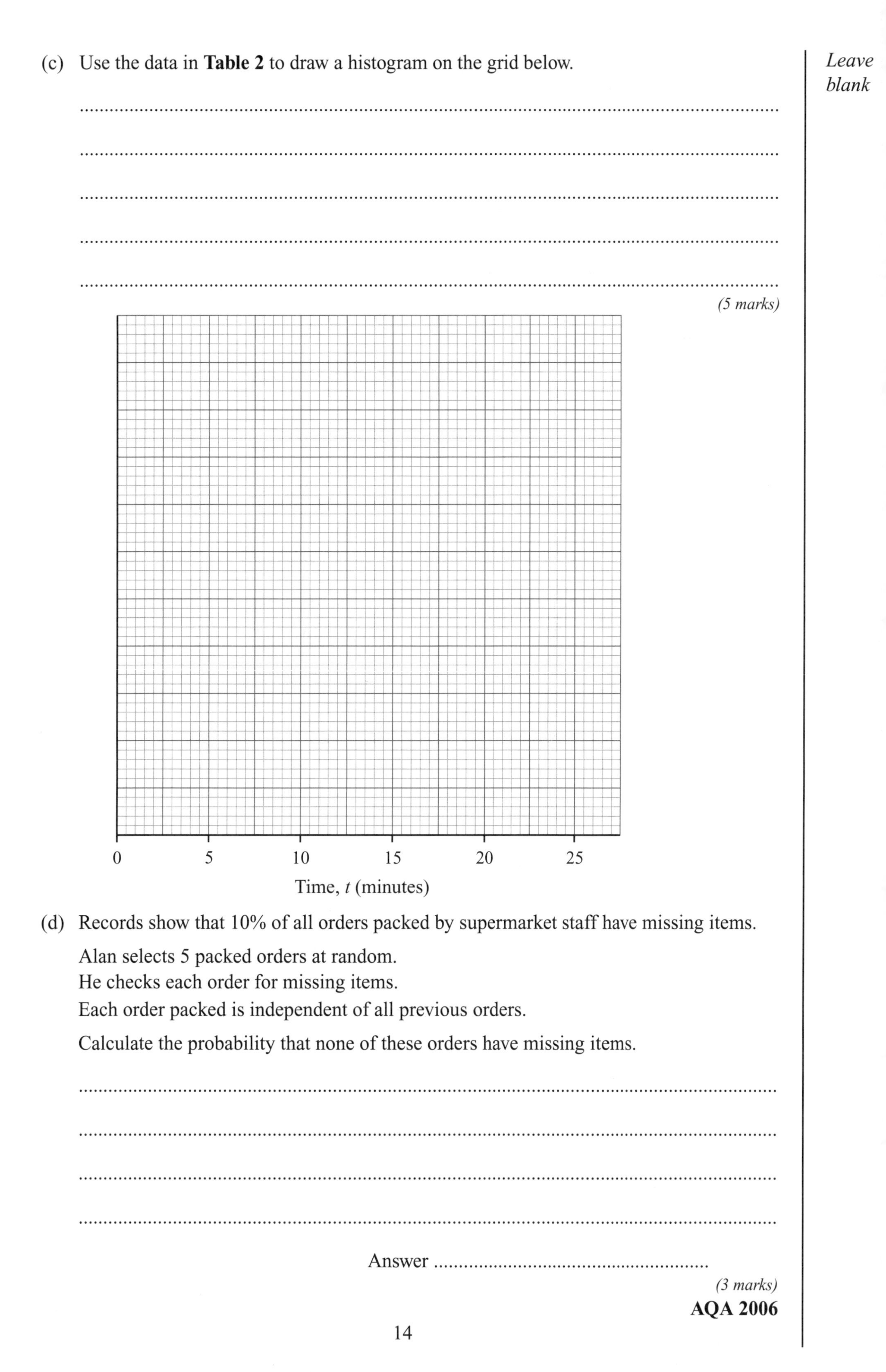

(d) Records show that 10% of all orders packed by supermarket staff have missing items.

Alan selects 5 packed orders at random.
He checks each order for missing items.
Each order packed is independent of all previous orders.

Calculate the probability that none of these orders have missing items.

....

....

....

....

Answer ....

(3 marks)

AQA 2006

8 Records for a local library show for each book whether it is in the fiction, non fiction or classics category and whether it is a hard back or soft back version.

When the library closed on Wednesday last week 2700 books were out on loan.

Of the books on loan 72% were in the fiction category.

Of the 620 hard back books on loan 55% were in the non fiction category and 25% in the classics category.

In total 176 classics books were on loan.

(a) Complete the table, entering the number of books on loan in each case.

Version / **Category**	Hard back	Soft back	Totals
Fiction			
Non Fiction			
Classics			176
Totals	620		2700

(4 marks)

(b) A library record for a book on loan is chosen at random.

Use the table to calculate the probability that the book is

(i) non fiction and a soft back version

....

Answer ....

(1 mark)

(ii) non fiction or a hard back version

....

Answer ....

(2 marks)

(iii) fiction, given that it is a soft back version.

....

Answer ....

(2 marks)

(c) How many of the first 200 books taken out on loan on the following day would you expect to be hard back classics?

....

....

Answer ....

(2 marks)

AQA 2006

Leave blank

9 An expert from the local antiques club agreed to challenge a number of contestants to correctly rank eight items of Victorian furniture according to their value.

John agreed to take part and his **rankings** along with those of the expert were as follows:

Exhibit	**A**	**B**	**C**	**D**	**E**	**F**	**G**	**H**
Expert	1	3	6	7	8	2	5	4
John	8	5	2.5	4	1	6	2.5	7

(a) Calculate the value of Spearman's rank correlation coefficient for the two sets of data.

....

....

....

....

....

Answer ....

(4 marks)

(b) Interpret, in context, your answer to part (a).

....

....

(1 mark)

(c) A further eight contestants entered the competition.
The values of the correlation coefficients were

0.35 -0.43 0.71 0.05 -0.36 -0.02 0.92 -0.81

(i) Which two of these values show that there is almost no correlation between the individual rankings of that contestant and those of the expert?

Answer ....

(2 marks)

(ii) Which of these values shows the strongest correlation between the expert and contestant?

Answer ....

(1 mark)

Question 9 continues on page 17

(d) John was asked to draw two comparative pie charts to show the value of UK exports of Victorian furniture to Europe in 1994 and 2004.

A pie chart of radius 3 cm was drawn to show the 1994 export figure of £107 000. The export figure for 2004 was £196 400.

Calculate the radius of the pie chart used for the 2004 total.

Give your answer to two decimal places.

....

....

....

....

Answer .... cm

(4 marks)

AQA 2006

10 A company runs holiday tours.

In 2005, 400 people made provisional bookings.

Of these 320 went on to confirm the booking.

In 2006 one person makes a provisional booking.

(a) Write down an estimate of the probability that this person will go on to confirm the booking.

....

....

....

Answer ....

(1 mark)

(b) Estimate the probability that the person will not go on to confirm the booking.

....

....

....

Answer ....

(1 mark)

Leave blank

(c) The tour company has just had 4 people who made provisional bookings.

(i) Calculate the probability that exactly three of these people will go on to confirm their booking.

You may use $(p + q)^4 = p^4 + 4p^3q + 6p^2q^2 + 4pq^3 + q^4$.

....

....

....

....

....

....

Answer ....

(2 marks)

(ii) For these 4 provisional bookings, find which are the **two** most likely numbers of people who go on to confirm their bookings. Show your working.

....

....

....

....

....

....

....

....

Answer ....

(3 marks)

EDEXCEL 2006

11 The scatter diagram shows the ages, x million years, and the volumes, y cm^3, of eight skulls of a particular type of ape.

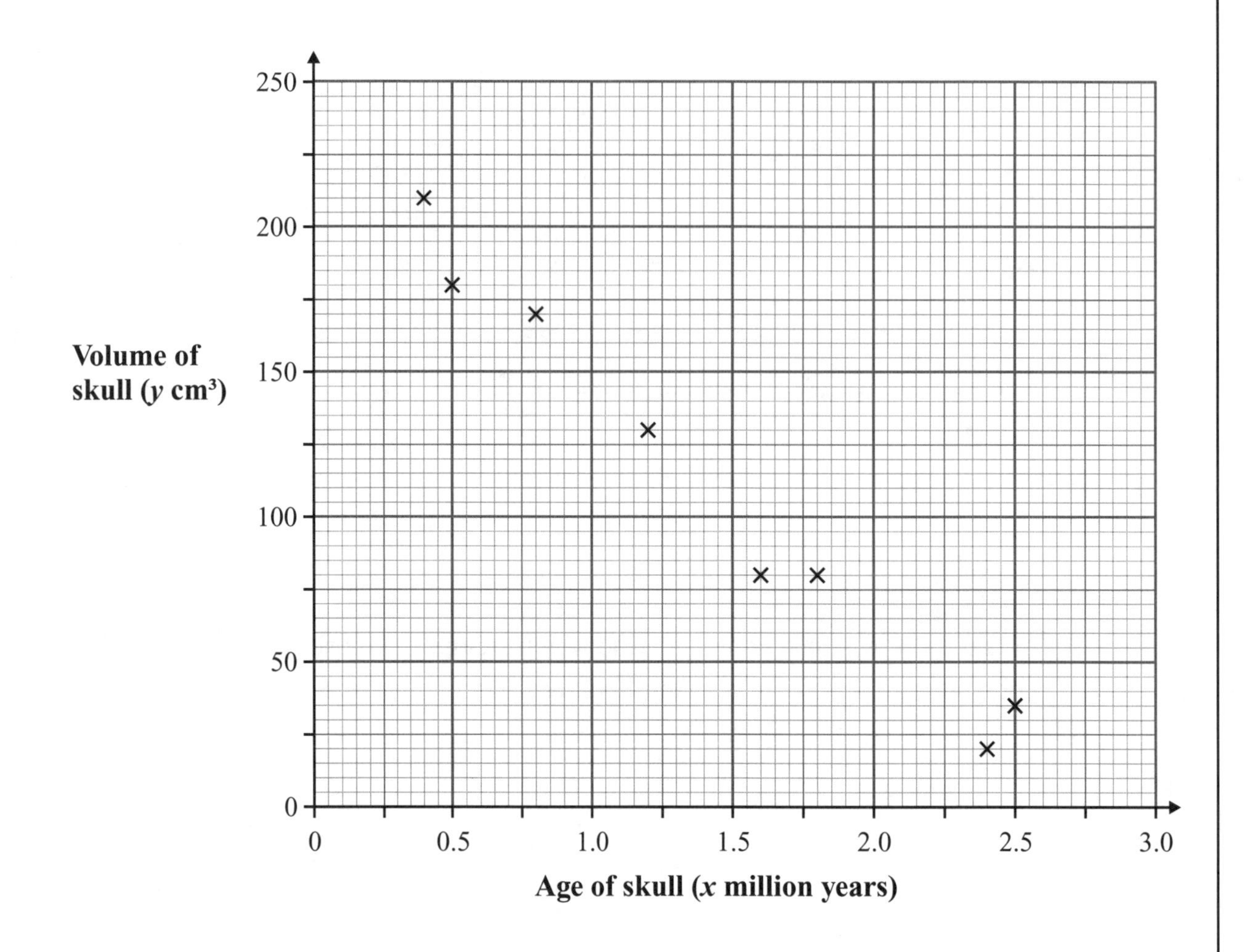

(a) Describe the correlation between the volume of a skull and the age of a skull for this type of ape.

....

(1 mark)

The table gives the ages, x million years, and the volumes, y cm^3, of the eight skulls shown in the scatter diagram.

x	2.5	1.8	0.8	2.4	1.6	0.5	0.4	1.2
y	34	80	170	20	80	180	210	130

(b) Calculate the coordinates of the mean point $(\bar{x}, \bar{y})$ for these data.

....

Answer (.................... , ...)

(2 marks)

Leave blank

(c) On the scatter diagram

(i) plot the point $(\bar{x}, \bar{y})$,

(1 mark)

(ii) draw the line of best fit.

(1 mark)

A skull of this particular type of ape has an age of one million years.

(d) Find an estimate for the volume of this skull.

Answer .... cm^3

(1 mark)

The skull of another ape is to be classified. It has an age of 1 million years and a volume of 75 cm^3.

(e) Discuss whether this skull is likely to be from the same type of ape.

....

....

....

....

(2 marks)

(f) Give a reason why your line of best fit may not be used reliably to predict the volume of a skull with an age of 3 million years.

....

....

(1 mark)

The equation of the line of best fit has the form $y = ax + b$.

(g) Use your line of best fit to find the value of a and the value of b.

....

....

Answer $a =$ ....

$b =$ ....

(3 marks)

(h) Give a practical interpretation of the meaning of a.

....

....

(2 marks)

EDEXCEL 2007

Page 6 (Warm-Up Questions)

1) Primary data is raw data that has probably been collected by you and has not been interpreted by anyone yet. Secondary data is data that has been collected by someone else and has already been processed.
2) May be biased, may be out-of-date.
   You could also say that you don't know whether the data is accurate or not.
3) Data that is not numerical, or data that is completely descriptive.
4) Discrete
5) Interval scale
6) Bivariate data

Page 7 (Exam Questions)

2 (a) Total number of boys surveyed = 42 + 38 + 103 + 17 = 200,
200 – 64 – 38 – 54 = **44**. ***(2 marks for the correct answer, otherwise 1 mark for finding the total number of boys surveyed.)***

(b) 103 + 87 = **190** ***(1 mark)***

(c) Maths ***(1 mark)***

(d) Total number of girls surveyed = 63 + 45 + 87 + 5 = 200
Total number of boys surveyed = 200 [from part (a)]
So, total number of students surveyed = 200 + 200 = **400**
(1 mark)

(e) A bad idea as the data has been collected for the Essex school only and so isn't relevant to the school in Dorset. For example, more of the Dorset students might live further away. So the data would be biased.
(1 mark for saying it was a bad idea and giving a valid reason why.)

3 (a) Rank scale ***(1 mark)***

(b) Neither (the data is qualitative — the numbers are only used to represent opinions). ***(1 mark)***

(c) Primary ***(1 mark)***
Martin has carried out the survey himself, so the data is primary.

Page 15 (Warm-Up Questions)

1) 100%
   A census surveys every member of the population.
2) It does not include every member of the population.
3) The population is all the penguins in the zoo.
   The sample frame is a list of all the penguins in the zoo.
4) Stratified sampling should be used.
   There should be 12 boys on the committee $\left(\frac{300}{350} \times 14 = 12\right)$.
5) Quota sampling
6) The wrong population might have been sampled from or a non-random sampling method might have been used.

Page 17 (Exam Questions)

5 (a) Jack ***(1 mark)***
Remember, Convenience sampling is just what it says — convenient. Jack has just asked a group of people who happen to be in one place at one time.

(b) Possible answers include:
She has only surveyed women, her town may not fairly represent the whole of England, she may have conducted her survey nearer to one shop than the other, elderly people are likely to be under represented because they are less likely to be walking around in the town centre. ***(1 mark)***

6 (a) Number of students ÷ sample size = 40 ÷ 10 = 4
So sample is every 4th student starting with the 2nd student (who has a height of 1.67 m). Next student is 6th, with height 1.68 m and weight **54 kg**.
(3 marks for correct answer, otherwise 1 mark for finding sample is every 4th student and 1 mark for saying it's the sixth student.)

(b) One way would be to number the list from 1 to 40 and select 20 numbers between 1 and 40 at random. E.g. random select on a calculator or draw numbers from a hat. The students with those numbers would then form the sample. ***(1 mark)***

(c) Adam's results should be the most reliable because he has used all the available data. ***(2 marks available — 1 mark each for correct name and correct reason.)***

(d) No, Adam's investigation is not a census. Although he has used all the data he has not used the whole population which would consist of all 16 year old girls in Wales. ***(1 mark for saying that the investigation is not a census and for stating the correct reason why.)***
Make sure you know the difference between a sample and a census. If you're not sure you do know, check out pages 8 and 9.

Page 25 (Warm-Up Questions)

1) The more pages a book has, the longer it will be out for when borrowed *(or equivalent)*.
2) The survey is restricted to people who have email, so may be biased.
3) It is a leading question, prompting an answer of "No".
4) Use a pilot study to test the questionnaire on a small group of people first. Any problems can be ironed out before asking the whole sample.
5) a) Open
   b) Closed
6) An opinion scale *(it would allow people to express the strength of their feelings)*.
7) Some of the men interviewed might want to impress Vicky by saying they preferred blondes, or feel under pressure to say they preferred blondes.
8) 1-5 *(a larger scale gives you more precise results)*.

Page 27 (Exam Questions)

4 (a) One of:
Hayley's employees may not be honest about whether they had done the exercise.
It would be difficult for the employees to judge their own performance.
(1 mark)

(b) Hayley could conduct an experiment to compare a week with exercise to a week without exercise. For the first week, she could supervise half an hour of exercise before work and then monitor her employees' performance throughout the day. For the second week, she would monitor performance in the same way.
(2 marks available for a sensible explanation.)

5 (a) One of:
It's a leading question, prompting an answer of 'yes'.
It doesn't allow for no preference.
(1 mark)

(b) E.g.

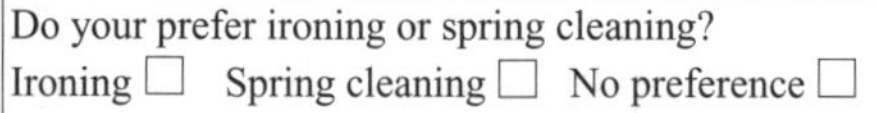

(2 marks available —1 mark for changing the question, and 1 mark for suitable response boxes.)

6 (a) She could ask each interviewee to throw the dice and answer 'No' if their number is even, but answer truthfully if their number is odd.
(2 marks available — 1 mark for using two groups of 3 numbers and 1 mark for saying that one group would lead to a definite 'No'.)

(b) 40 ÷ 2 = 20 — Of the 40 people asked, roughly 20 would have been forced to say 'No'.
32 – 20 = 12 — the other 12 would have answered honestly.
12 × 2 = **24** — With 12 out of 20 saying 'No' you would expect 24 out of 40 to say 'No'.

(3 marks for the correct answer, otherwise 1 mark for getting to '20' and 1 mark for getting to '12'.)
This question is a quite tricky — go back to page 23 if you're having a 'mare. If you're actually having nightmares, stop eating cheese at bedtime.

Page 34 (Warm-Up Questions)

1) Independent variable
2) The explanatory variable is the speed of the car.
   The response variable is the distance the car takes to stop.
3) Temperature should be plotted on the y-axis *(it's the response variable)*.
4) A control group is a group that's as similar to the experimental group as possible, but the members don't take part in the experiment. Any changes in the experimental group are compared to the control group to determine what effect the experiment has had.
5) Before-and-after experiment

6) Fresh air. *(It may be that simply being outside in the fresh air increases appetite. As the people jogging are both outside and exercising, it is difficult to know which is having the greater effect.)*

7) Any 10 numbers in the range 000-999.

Page 35 (Exam Questions)

2 (a) Take the 1st (or 2nd or 3rd) digit of each number, ignoring the digits 0, 6, 7, 8 and 9.
(2 marks for correct answer, otherwise 1 mark for not stating all the omissions.)
There are lots of different ways of generating a sample from a random number table. You'd get the marks for any correct method.

(b) Using the first digit of each number gives **3, 4, 5, 3, 1, 1, 2, 2, 1**.
Using the second digit of each number gives **5, 4, 2, 3, 2, 4, 1, 4, 2**.
Using the third digit of each number gives **1, 5, 1, 4, 3, 2, 2, 3, 2**.
(1 mark for the correct list of numbers for the method given in (a).)

3 (a) Experimental group ***(1 mark)***

(b) Control group ***(1 mark)***

(c) Placebo ***(1 mark)***

(d) He should make sure the groups' lifestyles are as similar as possible. They should eat similar food and do the same amount of exercise.
(1 mark for any answer expressing the need to keep the variables the same.)

(e) He will measure both groups' cholesterol levels again. A significant reduction in cholesterol for those in group A compared to those in group B, will be evidence that his pill works.
(2 marks available — 1 mark for each of the above points or similar.)

Page 44 (Warm-Up Questions)

1)

Lessons enjoyed	0	1	2	3	4	5	6
Tally	|	|	||	|||	||		|
Frequency	1	1	2	3	2	0	1

2)

Goals scored	0 - 1	2 - 3	4 - 5	6 - 7
Tally	~~||||~~	~~||||~~ ||	~~||||~~	|||
Frequency	5	7	5	3

3) The total number of football matches.

Page 45 (Exam Questions)

2 (a) The question states that she walked for 58 days.
The other groups total 1 + 17 + 22 + 15 = 55 days.
58 – 55 = 3, so ***x* = 3** ***(2 marks for the correct answer, otherwise 1 mark for getting to '55 days'.)***

(b) 1 + 17 + 22 = **40** ***(1 mark)***

(c)

Miles, m	$5 < m \leq 15$	$15 < m \leq 25$	$25 < m \leq 35$
Frequency	18	37	3

(1 mark)

(d) One of:
- The first table is more detailed / shows more information about the distribution.
E.g. you couldn't calculate the answer to part (b) from the second table.
- The second table seems to suggest that she may have walked over 30 miles on some days, which she didn't.
(1 mark)

3 (a)

Helicopter Type	Year			
	85-89	90-94	95-99	00-06
A	80	70	90	90
B	160	150	160	130
C	200	260	300	300
D	70	110	120	150
E	80	50	40	60
F	90	70	70	80
All Helicopters	680	710	**780**	**810**

(1 mark)

(b) There is an increase in total flying hours between 1985 and 2006.
(1 mark)

(c) The proportion for 00-06 is (150 000 ÷ 810 000) × 100 = 18.5%.
So the proportion of hours flown by Type D helicopters is much greater for the years 00-06 than for the years 85-89. ***(2 marks available — 1 mark for '18.5%' and 1 mark for the comparison.)***

Page 49 (Warm-Up Questions)

1) 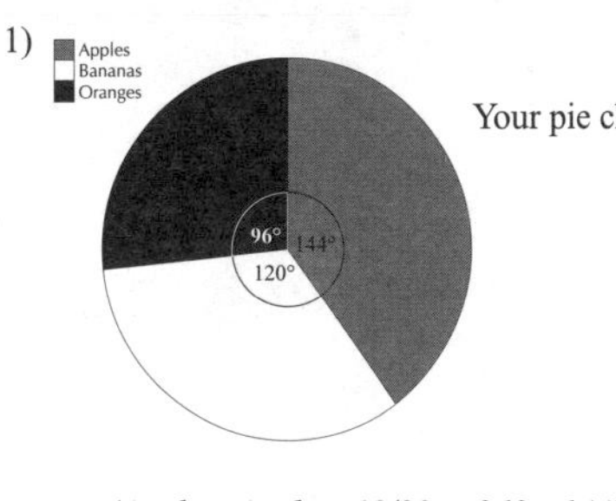

Your pie chart should have a radius of 3 cm

*(Angles: Apples: 12/30 × 360 =144°
Bananas: 10/30 × 360 = 120°
Oranges: 8/30 × 360 = 96°)*

2) a) 3

b) 14 *(sum of the frequencies = 4 + 6 + 3 + 1).*

3) a)

Goals Scored	≤ 0	≤ 1	≤ 2	≤ 3	≤ 4
Cumulative Frequency	1	4	9	11	12

b) 12 *(it's the total of the frequencies — i.e. the last cumulative frequency).*

Page 50 (Exam Questions)

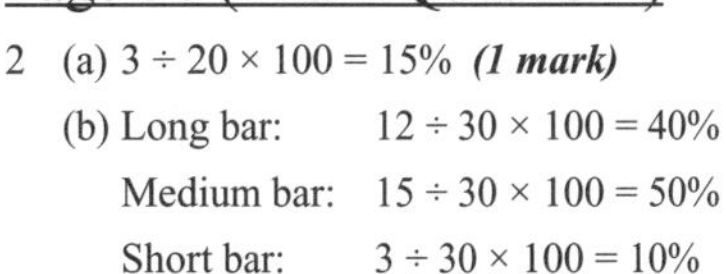

2 (a) 3 ÷ 20 × 100 = 15% ***(1 mark)***

(b) Long bar: 12 ÷ 30 × 100 = 40%
Medium bar: 15 ÷ 30 × 100 = 50%
Short bar: 3 ÷ 30 × 100 = 10%

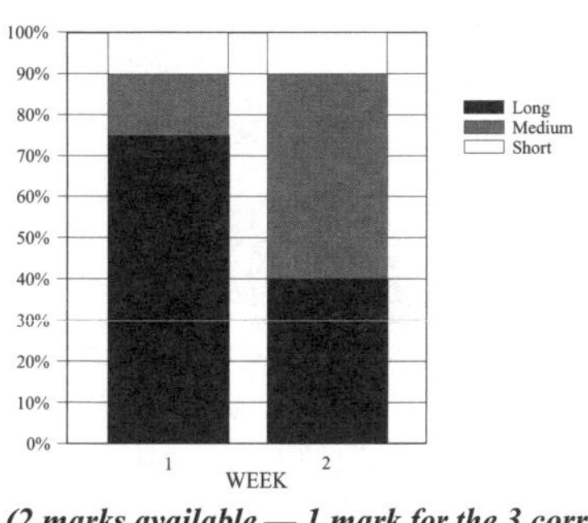

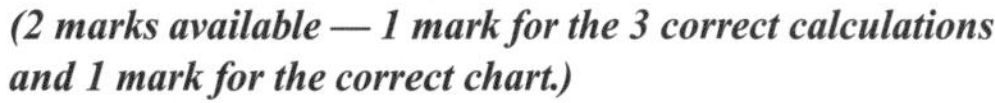

(2 marks available — 1 mark for the 3 correct calculations and 1 mark for the correct chart.)

(c) The same proportion (10%) chose the Short Route in both weeks **or** fewest people chose the Short Route each week.
(1 mark)

(d) (i)

Long rides per month	≤ 1	≤ 2	≤ 3	≤ 4	≤ 5
Cumulative Frequency	**0**	**3**	**5**	**10**	**12**

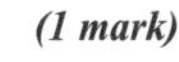

(1 mark)

(ii) 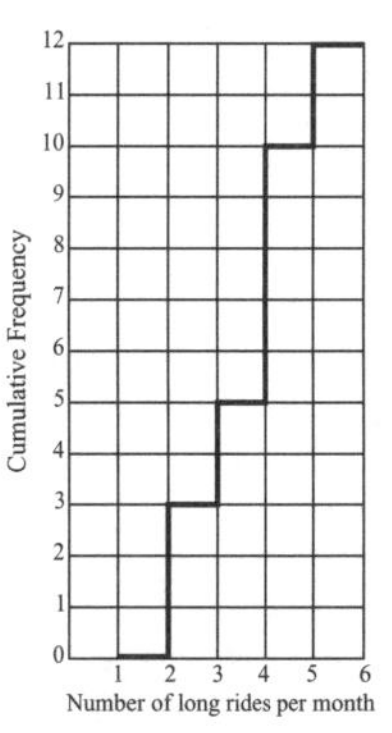

(2 marks available — 1 mark for numbering the axes sensibly and 1 mark for the correct graph.)
In the real exam you'll get much more space to draw diagrams. We're just trying to cram in as many questions as we can for you to have a go at.

Page 56 (Warm-Up Questions)

1)

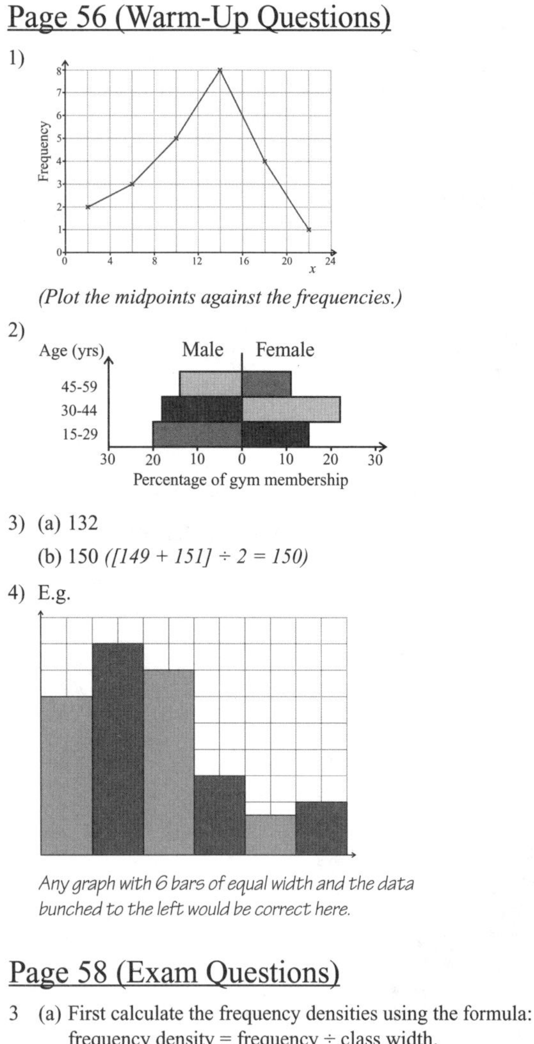

(Plot the midpoints against the frequencies.)

2)

3) (a) 132

(b) 150 *([149 + 151] ÷ 2 = 150)*

4) E.g.

Any graph with 6 bars of equal width and the data bunched to the left would be correct here.

Page 58 (Exam Questions)

3 (a) First calculate the frequency densities using the formula:
frequency density = frequency ÷ class width.
$4 \div 5 = 0.8$
$10 \div 5 = 2.0$
$18 \div 10 = 1.8$
$15 \div 30 = 0.5$

(5 marks available — 2 marks for calculating all 4 frequency densities correctly, or 1 mark for calculating 3 correctly, 1 mark for correctly numbered vertical axis with sensible scale, 1 mark for correct bar heights and 1 mark for correct bar widths.)

Remember — with histograms, it's not frequency but frequency density that goes on the vertical axis. If you put frequency up there instead, you're just waving goodbye to loads of marks in the exam. And that would be pretty silly.

(b) $10 < x \leq 20$ ***(1 mark)***

(c) The claim is false. The normal distribution is symmetrical with median = mean, but for this data, the median < mean, which gives a positive skew, not a symmetrical distribution.
(1 mark for saying the claim is false and giving a correct reason why.)

Page 67 (Warm-Up Questions)

1) Seasonal with random fluctuations.
2) Chart 3 is likely to be misleading because it is shown in 3-D. Section A dominates the visible part of the solid and appears to represent a higher proportion of the chart than it actually does.
3) No correlation *(the points are randomly scattered — there's no pattern).*
"No correlation" can also be called "zero correlation".

Page 69 (Exam Questions)

3 (a)

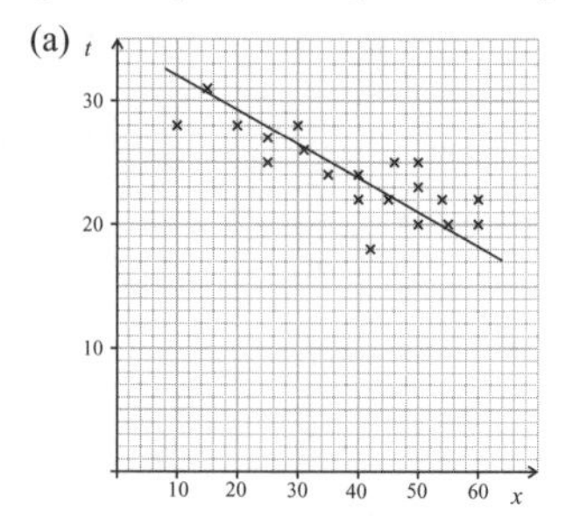

(2 marks for all 20 points plotted correctly, otherwise 1 mark for at least 15 points plotted correctly.)

(b) See graph above. Any suitable line of best fit similar to the one drawn. ***(1 mark)***

(c) Negative correlation **or** as age increases the number of teeth with no fillings decreases. ***(1 mark)***

(d) The line of best fits indicates that for $0 < x < 10$ you can expect $t > 32$, but the maximum number of teeth is 32. ***(1 mark)***
Hint: In the exam, always read the whole of the question and read it properly. If you didn't, you might miss important information — like the fact that humans usually have no more than 32 teeth. And then you'd be in a right old pickle.

Page 75 (Warm-Up Questions)

1) 5.5 *([10 + 1] ÷ 2 = 5.5 — the 5.5th value is 5.5 itself).*
2) 1 *(there is a total of two 1's in the numbers 1-10).*
3) 986 *(take 980 from all the numbers first, then find the average of 1, 5, 6 and 12 which is 6 and add it back on to 980).*
4) Mode
5) The mean can be distorted by outliers but the median remains unaffected.
6) 4 $\left(\sqrt[3]{(1 \times 4 \times 16)} = 4\right)$

Page 76 (Exam Questions)

3 (a) $[(22 \times 5) + (32 \times 15) + (45 \times 25) + (18 \times 35) + (3 \times 45)] \div 120$
= **20.67 minutes**
(3 marks for correct answer, otherwise 1 mark for attempting to find midpoints of the groups and 1 mark for 120.)

(b) Because grouped data is being used, not the times for individual employees. ***(1 mark)***
Remember — as soon as data is grouped, it's impossible to calculate the exact mean, you can only estimate it.

(c) $20 \leq t < 30$ minutes — it has the highest frequency. ***(1 mark)***

(d) There are 120 employees, so the median time is in position (120 + 1) ÷ 2 = 60.5. 60.5th time is in group **$20 \leq t < 30$ minutes**. ***(1 mark)***

(e) It would increase because the values removed are less than the mean time. ***(1 mark for saying the mean would increase and a valid reason why.)***

4 For the first building society — geometric mean = $\sqrt{(1.04 \times 1.09)} = 1.0647$ which gives an overall rate of 6.47%. The second building society at 6.6% fixed is better.
(3 marks for the correct answer with working, otherwise 1 mark for trying to find the geometric mean for the first building society and 1 mark for 1.06...)
If you can't get your head round this, go back to page 74 and learn the stuff about the geometric mean. You need to learn that formula — it won't be on the formula sheet.

5 (a) Total sum of numbers = 12 × 5 = 60. Sum of ten numbers is 50, so sum of missing numbers = 60 – 50 = 10. For mode to be 7, one missing number is **7** so the other must be **3**.
(2 marks available — 1 for each missing number.)

(b) Put the numbers in order: 1, 2, 2, 3, 3, 5, 6, 7, 7, 7, 8, 9.
The median is the 6.5th value, which is between 5 and 6, so median is **5.5**.
(2 marks for correct answer, otherwise 1 mark for ordering the numbers.)

Page 86 (Warm-Up Questions)

1) 99 *(100 – 1)*
2) 6 *(position no. = [3(7 + 1) ÷ 4] = 6)*
3) 3.39 to 2d.p. *(√11.5)*
4) 40 $\left(\sum(x-\bar{x})^2 \div 7 = \left[1^2+9^2+(-12)^2+2^2+(-5)^2+5^2+0^2\right] \div 7\right)$
5)

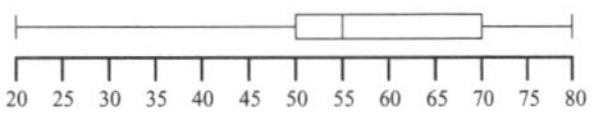

6) 5 *([80 – 58] ÷ 4.4)*

Page 88-89 (Exam Questions)

4 (a)

Number of tins (n)	$0 \le n < 5$	$5 \le n < 10$	$10 \le n < 15$	$15 \le n < 20$	$20 \le n < 25$	$25 \le n < 30$
Frequency	5	24	38	19	12	2
Cumulative Frequency	**5**	**29**	**67**	**86**	**98**	**100**

(1 mark)

(b)

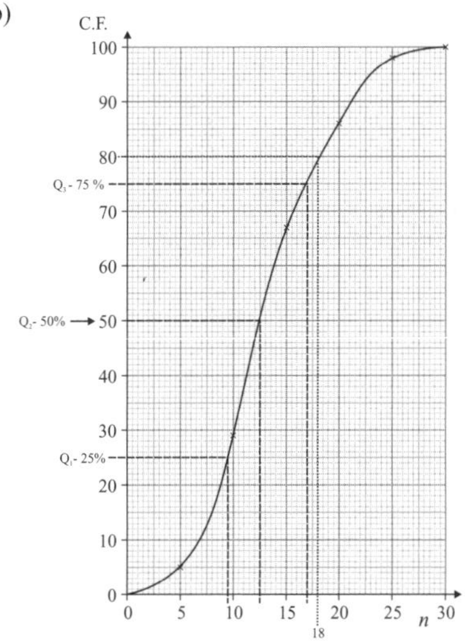

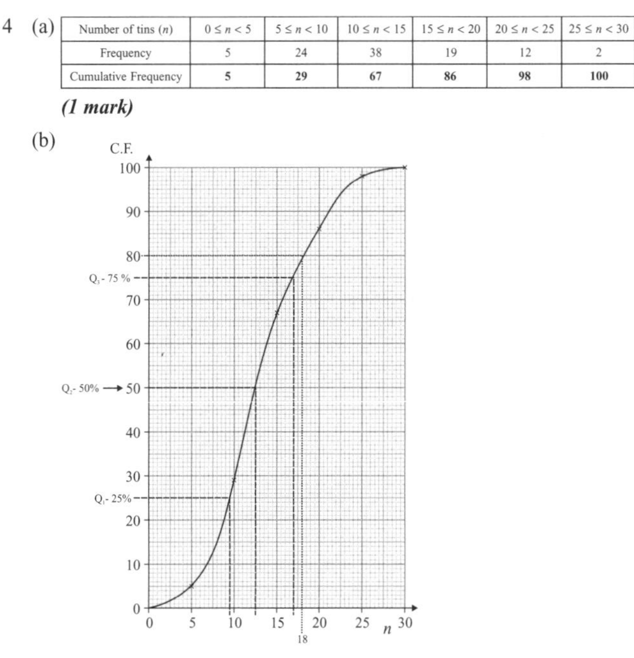

(4 marks available — 3 marks for all points correctly plotted (± 1 mm), or 2 marks if 4 or 5 points are correct, or 1 mark if all points are at the correct heights but at the wrong x-values. Plus 1 mark for a smooth curve.)

(c) (i) See graph above. Interquartile range = $Q_3 - Q_1$ = 17 – 9.5 = **7.5**
(2 marks for correct answer ± 2, otherwise 1 mark for correct method.)

(ii) See graph above. Median = Q_2 = **12.5** ***(1 mark for 12.5 ± 1)***

(d) See graph above. **80%** ***(1 mark for 80 ± 1)***

5 (a) $\sum fx^2 = 1568 + 5445 + 11\ 552 + 7396 + 2304 = 28\ 265$

$\bar{x} = 37.25$ and $\sum f = 20$

So, Variance $= \dfrac{\sum fx^2}{\sum f} - \bar{x}^2 = \dfrac{28\ 265}{20} - 37.25^2 = \mathbf{25.6875}$

Standard deviation $= \sqrt{\text{Variance}} = \mathbf{5.07}$ (3 s.f.)
(3 marks for both correct answers, otherwise 1 mark for 28 265 and 1 mark for the correct variance.)
Examiners often ask you to just find the standard deviation of some data. Remember that this is just the square root of the variance — you always have to find the variance first.

(b) (i) Standardised score for compulsory = (40 – 37.25) ÷ 5.07 = 0.54
Standardised score for freestyle = (44 – 41.7) ÷ 3.2 = 0.72
Total standardised score = 0.54 + 0.72 = **1.26**
(3 marks for correct answer, otherwise 1 mark for correct method and 1 mark for finding at least one of the standardised scores.)

(ii) Standardised score for Nathan =
[(43 – 37.25) ÷ 5.07] + [(41 – 41.7) ÷ 3.2] = 0.92
1.26 > 0.92, so Zac gave the best overall performance.
(3 marks for correct answer with working, otherwise 1 mark for correct method and 1 mark for finding at least one of Nathan's standardised scores correctly.)
Dead easy this one — when you've found the total standardised score for each guy, just compare them and find the biggest one. That's the best performer. I could've been a dancer you know — gave it all up to make the best revision guides money can buy.

6 (a) Both schools have a range of marks of 100%. Both schools have an upper quartile of 80% — i.e. 25% of the candidates in both schools scored 80% or more.
(2 marks available — 1 mark for each similarity.)

(b) Blakeney had the better results. The interquartile range is much smaller for Blakeney, showing that the marks were more consistent. The median score for Blakeney is also higher.
(1 mark for Blakeney with a valid reason why.)

Page 93 (Warm-Up Questions)

1) 164.7 *([1.12 ÷ 0.68] × 100)*
2) 7.69 *([400 ÷ 52 000] × 1000)*
3) 73.33 *([11 000 ÷ 15 000] × 100)*
4) Because birth rate is based on total population, and there's no information on the population of each town.
5) Retail Price Index

Page 94 (Exam Questions)

3 (a) Standard population column should total 100%, so 100 – 42 – 24 = **34%**
(1 mark)

(b) Population of Mudgrave = 57 000 + 30 000 + 44 000 = 131 000
Total number of deaths in Mudgrave = 120 + 320 + 5260 = 5700
Crude death rate = (5700 ÷ 131 000) × 1000 = **43.5**
(2 marks for correct answer, otherwise 1 mark for correct method.)

(c) Mudgrave:

$$\frac{\left(\dfrac{120\times1000}{57000}\times42\right)+\left(\dfrac{320\times1000}{30000}\times34\right)+\left(\dfrac{5260\times1000}{44000}\times24\right)}{42+34+24}$$

$$=\frac{88.421+362.667+2869.091}{100}=33.2$$

Ollington:

$$\frac{\left(\dfrac{100\times1000}{80000}\times42\right)+\left(\dfrac{500\times1000}{49000}\times34\right)+\left(\dfrac{8050\times1000}{86000}\times24\right)}{42+34+24}$$

$$=\frac{52.500+346.939+2246.512}{100}=26.5$$

The standardised death rate in Ollington is lower than that in Mudgrave, so it is likely that the population of Ollington is healthier.
(6 marks available — 1 mark for attempting to find crude death rates, 1 mark for attempting to multiply by standard population, 1 mark for attempting to divide by sum of standard populations, 1 mark for each correct standardised death rate and 1 mark for identifying Ollington as likely to have a healthier population, with explanation.)
In this case both the crude and standardised death rates are lower for Ollington, but it might not be like this in other questions. Examiners like examples where the crude rate is higher for one place, but the standardised rate is lower.

4 (a)

Year	2007	2008	Weight
Length of steel	275.00	350.00	**2**
10 rivets	12.00	15.00	**6**

(1 mark)

(b) Index number for steel = (350 ÷ 275) × 100 = 127.27...
127.27... × 2 = 254.54...
Index number for rivets = (15 ÷ 12) × 100 = 125
125 × 6 = 750
Weighted index number = (254.54... + 750) ÷ 8 = **125.6**
(4 marks for correct answer, otherwise 1 mark for correct method and 1 mark each for finding the two index numbers.)

Page 103 (Warm-Up Questions)

1) 6.5 *([4 + 6 + 9 + 7] ÷ 4)*
   6.75 *([6 + 9 + 7 + 5] ÷ 4)*
   7 *([9 + 7 + 5 + 7] ÷ 4)*
   7.75 *([7 + 5 + 7 + 12] ÷ 4)*
2) (a) Positive Correlation
   (b) No Correlation
   (c) Negative Correlation
3) 0.6

Competitor	a	b	c	d	e
Judge A Rank	5	3	1	4	2
Judge B Rank	4	1	2	5	3
d	1	2	1	1	1
d^2	1	4	1	1	1

($\sum d^2 = 8$, so $r_s = 1 - [6(8) \div 5(24)] = 0.6$)

4) $y = 2/3x + 74$ *(gradient: (78 – 74) ÷ (6 – 0) = 2/3, y-intercept is 74)*
   80 badgers *((2/3 × 9) + 74)*
5) 600 *((20 ÷ 50) × 100 = 40%, 40% of 1500 = 0.4 × 1500 = 600)*

Page 105-106 (Exam Questions)

4 (a)

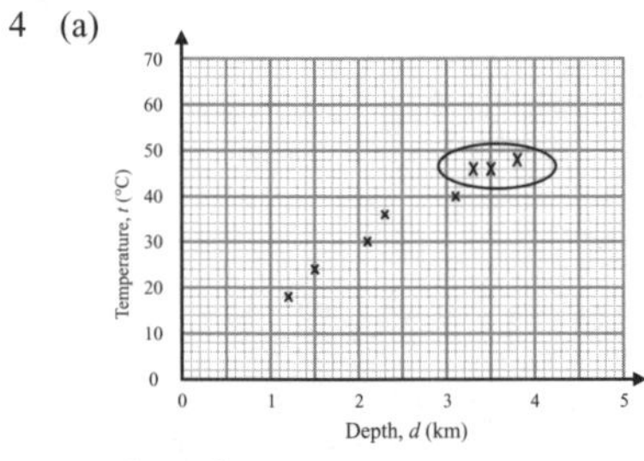

(1 mark)

(b) Positive correlation / The deeper the ship drills the higher the temperature. ***(1 mark)***

(c) Mean t = (18 + 24 + 30 + 36 + 40 + 46 + 46 + 48) ÷ 8 = **36 °C** ***(1 mark)***

(d)

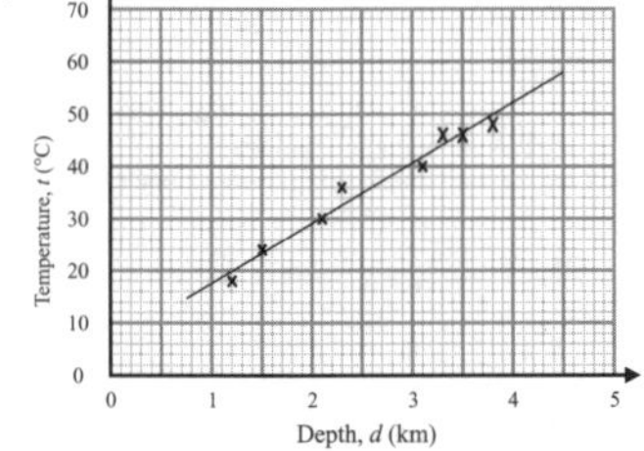

(2 marks available for a suitable line of best fit — 1 mark for a line through the mean point (2.6, 36), and 1 mark for reasonable gradient of line, i.e. passes on or between the first two points in the table.)

(e) (i) Reading up from 1.9 on the x-axis to the line of best fit, then across to the y-axis gives a temperature of **28°C**.
(1 mark, allowing ± 1 square from your line of best fit.)

(ii) Extending the line of best fit so it crosses the x-axis gives **6°C**. Extrapolation of best fit lines is not a reliable method because you can't assume the trend will continue.
Another valid answer for the second mark is that the seabed is where water starts and so is unlikely to relate to the rest of the data in the same way.
(2 marks available — 1 mark for temperature (allowing ± 1 square from line of best fit) and 1 mark for a valid explanation.)

5 (a)

Dancer	A	B	C	D	E	F	G	H
Judge 1	8	6	10	9	5	7	4	8
Judge 2	6	7	9	10	5	6	4	8
Rank 1	3.5	6	1	2	7	5	8	3.5
Rank 2	5.5	4	2	1	7	5.5	8	3
d	2	2	1	1	0	0.5	0	0.5
d^2	4	4	1	1	0	0.25	0	0.25

When scores are equal for two dancers the ranks are divided equally.
For Judge 1 dancers A and H both scored 8.
This is the 3rd highest score but with two dancers getting it you'll use the two rank positions 3 and 4. (3 + 4) ÷ 2 = 3.5.

$\sum d^2 = 4 + 4 + 1 + 1 + 0 + 0.25 + 0 + 0.25 = 10.5$
$r_s = 1 - [6(10.5) \div 8(64 - 1)] =$ **0.875**
(4 marks for correct answer, otherwise 1 mark for correct ranking of both judges' scores, 1 mark for 10.5 and 1 mark for correctly substituting in Spearman's rank formula.)

(b) Strong positive correlation ***(1 mark)***

(c) With a correlation of 1.0 Judge 2 and Judge 3 must have ranked the dancers in the same order.
So, **Judge 3 must have had Dancer F tied for 5th place.**
(1 mark)

6 (a) (690 + 770 + 820 + 860) ÷ 4 = 3140 ÷ 4 = **785**
(770 + 820 + 860 + 680) ÷ 4 = 3130 ÷ 4 = **782.5**
(2 marks for both correct answers, otherwise 1 mark for correct method used twice or for one correct answer only.)

(b)

Number of Guests
Quarter and Year

(3 marks available — 1 mark for plotting points correctly on x-axis [i.e. at midpoints of intervals], 1 mark for correct vertical plotting and 1 mark for trend line.)

(c) The trend line at 2009 2nd quarter should be in the interval 760-790.
760 + 30 = 790 and 790 + 30 = 820. So number of guests is **790-820**.
(3 marks for an answer between 790 and 820, otherwise 1 mark for trend line value between 760 and 790 and 1 mark for adding average seasonal effect.)

7 (a) The line of best fit passes through the points (30, 1100) and (100, 1800)
Using these points the gradient of the line is:
(1800 – 1100) ÷ (100 – 30) = 10.
Extending the line of best fit so that it intercepts the y-axis will give a value of b = 800.
So the equation of the line is **$y = 10x + 800$.**
(3 marks for correct answer, otherwise 1 mark for the correct gradient and 1 mark for the correct intercept.)

(b) The gradient, 'a', is the number of extra pairs of boots sold in a month for each extra 1 mm of rainfall. ***(1 mark)***

Page 115 (Warm-Up Questions)

1) 8 *(2 × 2 × 2 = 8 — HHH, HHT, HTH, HTT, THH, THT, TTH, TTT)*
2)

	2	4	7
7	9	11	14
8	10	12	15
9	11	13	16
10	12	14	17

P(odd) = 6/12 = 1/2 *(6 of the 12 outcomes are odd)*
P(square) = 2/12 = 1/6 *(only 9 and 16 are square)*

3) 7 *(P(5) = 1/6, 42 × 1/6 = 7)*

Page 116 (Exam Questions)

2 (a)

	Car	Moped	Foot	Total
Male	**15**	**6**	**4**	**25**
Female	**5**	**2**	**8**	15
Total	20	**8**	**12**	40

There are several ways to fill in the table. One is:

The male total is 40 – 15 = **25**

30% of all employees are on foot:

30% of 40 = 0.3 × 40 = **12**

Therefore, total on moped = 40 – 20 – 12 = **8**

$\frac{1}{3}$ of total females use a car: $\frac{1}{3}$ of 15 = **5**

So, male car users = 20 – 5 = **15**

$\frac{1}{3}$ of those on foot are male: $\frac{1}{3}$ of 12 = **4**

So, male moped = 25 – 4 – 15 = **6**

So, female moped = 8 – 6 = **2**

So, female on foot = 15 – 5 – 2 = **8**

(3 marks for all entries correct, 1 mark lost for each error or empty cell.)

(b) (i) $\frac{8}{40} = \mathbf{\frac{1}{5}}$ ***(1 mark)***

(ii) $\frac{(6+4)}{25} = \frac{10}{25} = \mathbf{\frac{2}{5}}$

(2 marks for the correct answer, otherwise 1 mark for "10".)

(iii) $\frac{(15+6+4+2)}{40} = \mathbf{\frac{27}{40}}$

(2 marks for the correct answer, otherwise 1 mark for the correct method, i.e. male moped "6" not counted twice.)

3 (a) The frequency for a score of "1" is higher than the others. ***(1 mark)***

(b) The frequencies for all the scores are quite similar. Although "1" has the highest frequency, it's only slightly higher than the others.

There were only 50 spins in the experiment, so it's difficult to know how accurate the results are. A greater number of spins would give more reliable results.

(2 marks available — 1 mark for each reason.)

Page 123 (Warm-Up Questions)

1) 3/8 *(P(Flying Saucer) + P(Liquorice) = 1/8 + 1/4)*

2) 6/35 *(P(1st Cube) × P (2nd Cube) = (2/5) × (3/7))*

3)

3/5 R — 3/5 R, 2/5 Y

2/5 Y — 3/5 R, 2/5 Y

13/25 *(P(RR or YY) = P(RR) + P(YY) = (3/5×3/5) + (2/5×2/5) = 9/25 + 4/25)*

4) 25/204

(P(Diamond) × P(Red given that the first card was a Diamond) = 1/4 × 25/51 = 25/204)

The second fraction is over 51 as a card's already been taken from the pack.

5) 9/64 or 0.14 (2 d.p.)

(For binomial method: p = 1/4, q = 3/4, n = 3

The expansion of $(p + q)^3$ you need will be the one with p^2 in it.

$3p^2q = 3(1/4)^2(3/4) = 3 \times (1/16) \times (3/4) = 9/64$)

You could list all the possibilities instead — but this method is far quicker.

Page 124 (Exam Questions)

2 (a) The first card was a vowel, leaving 7 cards of which 3 are consonants.

P(C given V) = $\mathbf{\frac{3}{7}}$ ***(1 mark)***

(b)

$\frac{5}{8}$ V — $\frac{4}{7}$ V, $\frac{3}{7}$ C

$\frac{3}{8}$ C — $\frac{5}{7}$ V, $\frac{2}{7}$ C

(3 marks for all correct, lose 1 mark for each error or omission.)

(c) P(2nd Card Vowel) = P(V, V) or P(C, V)

$$= \left(\frac{5}{8}\times\frac{4}{7}\right)+\left(\frac{3}{8}\times\frac{5}{7}\right)$$

$$= \frac{20}{56}+\frac{15}{56}$$

$$= \frac{35}{56} = \frac{5}{8}$$

(2 marks for the correct answer with working, otherwise 1 mark for the first line of fractions above.)

(d) P(VVVC) = $\frac{5}{8}\times\frac{4}{7}\times\frac{3}{6}\times\frac{3}{5} = \mathbf{\frac{3}{28}}$

(2 marks for the correct answer, otherwise 1 mark for the correct method.)

3 (a) Method 1: Binomial

$n = 5, p = \frac{1}{3}, q = \frac{2}{3}$

Using $(p + q)^5 = p^5 + 5p^4q + 10p^3q^2 + 10p^2q^3 + 5pq^4 + q^5$, the term needed for 1 head is where the power of $p = 1$, i.e. $5pq^4$

$$5pq^4 = 5\left(\frac{1}{3}\right)\left(\frac{2}{3}\right)^4 = \mathbf{\frac{80}{243}}$$

(2 marks for the correct answer, otherwise 1 mark for correct substitution.)

Method 2: Listing

P(H) = $\frac{1}{3}$, P(T) = $\frac{2}{3}$

P(1 Head)

= P(HTTTT) + P(THTTT) + P(TTHTT) + P(TTTHT) + P(TTTTH)

$$= P\left(\frac{1}{3}\times\frac{2}{3}\times\frac{2}{3}\times\frac{2}{3}\times\frac{2}{3}\right)+P\left(\frac{2}{3}\times\frac{1}{3}\times\frac{2}{3}\times\frac{2}{3}\times\frac{2}{3}\right)+P\left(\frac{2}{3}\times\frac{2}{3}\times\frac{1}{3}\times\frac{2}{3}\times\frac{2}{3}\right)$$

$$+P\left(\frac{2}{3}\times\frac{2}{3}\times\frac{2}{3}\times\frac{1}{3}\times\frac{2}{3}\right)+P\left(\frac{2}{3}\times\frac{2}{3}\times\frac{2}{3}\times\frac{2}{3}\times\frac{1}{3}\right)$$

$$= \frac{16}{243}+\frac{16}{243}+\frac{16}{243}+\frac{16}{243}+\frac{16}{243}$$

$$= \mathbf{\frac{80}{243}}$$

(2 marks for the correct answer, otherwise 1 mark for the correct method.)

(b) P(3 or More) = P(5) + P(4) + P(3)

Using Binomial method:

$$p^5 + 5p^4q + 10p^3q^2 = \left(\frac{1}{3}\right)^5 + 5\left(\frac{1}{3}\right)^4\left(\frac{2}{3}\right) + 10\left(\frac{1}{3}\right)^3\left(\frac{2}{3}\right)^2$$

$$= \frac{1}{243}+\frac{10}{243}+\frac{40}{243}$$

$$= \mathbf{\frac{51}{243}} = \mathbf{\frac{17}{81}}$$

(3 marks for correct answer, otherwise 1 mark for use of the correct binomial terms and 1 mark for $\frac{1}{243}+\frac{10}{243}+\frac{40}{243}$.)

Don't be tempted to simplify fractions between these last two lines of working. They're easier to add up with the same denominators.

(c)

Number of Heads	0	1	2	3	4	5
Working	$(2/3)^5$	$5(1/3)(2/3)^4$	$10(1/3)^2(2/3)^3$	$10(1/3)^3(2/3)^2$	$5(1/3)^4(2/3)$	$(1/3)^5$
Probability	32/243	80/243	80/243	40/243	10/243	1/243

The most likely number of heads is **1 or 2**.

(3 marks for the correct answer, otherwise 1 mark for the correct method for 2 or 0 heads, and 1 mark for the correct probability for 2 or 0 heads.)

This question isn't too bad once you've noticed that you've already worked out the probabilities for 1, 3, 4, and 5 heads earlier in the question.

PRACTICE EXAM PAPER ANSWERS

Please note: The answers to the following exam questions have not been provided or approved by the examining bodies (AQA and Edexcel). As such AQA and Edexcel Ltd do not accept any responsibility for the accuracy and method of the working in the answers given. CGP has provided suggested solutions — other possible solutions may be equally correct.

1 (a) (i) One to which a limited number of answers are possible. ***(1 mark)***

(ii) It is possible to give groups as choices, so people are not asked to give their actual age (which they might be embarrassed about). This means they are more likely to respond. ***(1 mark)***

(b) 1 mark for a sensible suggestion, e.g:
He could have collected them himself / offered rewards for completed questionnaires / included a prepaid envelope etc. ***(1 mark)***

(c) He should have tested the questionnaire on a small group of people first / he should have done a pilot study. ***(1 mark)***

(d) E.g. two of the following criticisms:
There is no idea of what he means by 'often'.
There are two different options — pub and restaurant, which might need different responses.
There are no response boxes.
He is asking about pubs when he is thinking of opening a restaurant.
(2 marks available — 1 mark for each of two criticisms.)

2 (a) (i) Each pair of branches should have 0.75 on the 'upper' branch and 0.25 on the 'lower' branch.
(3 marks for all branches correct, otherwise deduct one mark for each incorrect branch to a minimum of zero.)

(ii) Which phone the second call goes to is not affected by which phone the first call went to. ***(1 mark)***

(b) P(first call on mobile) = 0.75, P(second call on mobile) = 0.75
So, P(next two calls on mobile) = 0.75 × 0.75 = **0.5625** or **0.56**
(2 marks for the correct answer, otherwise 1 mark for some correct working. Allow marks if wrong answer from (a)(i) carried forward.)

3 (a) (i)

15	01	20	16	22	30	19	08
M	M	M	M	M	M	M	M
4	4	4	3	3	2	2	2

(3 marks for all 8 columns correct, otherwise 2 marks for 6 or 7 correct or 1 mark for 5 correct.)

(ii) Mean = total number of passes ÷ number of students = 24 ÷ 8 = **3**
(1 mark. Allow mark if wrong answers from (a)(i) carried forward.)

(b) (i) 20 out of the 30 students are male — the proportion of males is $^{20}/_{30} = ^{2}/_{3}$. So you want $^{2}/_{3}$ of the sample of 6 to be male and $^{1}/_{3}$ to be female — that's 4 males and 2 females.

04	29	13	14	23	24
M	M	F	M	F	M
8	6	5	5	7	2

(4 marks available — 1 mark for correct number of males, 1 mark for correct number of females, 1 mark for 5 correct columns and 1 mark for the 6th column correct.)

(ii) Mean = total number of passes ÷ number of students = 33 ÷ 6 = **5.5**
(1 mark. Allow mark if wrong answers from (b)(i) carried forward.)

(c) Because it has the correct proportion of males to females. ***(1 mark)***

(d) Strongly agree, Agree, Don't know, Disagree, Strongly disagree (or equivalent) ***(2 marks for a correct answer, otherwise 1 mark if numbers are used but not defined.)***

4 (a) Q3 ***(1 mark)***

(b) Any one from: holiday season, main school holiday, higher prices, better weather, more tourists, summer. ***(1 mark)***

(c) $\frac{2815+3819+2265+1901}{4}$ = 2700 = **£2700 million**

$\frac{3819+2265+1901+2815}{4}$ = 2700 = **£2700 million**

(2 marks for both answers correct, otherwise 1 mark for at least one attempt to add and divide.)

(d) First point plotted halfway between 2001 Q3 and Q4 on the x-axis and at 2700 on the y-axis. Second point plotted halfway between 2001 Q4 and 2002 Q1 on the x-axis and at 2700 on the y-axis. ***(1 mark. Allow mark if wrong answers from (c) carried forward.)***

(e) The earnings remained fairly level (or rose slightly) until the end of 2000. From the beginning of 2001 they started to decrease.
(2 marks available — 1 mark for each of the above observations.)

5 (a) There are 10 data values, so the median is the (10 + 1)/2th value — i.e. the 5.5th value. (96 + 97) ÷ 2 = **96.5**. ***(1 mark)***

(b) Lower quartile = value in position (10 + 1)/4 = 2.75th value.
Rounding this up to 3 gives a **lower quartile** of **93**.
Upper quartile = value in position 3(10 + 1)/4 = 8.25th value.
Rounding this up to 9 gives an **upper quartile** of **113**.
(2 marks available — 1 mark for each correct answer.)

(c) Interquartile range (IQR) = 113 – 93 = 20
1.5 × IQR = 30
Limit of outliers = 113 + 30 = 143
(3 marks available — 1 mark for finding IQR, 1 mark for calculating 1.5 × IQR and 1 mark for finding the limit of outliers.)

(d)

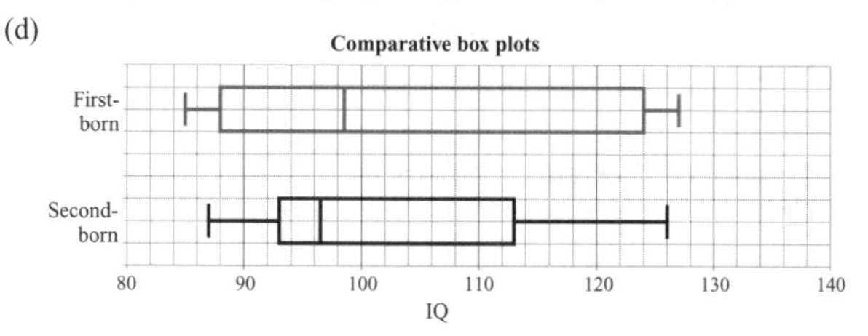

(3 marks available — 1 mark for drawing a box with correct whiskers, 1 mark for correctly placed median and 1 mark for correctly placed quartiles. Allow marks if wrong values from (a) and (b) carried forward.)

(e) Any two from:
Both data sets have positive skew.
The first-born twins have a higher median IQ.
The first-born twins' IQs have a greater (interquartile) range / are more variable.
(2 marks available — 1 mark for each statement.)

(f) By increasing the number of sets of twins tested. ***(1 mark)***

6 (a) $\sum fx = 450$ and $\sum f = 150$, so **Mean** = 450 ÷ 150 = **3**

$\sum f(x-\bar{x})^2 = 376$ **or** $\sum fx^2 = 1726$

Variance = 376 ÷ 150 = **2.507** **or** **Variance** = (1726 ÷ 150) – 3^2 = **2.507**

Standard deviation = $\sqrt{2.507} = \mathbf{1.58}$

(5 marks available — 1 mark each for: calculating sum of fx, finding the mean, calculating sum of squares of differences, finding the variance and calculating standard deviation. Allow mark for standard deviation if error is carried forward from earlier in the calculation.)

(b) (i) (21 – 16.5) ÷ 2.8 = **1.61**
(2 marks for correct answer, otherwise 1 mark for correct method.)

(ii) Call the unknown time x, so (x – 14) ÷ 4.5 = 2.4
Rearranging gives: x = (2.4 × 4.5) + 14 = **24.8 minutes**
(3 marks for the correct answer, otherwise 1 mark for correctly substituting numbers into formula and 1 mark for correctly rearranging formula.)

(iii) Approx. 99.9% of values lie within ± 3 standard deviations of the mean, i.e. 16.5 ± (3 × 2.8). So values in the range **8.1 – 24.9**.
(3 marks for correct answer, otherwise 1 mark for knowing that approx. 99.9% of values lie within ± 3 s.d. of the mean and 1 mark for correctly substituting numbers into the formula but incorrect final answer.)

7 (a) Table 1 has equal class widths and shows more detail about the distribution as it has more classes.
(2 marks available — 1 mark for each correct reason.)

(b) Table 1: $9 \le t < 12$ and $12 \le t < 15$
Table 2: $10 \le t < 11$
(2 marks for all three intervals correct, otherwise 1 mark for two correct.)

(c) Calculate the frequency densities using the formula:
frequency density = frequency ÷ class width.
So the frequency densities are **1**, **2**, **22**, **6** and **3**.

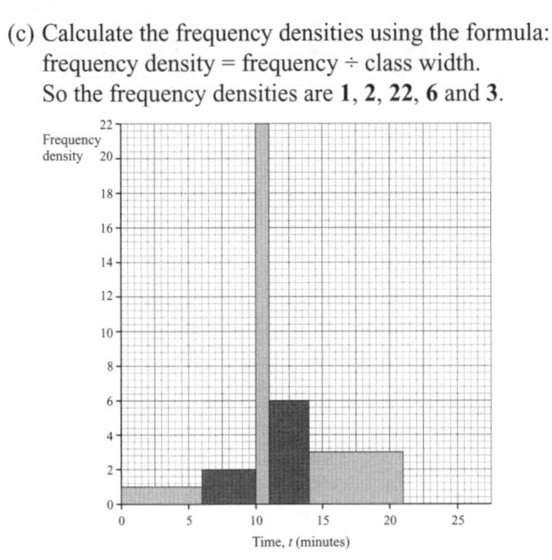

(5 marks available — 2 marks for calculating all five frequency densities correctly or 1 mark for calculating three or four correctly, 1 mark for correctly labelled vertical axis with sensible scale, 1 mark for correct bar heights and 1 mark for correct bar widths.)

(d) P(order has no missing items) = 1 – 0.1 = 0.9
$(0.9)^5$ = **0.59** (2 s.f.) ***(3 marks for correct answer, otherwise 2 marks for $(0.9)^5$ or 1 mark for 0.9.)***

8 (a)

Category \ Version	Hard back	Soft back	Totals
Fiction	124	1820	1944
Non Fiction	341	239	580
Classics	155	21	176
Totals	620	2080	2700

(4 marks for all entries correct, otherwise deduct 1 mark for each incorrect or missing entry down to a minimum of zero marks.)

(b) (i) P(non fiction and soft back) = $\frac{\mathbf{239}}{\mathbf{2700}}$ = **0.0885**

(1 mark. Allow mark if incorrect numerator carried forward from table.)

(ii) P(non fiction or hard back)
= P(non fiction) + P(hard back) – P(non fiction and hard back)

$$= \frac{580}{2700} + \frac{620}{2700} - \frac{341}{2700} = \frac{\mathbf{859}}{\mathbf{2700}} = \mathbf{0.318}$$

(2 marks for correct answer, otherwise 1 mark for correct method. Allow marks if incorrect numerators carried forward from table.)

(iii) P(fiction, given that it is soft back)
= P(soft back and fiction) ÷ P(soft back)

$$= \frac{1820}{2700} \div \frac{2080}{2700} = \frac{1820}{2700} \times \frac{2700}{2080} = \frac{\mathbf{1820}}{\mathbf{2080}} = \frac{\mathbf{7}}{\mathbf{8}} = \mathbf{0.875}$$

(2 marks for correct answer, otherwise 1 mark for correct method. Allow marks if incorrect numerators carried forward from table.)

(c) P(hard back classic) = $\frac{155}{2700}$

So expected frequency = $\frac{155}{2700} \times 200 =$ **11**

(2 marks for correct answer, otherwise 1 mark for correct method or for 11.48 or 11.5. Allow mark if incorrect numerator carried forward from table.)

9 (a) Spearman's rank correlation coefficient = $1 - \frac{6\sum d^2}{n(n^2-1)}$

$\sum d^2 = 154.5$, so $1 - \frac{6 \times 154.5}{8 \times 63}$ = **-0.839** (to 3 s.f.)

(4 marks for correct answer, otherwise 1 mark for attempting to find the differences, 1 mark for finding the sum of d^2 and 1 mark for correct substitution in the formula.)

(b) There is a negative correlation between the rankings, which means John disagrees with the expert. ***(1 mark)***

(c) (i) 0.05 and -0.02 (the values closest to zero)
(2 marks available — 1 mark for each correct answer.)

(ii) 0.92 ***(1 mark)***

(d) Area of 1994 pie chart = π × 3² = 28.274 cm²

Area of 2004 pie chart needs to be equal to 28.274 × $\frac{196\,400}{107\,000}$ = 51.9 cm²

$\pi r^2 = 51.9$, $r^2 = 16.519...$
r = **4.06 cm**
(4 marks for correct answer, otherwise 1 mark for finding area of 1994 pie chart, 1 mark for finding area of 2004 pie chart and 1 mark for finding r^2.)

10 (a) Using relative frequency, P(confirm) = $\frac{320}{400} = \frac{\mathbf{4}}{\mathbf{5}}$ = **0.8** or **80%** ***(1 mark)***

(b) P(not confirm) = 1 – P(confirm) = $1 - \frac{4}{5} = \frac{\mathbf{1}}{\mathbf{5}}$ = **0.2** or **20%** ***(1 mark)***

(c) (i) P(3 confirm) = $4p^3q = 4 \times \left(\frac{4}{5}\right)^3 \times \frac{1}{5} = \frac{\mathbf{256}}{\mathbf{625}}$ = **0.41** (2 s.f.)

(2 marks for correct answer, otherwise 1 mark for correct method.)

(ii) From above, P(3 confirm) = 0.4096
P(4 confirm) = p^4 = 0.4096
P(2 confirm) = $6p^2q^2$ = 0.1536
P(1 confirm) = $4pq^3$ = 0.0256
P(no confirm) = q^4 = 0.0016
Two most likely numbers of confirmations: **3 and 4**
(3 marks for correct answer and working, otherwise 2 marks for working out all probabilities correctly, or 1 mark for working out 1 probability [other than P(3 confirm)] correctly.)

11 (a) Negative correlation **or** volume of skull decreases as age increases.
(1 mark)

(b) $\bar{x}$ = 11.2 ÷ 8 = 1.4, $\bar{y}$ = 904 ÷ 8 = 113. So coordinates are **(1.4, 113)**.
(2 marks for correct answer, otherwise 1 mark for (113, 1.4) or only one of the pair of coordinates.)

(c) (i) (1.4, 113) correctly plotted
(1 mark. Allow mark if within ± one 2 mm square of correct point.)

(ii) Line of best fit drawn with y-axis intercept in the range 200 - 250 and x-axis intercept in the range 2.5 - 3. ***(1 mark)***

(d) Answer in the range 130 cm³ - 170 cm³. ***(1 mark)***

(e) This skull is unlikely to be from the same type of ape because the point (1, 75) lies a long way from the rest of the data. The skull is smaller than expected. **OR** The skull could be from the same species — it could be smaller than expected because it's from a young ape.
(2 marks for either explanation, or similar.)

(f) It would predict an impossibly small or negative volume. **Or**, you can't assume the trend will continue beyond the given data. ***(1 mark)***

(g) a = (change in y) ÷ (change in x), so $\boldsymbol{a}$ **= -80** ± 20
b = y-intercept, so $\boldsymbol{b}$ **= 225** ± 25
(3 marks for correct answer, otherwise 1 mark for attempting to find gradient of line by any appropriate method and 1 mark for correctly finding one of a and b. Allow mark for finding b if incorrect y-intercept from (c)(ii) carried forward.)

(h) a tells you the decrease in volume of the skulls, on average, per million years.
(2 marks for correct answer, otherwise 1 mark for incomplete description involving rate, e.g. 'decrease in volume' or 'decrease per million years'.)

Working out your Grade

- *Find your percentage mark for the exam.*
- *Look it up in this table to see what grade you got. If you're borderline, don't push yourself up a grade — the real examiners won't.*

Percentage Mark	73+	59 – 72	46 – 58	33 – 45	22 – 32	15 – 21	—	—	under15
Grade	A*	A	B	C	D	E	F	G	U

Important
- *This is a Higher paper — if you're doing Foundation, the top grade you can get in the real exam is a C. The questions will be easier, but you'll need more marks to get each grade than shown above. E.g. you'll need about 61% to get a C grade.*
- *Obviously these grades are only a guide — and the more practice you do the better...*

Index

Index